Prospect Shaft.

EXAMINATION AND VALUATION
OF MINERAL PROPERTY

BAXTER AND PARKS

Third Edition 1949
by
ROLAND D. PARKS
Associate Professor of Mineral Industry
Massachusetts Institute of Technology

OIL PROPERTY VALUATION

By WALTER L. WHITEHEAD

Associate Professor of Geology
Massachusetts Institute of Technology
in collaboration with the author

THE MICHIGAN MINE APPRAISAL SYSTEM

By FRANKLIN G. PARDEE
Mining Engineer and Appraiser of Mines
Michigan Geological Survey
Lansing, Michigan

Published by
ADDISON-WESLEY PRESS INC.
CAMBRIDGE 42, MASSACHUSETTS

First and Second Edition

MINE EXAMINATION AND VALUATION

Copyright 1933 and 1939

CHARLES H. BAXTER and ROLAND D. PARKS

Third Edition

EXAMINATION AND VALUATION OF MINERAL PROPERTY

Copyright 1949

ROLAND D. PARKS

ADDISON-WESLEY PRESS INC.

Cambridge 42, Mass.

Printed in U.S.A.

961

CONTENTS

CHAP. 3 GEOLOGICAL INVESTIGATION

CHAP. 4 SAMPLING

CHAP. 5 SAMPLING CALCULATIONS

PART II
MINE VALUATION

CHAP. 11 MATHEMATICAL PREMISES—COMPOUND INTEREST

CHAP. 12 MINE VALUATION—UNIFORM ANNUAL INCOME

CHAP. 13 MINE VALUATION—NONUNIFORM ANNUAL INCOME

PART III
VALUATION OF OIL PROPERTY

PART IV
OTHER VALUATION THEORIES

PART V
VALUATION TABLES

PREFACE TO THIRD EDITION

This third edition of the original "Mine Examination and Valuation," by Baxter and Parks, has been revised and expanded and for that reason has been given the new title of "Examination and Valuation of Mineral Property."

The major additions are the chapters on Valuation of Oil Property by Dr. Walter L. Whitehead, Associate Professor of Geology, Massachusetts Institute of Technology; the descriptions of sampling practice by Messrs. Edward P. Shea, Alfred T. Barr, and John A. Lentz, Jr.; the chapter on geological investigation of mineral property; an oil-field valuation problem; a new case valuation problem and text to illustrate treatment and marketing of complex lead-zinc ores; a discussion of the royalty interest in lessor-lessee operation; and the derivation and application of the Hoskold premise to mineral properties producing unequal annual income.

Mr. Franklin G. Pardee, in addition to revising his summary of the Michigan Mine Appraisal System, has made many helpful suggestions and assisted with the new material on iron ore sampling practice.

Considerable rearrangement has been made of the material in Part II to present it in better sequence for the student. Figures have been provided to illustrate the principles of interest accrual and discount; tables have been expanded to provide for lower interest rates on redemption fund, and a full five-place logarithm table is included for calculation of factors not covered by the tables.

We assume that the student or engineer has a knowledge of geology, methods of mining, mining practice, principles of accounting and cost finding, and economics. A knowledge of these arts and sciences is the foundation on which the valuation rests and without it the superstructure is worthless. In fact, the use of a scientific method of procedure when based on false premises may give an appearance of soundness that is entirely unwarranted. Wherever these underlying sciences are touched upon in this volume, the purpose is merely to show an application to the work. We have tried to limit the discussion to the procedure of the examination, the collection of data, and the calculation of the valuation of the mining property.

The authors make no claim to originality. In order to cover even the limited field of this volume, one must draw not only on a large number of books, but also freely from the transactions of the technical societies and mining journals. We have taken material wherever we could find it; whenever the source was known, we have given credit; and in many cases we have obtained the permission of the author or publisher.

One of the outstanding jobs in mine valuation is the annual appraisal of the iron and copper mines of the State of Michigan for the purposes of taxation. Mr. Franklin G. Pardee, Mining Engineer and Appraiser of Mines for the State of Michigan, has written a brief history of this appraisal and the method used. We are grateful for his permission to incorporate it as an appendix to this book. Mr. Pardee has also read the text and made many valuable suggestions which are incorporated therein. We also wish to acknowledge the suggestions and encouragement of Dr. W. O. Hotchkiss, President of the Michigan College of Mining and Technology, and likewise the aid of Dr. E. L. Wood and Professor L. A. Rose of the English Department of this college in preparation and proofreading of the manuscript and text, and of Miss A. Margaret Sullivan for her stenographic cooperation.

CHARLES H. BAXTER
ROLAND D. PARKS

Houghton, Michigan,
January 1, 1933.

PREFACE TO FIRST EDITION

This book is designed specifically as the foundation for a course in Mine Examination and Valuation at the Michigan College of Mining and Technology. Collateral reading is assigned in order to give the student a broader knowledge of the subject. Much of the material has been used in the form of department notes for the past five years. The liberal use of examples and problems, abundant throughout the text, has been found to aid students in grasping the method of employing the formulas and tables.

Examples and problems may also prove of assistance to engineers in the field who are somewhat "rusty" in their algebra. Hoskold's classic "Engineer's Valuing Assistant," to which they previously referred, is out of print and unobtainable. Though several good volumes with excellent tables covering the principles of valuation have been written, we have found none of these which includes a discussion of the examination.

We have limited our tables to the more common rates and have carried them only to four decimal places, which is of sufficient accuracy for any mine valuation. They are designed to familiarize the student with the use of such tables and also to permit the assignment of a larger variety of problems in a limited time than would be feasible if each problem had to be solved from the equations. The tables have been checked; but errors will creep in, as we have yet to find any volume of interest tables that has been entirely free from them. The mathematical calculation involved in any mine valuation takes so little time that the engineer should always check the particular figure he uses.

The author has missed particularly the thoughtful discussions and collaborations with his former associate, Professor Charles H. Baxter.

In addition to those mentioned above, grateful acknowledgment is made to Professor H. E. Krumlauf and Mr. P E. Malozemoff for their detailed criticisms; to Dr. W. J. Mead, Dr. W. O. Hotchkiss, Mr. A. E. Anderson, Mr. F. W. Wolff, and Dr. R. Schuhmann, Jr., for their valuable suggestions; and to all others who assisted in the preparation.

Cambridge, Mass.   ROLAND D. PARKS.
June 1, 1948

PART I

MINE EXAMINATION

Open Pit Mine.

CHAPTER 1

EXAMINATION OF MINERAL PROPERTY

DEFINITIONS — A mine examination is a careful scrutiny of a mineral property made in order to form an opinion or judgment of its present worth or future possibilities. The term "mine," in its strict sense, represents any artificial excavation made for the purpose of winning mineral values. It therefore includes both open-pit and underground, metal and coal workings, as well as quarries and oil, gas, salt, and sulphur wells, but excludes borrow pits, railway, sewer, and water tunnels, and all diggings made for commercial purposes other than the exploiting of minerals. Although gravels, rock (coarse and crushed), sand, and clay are not ordinarily classed as minerals, they have commercial value for construction and industrial purposes, and their examination, estimation, and excavation do not differ, in most instances, from those of a true mineral deposit. Such workings will be here included as mines. The term also covers all plant equipment, machinery, etc., used either directly or indirectly in working a mineral deposit. A survey of an entirely undeveloped region to determine its mineral possibilities might be termed a "mineral survey."

"Ore," as defined by the U.S.G.S.,[1] is "a natural aggregation of one or more minerals from which useful metals may be profitably extracted." It thus includes not only mineral in its natural place in the earth's crust but also mine dumps,

---

[1] United States Geological Survey.

tailings piles, etc., which can be reworked at a profit. A broader definition, in line with common usage, would cover extraction of nonmetallic mineral products as well as metals.

The distinguishing point between "ore" and "metal or mineral bearing material" is the grade above which extraction of the end product is profitable under a given set of cost-price circumstances. Economic factors are important to this determination. Without change of grade or location what is "mineral bearing material" at one time may become "ore" at another through development of cheaper mining or extraction processes or because of changes in one or more of the factors entering into cost of production vs. sale of product. Likewise, the mere transfer of a property at forced sale may so reduce the capital charges to the new owner as to make the operation profitable.

PURPOSE — Every examination has a definite purpose, although its scope may be limited or broad. It may deal solely with a single phase of the business or it may encompass the entire operation. This condition is necessarily true because clients' circumstances differ and because each mine represents an individual problem. No two mineral deposits are alike, no two companies operate alike, no two localities are favored with the same economic conditions, and no two examiners are of the same temperament. A mine may be in any stage of development from a mere prospect pit to a fully equipped and operating plant; it may be in its extreme youth, in its prime years, or in its declining old age.

Examination of mineral property is usually called for in the following circumstances:

1. When change of ownership is considered, either by outright purchase or sale, or through consolidation with other properties.
2. Appraisal for tax purposes.
3. When funds are to be solicited through sale of stock or bonds or by bank loan.

4. When planning broad revision of operating methods or installation of important, long-life equipment.

TYPE AND SCOPE OF EXAMINATION — The type of examination to be conducted is dependent upon the client's reason for instituting the investigation, and its scope and thoroughness are related to the other factors named above.

In general, all mine examinations may be grouped into two classes, preliminary examinations and formal examinations.

Preliminary examination may be defined as a rapid survey of a property covering only the more essential features and touching lightly upon the others. In the case of a property up for sale, the object of such an examination may be merely to discover the reasons for selling the mine. A preliminary examination usually includes some sampling (important check points, etc.), a brief geological survey, some mapping, a short study of methods, a rough cost setup, and an estimation of management. The survey should be so planned that the data taken and the results derived may be augmented without repetition if a formal examination is warranted.

Formal examination is a detailed survey of a property to determine completely the facts regarding the mine and its future prospects. It is an expensive and long process, usually requiring from one to six months and often involving a large force of experts and workmen. A formal examination should never be instituted until a preliminary examination has shown that the expense will be justified. Formal examinations are usually conducted when consolidation of properties or the purchase of an operating mine is under consideration.

RESPONSIBILITY OF EXAMINING ENGINEER — The engineer is responsible to the client for the examination and subsequent report stating his judgment and decisions. None of the factors involved in a mine examination is absolutely definite. It is the engineer's problem to consider each of these items in its true aspect in regard to the investigation at hand, to weigh each of the parts with respect to the whole, and to arrive at as close an approximation to the true facts of the case as possible. The client expects no less of the examiner when he retains him, and the engineer should feel that he owes the client a conclusion based upon his best, unbiased judgment.

It is sound practice to be conservative, especially in mining enterprises, where valuations must necessarily be based upon estimates of probabilities. Too decided a leaning to the conservative, however, may mean the loss to the client of a good proposition and, therefore, the engineer must guard against timidity as well as against overenthusiasm. His final decision should represent a true estimate of value qualified slightly on the conservative side.

To obtain such a result, the estimator will gather all his data, consider the respective importance of each item, weigh them all in their true aspects, arrive at the approximate total figure, and then, if circumstances warrant, apply a proper margin of safety. As an example, suppose that there are ten items entering into a valuation as multipliers of each other and that the whole proposition is slightly speculative, to the extent of 10%. If this 10% factor is applied to each item before the items are combined, the final result will be $100 \times (\%_{10})^{10}$ or .35, an underestimate of 55%; whereas if each item is entered into the whole at its full value the result will be 100%. Then the factor of 10% will produce a final figure of 90%, thus giving the desired margin for speculative value.

In the sale or purchase of a mine the examiner should report a valuation that represents his judgment of the value of the property. Whether for buyer or seller, his report should contain the same basic facts. To evaluate these basic facts without bias may require courage, and always demands clear thinking and a lively regard for the good name of the profession.

In the valuing of a mine for bond issue or loan it falls to the engineer to be especially conservative. The same is true if the valuation is to be used to induce the sale of stock. In this instance, the examiner should bear in mind the many slips that may occur between the ore in the ground and the realization of profit from this ore.

An engineer is sometimes retained by a client to examine a mineral property because of his knowledge of the particular mine or district; more often he is retained because the client has confidence in his ability, integrity, and judgment. If the engineer is not familiar with the district and its particular problems, he may find it to the interest of his client to employ technical assistants who are familiar with local conditions, or specialists in certain phases of the problem. These assistants can usually be employed at a considerably lower rate per diem than is paid the examining engineer. They are responsible only to him and not to the client. The engineer takes full responsibility for their work and for opinions resulting therefrom. A local attorney can examine abstracts and titles more quickly and thoroughly than can the engineer. An assistant engineer working with the examiner can greatly expedite the field work, sampling, calculation, etc., and thus save money for the client. If a crucial point in the estimation is the separation of a complex ore and this is not the specialized field of the engineer, the employment of a technical expert is advisable.

QUALIFICATIONS OF EXAMINING ENGINEER — The essential qualifications of an examining engineer are:

1. Sound reasoning, that is, the ability to properly weigh component parts and deduce logical conclusions while still retaining a clear picture of the accuracy of the facts with which he is dealing.

2. Honesty, integrity, and straightforwardness.

3. A working knowledge of geologic principles and the ability to apply it to local conditions.

4. An understanding of sampling theory and practice.

5. Knowledge of mining methods and their effect upon production costs.

6. A working knowledge of mineral dressing.

7. Ability to compute production costs and estimate profits.

8. A knowledge of economic principles and business conditions and their effect upon the mining industry.

9. An understanding of money values.

PROFESSIONAL ETHICS — To be absolutely unbiased in his opinion, an examiner should have no personal or monetary interest in the property which he is inspecting. His relations with his client should be purely those of an impartial arbiter retained to render an opinion. To guard against criticism, the engineer has a right to demand his fee in money and should never accept payment in scrip dependent upon the future earnings of the property being examined. Before entering into any definite agreement with his client, he should also, as a precaution, assure himself of his client's integrity and ascertain the true purpose of the examination to make sure that it is entirely aboveboard and that he will not be furthering any scheme to the disadvantage of the entire organization involved.

F. W. Sperr[1] expressed these ethical considerations as follows: "Every precaution should be taken to avoid the influence of the question of compensation upon the engineer's judgment and opinion. If the parties are strangers to each other, it is best for both that the engineer's compensation should be wholly or in large part paid in advance, or be well secured for payment upon delivery of the report. The engineer should be entirely free from the pressure of financial necessities which might possibly influ-

---

[1] Prof. of Mining, Mich. Coll. of Mines, 1895—1926. Department Notes on "Mining Engineering"—4th Ed. 1924.

ence his judgment or opinions. If there arises the remotest suspicion that the prospective client desires to 'keep the engineer in line' by money considerations, the engineer must decline to undertake the work if he hopes to maintain his good repute as an engineer.''

The subject of ethics and responsibility has been covered in a concise manner also by C. Frank Allen[1] in his text "Business Law for Engineers.''

"Engineering skill required. Where an engineer or architect is employed in a private capacity, he undertakes to bring to his work the average skill of those engaged in a like kind of work. If he makes a specialty of some class of engineering, as structural, or as sanitary, he undertakes to use the average skill of others who make a similar specialty in such class of engineering. He does not in either case insure absolute accuracy, unless, by custom, checks are possible and in regular use which will allow absolute accuracy to be secured.

"What service is guaranteed. The engineer does guarantee: 1. Reasonable learning, skill, and experience. 2. The use of proper care and diligence. 3. The application of his best judgment. 4. Absolute honesty. The burden of proof is on him who disputes the engineer's skill and other qualifications. The engineer is, of course, liable if negligence on his part can be proved.

"What an engineer may attempt. If an engineer of good training and experience is called upon, as often happens, to carry out work not altogether within the line of previous experience, and he enters upon his duties modestly and with earnest purpose to succeed, it is probable that strong evidence would be necessary to hold him liable for faults in his work if there seemed reasonable probability of success when he attempted the work. An engineer who never attempts work which he has not already demon-

---

[1] "Business Law for Engineers''—C. F. Allen. McGraw-Hill Book Co., Inc., 1929.

strated his ability to carry out, is of little use in the world. Where the result of failure is likely to prove serious and the probability of success definitely doubtful, the engineer should decline the service, unless the necessity seems imperative with no better alternative apparently available.''

CHAPTER 2

PRELIMINARY PHASES
OF INVESTIGATION

PLANNING OF FIELD WORK — The field work involved in examining a mine varies widely, depending to a large extent upon the type of property under inspection, the object and type of the examination, and the familiarity of the engineer with the mine. It is obvious that the examination of an undeveloped prospect or claim involves a different field procedure from the evaluation of a fully developed operating mine.

Prospect — In examining a prospect, the engineer generally conducts his field work along the following lines:

1. Geology.
2. Drill records and drilling.
3. Sampling of outcrops and pits.
4. Estimate of plant cost, transportation, etc.
5. Market conditions and future possibilities.

The all-important question to be answered in examining a prospect is, "What chance has it to become a mine?" Since tangible evidences are usually lacking, the verdict will depend, necessarily, upon the engineer's opinion rather than upon demonstrable facts. A majority of prospects have usually been examined several times and as often turned down. Ordinarily, no brilliant showings will be found. At any time, however, a study of the local geology, access to new facts, or the discovery of other evidence not noticed or not utilized by preceding engineers may change the aspect of the situation and give the prospect a different valuation rating.

Ancient Workings — In the examination of ancient workings,[1] or antiguas, the first step is to make a map of the property and place the geology on it, because faulting was not understood in the early days. The workings can then be sampled to determine whether or not profits can be made by modern methods. The engineer will do well to guard against certain misconceptions in regard to this type of property. An ancient working does not necessarily imply rich ore or a valuable property. If slave labor was used the operators could work even lean orebodies at a profit. They did not have modern implements, however, and, as a result, could not mine much below water level. If, in the examination of an ancient mine, the engineer finds that the pay shoots were short and the stopes were narrow, there is little chance for further exploration except below water level or through an analysis of fault offsets.

Operating Property—An examination of an operating property should cover the following points:

1. Estimate of past and present management.
2. Study of office data, such as mine maps, surface and underground geological maps, drill records, sample maps, cost sheets, productive history, etc.
3. Underground geology inspection.
4. Check sampling at vital points.
5. Study of methods to find weak points.
6. Survey of plant, equipment, etc.
7. Estimate of future costs, life, and expected profits.
8. Computation of value.

A simple outline form is given here, listing important points to be covered in examining a property. The form, of course, is subject to change to suit the conditions found in the field, but the main points to be considered will probably be similar in all cases:

---

[1] "Examination of Prospects"—C. G. Gunther, McGraw-Hill Book Co., 1912, p. 4.

Outline for Mine Examination

Property_____

Location_____

_____

Date_____

Client_____

Engineer_____

Purpose and scope of examination Agreement between engineer and client as to details: field work, personnel, date of preliminary report, time for completion, fee, advance payment, etc.

1. *Geography.*

    Map of mine location and nearby territory, showing topography.

    Map of county or district, showing towns, roads, railroads, etc.

    Survey of transportation facilities and relation of mine to markets.

    Summary of freight rates, power rates, etc.

    Climatic conditions: snow, rainfall, etc.

2. *History.*

    (a) Legal.

    Claim recorded.

    Title recorded.

    Changes of ownership — abstract of title.

    Tax history.

    Leases, water and mill rights, royalties, etc.

    Suits in court, claim conflicts, litigations, etc.

    (b) Productive.

    Record of production since beginning.

    Record of all shutdowns and reasons.

    Production of surrounding district.

(c) Financial.

Pre-organization agreements.

Capitalization.

Stock issued for cash.

Stock issued for services.

Stock issued for property.

Profits, dividends, and assessments.

Reorganizations and consolidations.

Comparison of yearly statements.

Present financial structure and standing.

3. *Management.*

Personnel and organization.

Character, attitude, and capability.

Comparison with operators of other similar mines.

Efficiency; past and present.

4. *Geology.*

Study of district through:

1. U. S. G. S. reports and maps.
2. State publications.
3. Publications of technical societies.

Study of surface features.

Study of underground structures from:

1. Mine maps and underground examination.
2. Drill hole data and inspection of drill core and samples.

Deductions as to formations, structures, and orebodies.

5. *Sampling.*

Study of all records.

Check of previous results.

Sampling of new workings.

Correlation with geology.

6. *Estimate of Ore Reserves.*

Outlining of assured and probable ore reserves by correlation of geology, sampling, and mine maps.

Tests of tonnage factor.

Estimates of reserves: positive, probable, and possible.

7. *Methods and Costs.*

    Mining — Method in use; estimate of percent of recovery.

        Advisable improvements.

        Relation of development work to mining.

        Itemization of costs for recent periods.

        Estimate of most economical rate of mining and corresponding life of mine.

    Milling — Flow sheet and details of all unusual features, percent of recovery, costs, suggestions for improvement.

        Water supply.

        Space available for tailings.

8. *Marketing.*

    Sale of ore or metal.

    Smelter contracts.

      Open vs special schedules.

    By-product possibilities.

9. *Plant and Equipment.*

    Underground — Condition of shafts, plats, drifts, crosscuts, raises, stopes, etc.

        Condition of pumps, motors, and other underground machinery.

        Summary of equipment at hand and additional pieces needed.

    Surface — Condition of headframe, hoist, power plant, shops, mills, smelters, houses, hospitals, etc.

        Condition of machinery.

        Estimate of new equipment needed.

10. *Miscellaneous.*

    Timber, land, power sites, water, etc.

    Labor, unions, wages, disputes, welfare, safety practices, etc.

    Attitude of local government.

    Surface rights — liability for damage due to subsidence above mining operations.

11. *Economic Situation.*

  Average profits for recent periods.

  Average market in same periods.

  Future prospects.

  Estimate of future earning power.

12. *Valuation.*

  Determination of values for years' life, profit factor, interest rates, etc.

  Application of formulas and calculation of present worth.

GEOGRAPHICAL LOCATION — The question of geographical location is of greater moment in connection with the examination of a prospect or undeveloped mine than in the case of a fully developed property. For the ~~lway~~ facilities, roads, power lines, town sites, etc., ~~e~~ figured on; whereas the latter probably has these ~~facilities~~ at hand. Nearness to markets and reduction plants and the possibility of a shift in markets, however, are points which must be considered with either type of property; in fact, when translated into freight costs, these often become deciding factors in the consummating of a transaction. Freight charges are always an important item in the cost sheet of a mining enterprise and consequently affect the valuation of the property.

LEGAL HISTORY — TITLE RECORD — An inspection of the legal history of the property should cover all land and mineral titles and deeds, all transfers of title, and all recorded documents, to show just what acreage and rights are included in the property and to disclose any errors in title, conflicts, damage suits, delinquent taxes, etc., which might affect the validity of the title to any of the property in question. Rentals, leases, royalty and sale contracts, and especially any long-time agreements, should all be gone over carefully in order that the engineer may know the exact standing of the company with respect to those with whom it is dealing.

Unless he is well acquainted with legal procedure, court records, contracts, etc., the examiner should delegate this part of the investigation to an attorney or other reputable consultant in the field of legal transactions and documents. Because of the specialized nature of this work, many mining companies have found it wise to establish departments within their organizations to deal entirely with land, royalties, property and water rights, taxes, and other items related to ownership.

PRODUCTIVE RECORD — The productive history of the mine gives the engineer a record of past achievements upon which to base his estimates of future capabilities. A careful inspection of these records may reveal certain facts in regard to the past which will enable him to gauge the efficiencies of plant and operations. Particular attention should be paid to determining the causes and effects of any shutdowns.

Before accepting the cost figures on the past production of any property, the engineer should satisfy himself as to the correctness of accounting practice, particularly with reference to the proper distinction between capital and operating accounts. When expense items are improperly charged to capital accounts or when proper depreciation of capital accounts is not provided for, an actual loss in operation may be turned into a profit on the books.

FINANCIAL STRUCTURE — An itemization of the financial structure of the concern, in conjunction with cost summaries for past years, helps to confirm the engineer's judgment in regard to the efficiency of past work and also gives him a general picture of the financial standing of the business and the attitude of the shareholders or owners. Special attention should be paid to the causes and results of preorganization agreements and to any assessments which may have been called. A summary of yearly profits furnishes a rough gauge of the past success of the property. This estimate must, however, be qualified by further opinions as to efficiency and economic factors.

MANAGEMENT — Management is undoubtedly a most important factor in the success of a business; in fact, managerial ability is considered so vital that some authorities attribute as much as 90% of the success of an enterprise to this one item. Management is likewise vital in the operation of mineral property but the general statement must be qualified because one mine may be endowed naturally with a better grade of raw material and less difficult physical conditions than another, though each produces the same product. Given two mineral properties similar in all respects, the true measure of management then becomes as evident as with two grocery stores.

Management is the influence that coordinates land, capital, and labor. Efficient operation can be achieved only by a proper harmony of these three. A few mines are rich enough to "carry" the management, and some mines are too deficient in resources for any management to show a profit, but in the great majority of intermediate cases, the management "makes" the mine. A careful examiner, like a careful investor, will not overlook the management of a mine when he scrutinizes its mineral resources and productive record.

Costs obtained at a mine are largely dependent on management. In the determination of the proper cost figure to use, the engineer must ask himself whether the same quality of management will be maintained in the future. If the property has no operating record, what can be expected in the way of management when the mine is opened up? Naturally, it is more difficult to make this abstract valuation of a property than it is to predict its future under known management conditions. That good management will lose only a small amount of money on a poor property, will make a small profit on a fair property, and will make a bonanza out of a good one has proved itself time and again. Frequently an engineer examines and values a mine for an operating group whose abilities are well known to him. If he feels sure that his group can effect economies in operation, it is his province to consider this in his valuation.

The management of a property expresses itself in many ways, and each engineer builds up from his experience certain criteria upon which he bases his opinion. "Good housekeeping" at a mine may sometimes indicate efficient direction, but this is not always a good guide. Safety conditions at the mine are often used as a barometer. One engineer always pays particular attention to the loading and condition of the cars used for hauling rock and ore. He has found that partially loaded cars being hauled to the shaft and rolling stock that is not kept up show indifferent and expensive operation. These are only a few of the many telltale observations that can be revealing. No matter what the yardstick, the engineer making the valuation must be sure of the quality of the management before he makes any radical changes in cost figures.

Engineering and planning, of course, come under the heading of management. In fact, it is usually at this point that the examining engineer makes his first contact with the property. It is sufficient here to emphasize the importance of two questions: (1) are the records, maps and estimates in such shape that a clear presentation is made of the whole situation? (2) in the case of an operating property, does the engineer plan the work or merely measure it up after it is done? The complete answer to these questions usually furnishes a good insight into the operating efficiency.

The indirect charge for management is the item just discussed. The direct charge is represented by the salaries and wages paid to those who guide the operation. In a consideration of these items, the ratio between amounts paid and results obtained is worthy of notice.

CHAPTER 3

GEOLOGICAL INVESTIGATION

PURPOSE — Property has mineral value only when it contains a deposit from which a product can be won at a profit. Since evaluation necessarily contemplates the processes of mining and extracting the product, the size, shape, position and grade of the deposit are fundamental features that must be determined, at least within reasonable limits, as a basis. Determination of these features is largely a matter of geology. Sampling is an allied process.

Mineral deposits [1] range from thin, erratic veins to extensive bedded deposits and massive bodies such as the copper-porphyries. Processes of genetic concentration may have been igneous, sedimentary, or metamorphic. Some deposits are primary in that they have retained their original qualities and relationships to adjoining rocks; others have been altered, either by chemical or mechanical means, to secondary deposits. Structural relationships [2] range from inclusion in undisturbed series to distortion in tight folding and dislocation by complicated fault offsets. Solving the geology of a deposit may vary from a simple problem to one requiring advanced geological training and experience and some ingenuity in its application.

An orebody can be measured with absolute certainty only after it has been mined. It can seldom be seen as a whole body.

---

[1] Lindgren, W., ''Mineral Deposits,'' McGraw-Hill Book Co., 1933.
[2] Newhouse, W. H., Editor, ''Ore Deposits as Related to Structural Features,'' Princeton University Press, 1943.

In all forms of mining, open pit or underground, there is always a region beyond which one must visualize continuance or possible interruption of ore. In an open pit, this projection is downward or sidewise; in an underground operation, it may be in any direction.

The object of geologic study as a basis for evaluation of a mineral deposit is to locate and determine the boundaries of mineral values; or, as stated above, to determine the size, shape, position, and grade of the deposit.

SCOPE — In the main, this problem of delineation of ore bodies is a problem in structural geology aided by sampling, although the complete investigation would be concerned also with genesis, alterations, mode of occurrence, and mineral associations of the deposit.

Since mineral deposits are themselves three-dimensional and since their coordinate position and depth below the surface is likewise a three-dimensional problem, geologic field work is planned accordingly. Surface investigations are usually supplemented by drill-hole data and by underground observations whenever openings for such are available. Subsurface data are vitally important to proving up the third dimension. While there are occasions when the entire geologic study must be made from surface indications alone, it would be poor practice to be limited to surface data if there were underground openings that could be inspected. To do so would be to ignore the possibility of gaining additional evidence that might prove or disprove an important point.

Furthermore, surface study is often hindered by lack of rock exposures in the area under investigation. On the average, there is about one square foot of exposed bedrock per acre throughout the entire North American continent. Over the glaciated pre-Cambrian Shield of Canada and the Central Plains, large areas contain few exposures.

Geologic study seldom can be confined to the immediate mineral property. Knowledge of the regional geology is a prerequisite to working out the local geology. The effects of major forces, possibly not expressed locally, may control minor structural patterns to which the ore deposit is related.

PROSPECTS VS. MINES — Examination of prospects is quite different from examination of mines or mineral-producing property. A prospect is a long way from profitable production. Actual ore reserves are seldom evident and, in fact, sometimes not expected immediately; geological predictions are more or less speculative. In the usual instance, structures, ore limits, and other essential geologic features of a prospect are known somewhere between zero and a reasonable percent of final knowledge; the balance is inferred subject to correction with new evidence. In the case of the prospect, the geologist looks for favorable geological conditions, whereas in the case of the mineral producer, he looks for reserves.

USE OF AVAILABLE DATA — Several sources of geologic information are usually available to the examiner even though the property being examined is situated in remote territory. There are few land areas that are unknown at least as to general geology.

National and State Geological Surveys and Mines Departments are mapping and reporting continually on mineral areas and properties. These data, except in unusual instances, are available to the public. Company and private reports on mines or districts are sometimes available to the geologist. Geology texts frequently contain references or maps in sufficient detail to be helpful. Maps of adjoining mines, when available, may show assay results and geologic sections that will be of value in projecting structure and mineral trends across the property in question. Drilling and geophysical records are an additional source of information. The examiner should avail himself of all such data preparatory to making his own investigation. He can then plan his work more effectively.

FIELD WORK — It is not within the scope of this book to cover in detail the many geologic field procedures and the methods of interpretation of data that may be called upon in the course of a mine examination. These, appropriately, may be found in geology texts and handbooks in which mineral deposits, structural principles, and field practice [1] are treated at length.

CORRELATION WITH OTHER PARTS OF EXAMINATION — Mapping and sampling are usually part of the field work of examining mineral property. Each may be a rather lengthy undertaking, but is essential to the overall objective of determining location and grade of material. Insofar as the geology can be interpreted at the time, this knowledge should be used to guide the mapping and sampling programs. This plan will not only avoid duplication and unnecessary work, but will make for more effective observation of critical details.

There is no set procedure for the geological examination of mineral property. Too many variables are present. An efficient examiner will review constantly the sum of his geologic information on the property and keep revising the field program in order to obtain the next significant bit of key data.

For an undeveloped property, surface inspection should be in considerable detail before a sampling program is started. To keep proper record of observations, mapping may have to go along with the surface study, and some test samples may be

---

[1] Lahee, F. H., "Field Geology," McGraw-Hill Book Co., Inc., 4th Ed., 1941.

Forrester, J. D., "Principles of Field and Mining Geology," John Wiley & Sons, 1946.

McKinstry, H. E., "Mining Geology," Prentice-Hall, Inc., 1948.

needed. But until some picture is formed of the geology, or until evidence is found to support a theory of formation of the deposit, any extensive sampling would be haphazard and is to be avoided.

The task is much simplified when the examination is of an operating mine where plan, sectional, and assay maps have been kept up to date. Here the structure and formation, in part at least, are in evidence and the examiner need only check the results already at hand as background for planning his approach to the forward problem.

TYPE PROGRAMS — Examination of mineral property for purposes of valuation is to be distinguished from a program of exploration for ore. The one is a survey as of a given time; the other more often a continuing program allied to development or operation. In a sense, however, they are similar; each has the delimiting of ore as an objective and methods of approach frequently are alike.

Choice of method for the field program is often largely a matter of economics. The program may be determined by the expense warranted for the information that may be obtained.

Test Pitting and Trenching — Once traces of mineral or favorable geologic conditions have been found, test pits and trenches are among the simpler, direct methods of prospecting used to search out mineral values. Trenches are suitable for uncovering ledge under shallow soil; test pits can be used to penetrate overburden to about 100 feet in depth, providing large boulders and much water are not encountered. Both are adaptable to hand methods and, requiring no power equipment, to remote localities.

Simple drive-pipes or auger drills may be used to test relatively soft, shallow deposits.

With suitable topography, light overburden, and a supply of water under head, hydraulicking may be advantageous for exposing an area of bedrock to inspection. This method, however, will usually require too much capital outlay for the average examination.

Drilling [1] — Drilling, preferably coredrilling, is an excellent method of determining ore formations and structures. It greatly augments surface geological knowledge by correlating structures and checking presumed extensions of ore at depth. In prospecting, it is fully as important for the geological information which it brings to light as for any ore which it may discover. Where actual ore is being dealt with, drilling is apt to give misleading results, since drill holes have been known just to miss a large body of ore. When they cut obliquely through a small body, they may give the impression of greater ore thickness than actually occurs. Results of drilling should be correlated closely with structural observation to avoid misleading interpretation.

In coredrilling, the sludge obtained from a hole is a valuable adjunct. Sludge samples should be taken at regular intervals in significant sections and retained for analysis and for comparison with the core. In soft ore-bearing formations and in fracture zones where much of the core may be lost, sludge samples may be the sole criterion for judgment of the value of the material.

When churn drilling is used to test a deposit, special attention must be paid to recovery of the material and interpretation of results. Contamination is apt to occur even in cased holes, depending upon the formations penetrated. An analysis correction factor, determined empirically, may be necessary in such an event. Although portable churn and diamond-drill rigs with self-contained power are available to specification for

---

[1] Forrester, J. D., "Principles of Field and Mining Geology," John Wiley & Sons, 1946, Chap. XI.
McKinstry, H. E., "Mining Geology," Prentice-Hall, Inc., 1948, Chap. 3.

practically any examination work, contractors are often employed for the work, thus avoiding capital outlay for equipment.

Instrument Surveys — The dip needle and magnetometer are among the most useful instruments for geological work. Each is readily portable and rapid to operate. Choice depends, usually, upon accuracy desired. The airborne magnetometer may be employed advantageously to indicate major anomalies which can then be investigated more closely by ground observations within a limited area. These instruments record only the presence of magnetic minerals, but a knowledge of mineral associations may lead to using them on allied minerals and marker formations where the mineral under investigation is, itself, nonmagnetic. Asbestos, for instance, may be associated with enough magnetite for a survey of this type to outline the formations.

In respect to radioactive minerals, the Geiger counter is obviously useful. Portable field models are readily available. An understanding of types of emission is essential to proper interpretation of readings. Portable ultraviolet lamps are an aid to prospecting for fluorescent minerals, such as scheelite.

Geophysical methods,[1] such as gravitational, seismic, and electrical resistivity, are usually applied to large-scale exploration, as for petroleum. They may also be useful as aids to determining the geology of the ordinary mineral deposit. Advanced methods and instruments for well-logging, likewise, have been most helpful in petroleum work. To date, they have not been applied extensively to ore deposits.

---

[1] Lahee, F. H. "Field Geology," McGraw-Hill Book Co., Inc., 1941, Chap. XXII.
   Heiland, C. A., "Geophysical Exploration," Prentice-Hall, 1940.
   Jakosky, J. J., "Exploration Geophysics," Times-Mirror Press, Los Angeles, Calif., 1940.
   Nettleton, L. L., "Geophysical Prospecting for Oil," McGraw-Hill Book Co., 1940.
   "Geophysical Prospecting," A.I.M.E., 1929, 1932, 1934, 1940, 1945.

LABORATORY STUDIES — Laboratory work is called for in many mineral investigations. It may be for the purpose of optical or x-ray identification of minor minerals of value in association with the major ones in the deposit; for age determination to correlate series; or to point out chemical and physical qualities critical to the milling and metallurgy of the product.

The engineer or geologist examining a property, though he may not be proficient in these specialized fields, should be aware of the valuable help of such work. Interpretation of geological features may be verified by studies or tests of this type. Critical problems of treatment and marketing, solved in the laboratory, may be the determining factor in the success of the operation.

MAPPING — Measurements are essential to determining the location and size of a mineral deposit. Points of reference tie measurements together and are needed for legal record. Some form of surveying is the procedure by which this is done. Maps are the usual form of final record.

Most examiners of mineral property will be conversant with surveying techniques.[1] Others will appreciate the need for engineering assistance to conduct this phase of the work. The geologist or engineer may do his own surveying on a small job or may direct the work of one or more crews if considerable measurement and mapping are called for.

Surveys requiring special equipment are usually handled on a contract basis. Aerial mapping and airborne magnetic work are in this class, as are also geophysical surveys by gravity,

---

[1] Breed, Surveying, John Wiley & Sons, Inc.
Lahee, F. H., "Field Geology," McGraw-Hill Book Co., Inc., 1941, Chap. XV to XXI, inclusive.
Forrester, J. D., "Principles of Field and Mining Geology," John Wiley & Sons, 1946, Chap. V to VIII inclusive.
McKinstry, H. E., "Mining Geology," Prentice-Hall, Inc., 1948, Chap. 1.

seismic and electrical methods, and electrical or radioactive drill-hole logging. Aerial mapping and airborne magnetometer surveys usually require ground control, so will probably call for some surface surveying to give maps of the area that will be fully satisfactory.

Surface — Surface maps usually are of two types, property and topographic. The property map may show only land parcels and be plotted on form sheets printed to cover a regular township with its 36 numbered sections. Or it may be a map drawn to show property lines, railroads, highways, streams, buildings, mine dumps, etc., but usually without topography. The topographic map probably will show property lines also and will have on it the railroads, highways, etc., listed above. In addition, it will show topography (contours) and geology. Property lines, with tie-in lines to reference points, are usually surveyed with transit and tape for record purposes, although for a preliminary report and as a base for geologic work, stadia measurements will suffice for boundary lines but should be so noted. The plane table is the usual field instrument for topographic and geologic work, as it is somewhat more rapid than the transit. Choice of contour interval will depend on ruggedness of topography and scale will depend on area being worked. The compass is often used for some of the traversing. Solar observations are the usual means for determining meridian in remote areas. If the area is large, aerial mapping will be much faster and possibly more economical.

Underground — The Brunton compass, in some situations, may be sufficiently accurate for the underground survey for examination purposes. In any case, an instrument of this type is well adapted to making sketch maps of underground openings and for the mapping of geologic data. Measurements may be by tape or pace, as the situation requires. Side developments and extensions of main underground openings are frequently measured up by Brunton until such time as more accurate location is needed.

The transit is the usual instrument for underground surveying. Linear measurements are by tape to hundredths of a foot. Angular readings to one minute of accuracy are customary, with readings to one-half minute or even closer for important closures and for extended main-level developments. Elevations are carried by using the transit as a level and by vertical angle measurements through either main or auxiliary telescope. Corrections must be applied by computation for vertical angle measurements made by top telescope. Bearings (azimuths) are carried underground by transit or plumb wires as the openings demand.

Both **plan maps** and **sections** are usually needed to show underground workings and ore deposits. Elevation at which plans are drawn will probably coincide with main levels or sublevels. For a property undeveloped except by drilling and for projection of geologic inferences, the elevation of such a plan map or sketch will be determined by the data at hand and the purpose. Position of sectional veins and plane of projections usually depend on shape and position of the deposit; the footwall is often a controlling factor.

Underground maps show positions of openings such as shafts, drifts (entries), crosscuts, raises, and stopes, and are plotted accurately to scale.

On the background are recorded the geologic data and sampling results. These are often called **assay** or **geological maps** to distinguish them from operating maps for contract measurement. The geology maps will show rock and ore formations, dips, strikes, contacts, folds, slips, faults, fracture zones, and mineral associations and assays. In vein structures, width of vein vs. width of mining opening is important, as will be noted under sampling.

All relevant data are entered on the working maps which are drawn to a scale (often 40 ft. per inch) suitable for such record. Final maps for reports are more often at scales of 100 to 400 ft. per inch, with formations and geologic features displayed clearly by use of colors and symbols.

ORIGIN OF OREBODIES — In discussing classification of mineral deposits, Lindgren [1] states that in exploring and exploiting ore deposits, the miner is almost forced to form an idea of its origin in order to follow up the orebodies to best advantage. Therefore, in his opinion, a genetic classification according to geological processes is the most desirable both theoretically and practically. Lindgren's classification, as outlined in the reference cited, has withstood the test of time and continues to be authoritative.

Mineral deposits must have been formed by igneous processes, alteration, cementation, deformation, erosion, or sedimentation.

To have an ore or mineral deposit, there must have been a source of the elements that go to make up the mineral, a process of concentration, and a locus of deposition. The locus of deposition was determined by some combination of environmental factors that may be classed, broadly, as physical, chemical, and structural. In arriving at a deductive explanation for the genesis of an orebody, the examiner must consider all of these factors as an interrelated group. The results of the physical factors, such as pressure and temperature, and the chemical action are evidences from which the original system may be reconstructed but, of the three, only the structure can be seen in a relatively unchanged state.

Geology is not yet an exact science and, naturally, there are differences of opinion about the origin of any orebody. Although it may be difficult, in many deposits, for the investigator to gain much of practical value from ideas on ore genesis, nevertheless, relationships of ore to rock alteration and to structural features are at times great aids in locating and following ore bodies.

---

[1] Lindgren, W., Mineral Deposits, McGraw-Hill Book Co., 4th Ed., 1933, p. 204.

IMPORTANCE OF STRUCTURE — Structure refers to the build of the earth's crust. Those structural features which aid in mineral concentration or delimit orebodies may be primary sedimentational structures or deformational. Ore bodies may be found in sedimentary beds, may follow favorable horizons such as limestones, or may be concentrated in other sedimentary horizons. Deformational features, as fractures, folds, contacts, and barriers, may be causal determinants of ore deposition. Rock alteration associated with ore also is often related to structural features.

The examiner should be aware of the importance of thorough study of structure around and in an ore deposit as a basis for his deductions as to the extent and delineation of the ore. Hypotheses of origin and detailed description of the relations of structural features to orebodies may be found among the references already given.

Deformational structures, notably faults, may be post-ore in age. In this event, dislocation and displacement of part of an orebody may present a difficult problem to the investigator. Careful studies of both minor and major geological features in three-dimensional relationships are required to solve problems of this kind. Special drilling, trenching, or mine openings may be needed to give significant information. Methods of structural analysis applicable to cases of this kind involve descriptive geometry [1] or stereographic projection.[2]

As noted, three dimensions are involved. Maps and sections are means to an end; they help the examiner to see the three-dimensional picture and by contributing to an understanding of the geometry are a means for making quantitative measurements of features of importance. While geometry may be all-important in solving post-ore structural problems, structure has much broader implications on the genetic side.

---

[1] Billings, M. P., "Structural Geology," Prentice Hall, Inc., 1942.
[2] Fisher, D. J., "A New Projection Protractor," University of Chicago, Dept. of Geology, 1940.

CHAPTER 4

SAMPLING

THEORY — In the examination of a mining property the chemical and physical characteristics of the ore or mineral must be determined at least as accurately as other factors entering into the valuation, since upon these characteristics the value of the ore depends. This determination is generally made by "sampling."

Sampling is the process of taking a small portion of an article such that the consistency of the portion shall be representative of the whole. In precious-metal mining this consistency is generally known as "assay value" — the value of gold, silver, and other precious metals contained in the ore; in coal mining — the thermal units, fixed carbon, volatile ash, coking qualities, and any deleterious elements such as sulphur; in iron mining — the complete analysis of the ore, including iron, manganese, silica, alumina, lime, magnesia, phosphorus, sulphur, moisture, and also physical structure; in general, all characteristics, physical or chemical, which may affect the value of the ore or mineral.

The kind and amount of sampling depend upon the type of deposit and the degree of development — whether the property is a prospect, an exploration, or a partly or fully developed mine.

Sampling may be done at any exposed surface of the ore body, such as may be found in outcrops, shafts, drifts, crosscuts, or raises in the ore. Test pits or drill holes may be sunk for the express purpose of obtaining samples. Because of weathering, samples taken from outcrops are rarely representative of the unaltered ore.

As thorough sampling is usually expensive, the cost of a complete job is often unwarranted and a cheaper approximation must be substituted. The engineer should, however, weigh the situation thoroughly before subscribing to an alternative other than an accurate assay basis on which to build his conclusions.

The theory of sampling is that, if enough small portions of an article, properly spaced, are taken, their average value or consistency will approximate that of the whole very closely. Sampling should be, as nearly as possible, a mathematical-mechanical process, a mechanical collection of material at mathematically spaced intervals. It is not, and never should be considered, a haphazard procedure.

APPLICATION — Although, for all practical purposes, this mathematical-mechanical process may be accomplished in the sampling of sized material during the ore-dressing process, and closely approached in the sampling from drill holes of some types of uniform deposits, it is rarely applicable to sampling in a mine, because of the irregular distribution of exposures from which samples may be taken; but even in this case it does apply to each exposure sampled. From such irregular points the assembling of sample results becomes almost entirely a question of judgment.

The nature of the material to be sampled, its manner of occurrence, the amount of related evidence as to the properties of the ore or mineral — these may all vary so greatly that no set procedure can be prescribed. Each type of deposit presents an individual problem; hence, if the engineer expects to get satisfactory results at minimum expense, he must plan his sampling procedure with great care so as to suit the conditions at the individual property.

STANDARD PROCEDURES — In some mining districts and for some types of mineral deposits certain procedures, the result of much experience, become standardized and produce results of great accuracy.

For example: Through years of experience and the checking of results against methods, the techniques of sampling, preparation of samples, and analysis of iron ores from the Lake Superior District [1] have been so developed and standardized that samples taken in the mines, from diamond or churn drills, from test pits, or from stockpiles, railroad cars, or cargoes, check very closely in analysis.

This procedure is outlined in some detail in the example of sampling practice for iron ore in Chapter 6.

Whenever such a procedure has been developed for a certain type of ore or deposit, the engineer will do well to follow it unless thoroughly satisfied that an alternative method will be more accurate.

Current or past production in an operating property, or the experience of the district in which the property is located, may furnish collateral evidence of the type and grade of ore that may be expected; but the engineer should bear in mind that it is the ore to be mined which determines the value of the property, and that even in the same orebody the grade may change laterally or at depth. In fact, in metal mining uniformity is the exception.

SUPERVISION — If the engineer making the valuation has had charge of the sampling, he knows the limitations of the data he is using. If, however, the sampling and analysis

---

[1] "Methods of the Chemists of the U. S. Steel Corporation for the Sampling and Analysis of Iron and Manganese Ores," published by Carnegie Steel Company. 3rd Ed. 1926.

"The Iron Ores of Lake Superior"—Crowell & Murray. The Penton Press Co., Cleveland, Ohio. 7th Ed. 1930.

"Lake Superior Iron Ores"—The Lake Superior Iron Ore Association, Cleveland, Ohio. 1938.

have not been done under his supervision, he must question every phase of the work. It is not merely a matter of honesty, but of the technique necessary to give accurate results. Whenever possible a sufficient number of check samples should be taken to determine the degree of accuracy of the previous sampling. Where the sampling has been done honestly, but with faulty technique, it may be possible to determine a factor which, when applied to the results of such sampling, will give approximately the correct analyses.

METHODS OF SAMPLING

Channel and Chip Sampling — Exposed ore in place either underground or in open pits is usually sampled by channeling or chipping. Either method may be applied to test pits, drifts and crosscuts, raises, shafts, and backs or sides of stopes. The bottom or floor of mining openings is usually not a clean rock face and is avoided, whenever possible, as a spot for sampling. If necessary to sample the floor, it may be trimmed to expose a fresh face but care should be taken to clean off any fines that may have penetrated cracks in the rock.

Channeling consists of cutting grooves of uniform section across the face, usually at right angles to the formation. The customary size of the groove is from 1½ to 4 inches wide and about 1 inch deep, depending on the nature of the material. Hammer and moil are ordinarily used to cut the sample, for in hard or mixed formations a pick is easily deflected and is liable to chip too much of the softer material. In soft material, however, the pick is used, because it is faster than the moil and gives better results. The rock face should be brushed clean, or trimmed if necessary, at the point where the channel is to be cut, and the cuttings caught on a canvas or oilcloth which is cleaned prior to collecting each sample. If the quantity is large, it may be coned and quartered before being placed in the sample bag. Attention should be paid, particularly in reducing the

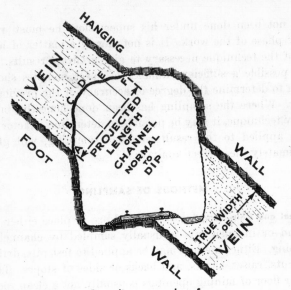

Fig. I. Sampling curved surfaces.

quantity of a sample, to the maximum size[1] of the individual piece or metal particle that may be retained in the final sample without abnormal effect on the assay. This limit varies among ores.

Since the backs of drifts and stopes are usually curved surfaces, the channel cut will be in the form of a curved groove instead of a straight line. Fig. 1 represents a cross section of a drift from which a relatively narrow vein, dipping at about 45°, is being sampled. The sample of the channel A-B-C-D-E-F is cut in the exposed face of the vein and is necessarily longer than the true thickness of the vein. In the field notes for a channel of this type, its projected length — the length it would have were it cut on a plane face normal to the dip — must be

[1] Richards, R. H. and Locke, C. E., ''Ore Dressing,'' McGraw-Hill Book Co., 2nd Ed., 1925, p. 316.
    Louis, H., ''Mineral Valuation,'' Chas. Griffin & Co., Ltd., 1923, p. 147.

recorded, and not the curved length. Otherwise an erroneous conception would be given of the vein thickness. When a channel of this type is being cut, the size of groove should be varied so that an equivalent amount of sample will be obtained from each projected foot of length.

A single sample is usually limited to about five feet of channel cut. Longer channels are subdivided into separate samples as called for. In channeling across layer structure, the natural breaks from one type of rock to another often offer the best dividing line between samples. Assays are thereby correlated with the geologic structure and hardness differences are kept separate, thus making it less difficult to cut uniform channels.

The spacing of channels is highly important; the intervals must be close enough to yield a representative part of the whole. In general, the richer and more irregular the ore, the closer will the samples have to be spaced; and the more uniform the ore, the greater may be the sample interval that will retain the required accuracy. Wherever possible, it is better practice to have the channels at regular intervals, as this makes the process more purely mathematical and eliminates one factor in the subsequent computations.

Chip sampling is used for hard or uniform ores where it is difficult to cut a channel and where the rock fractures independently of the values. The sample is obtained by breaking off small, equal-sized pieces from points uniformly distributed over the breast. The distance between any two points, horizontally and vertically, should be the same on any one face and may vary with the character of the ore.

Sampling Drill Holes — Both diamond and churn drills are used in prospecting and exploration and are often an important factor in determining the extent and the physical and chemical characteristics of the ore or mineral. The sampling of the core and cuttings (sludge) is of great importance. In drilling the hole, sampling is begun as soon as the ore is reached; and thereafter, if there is no change in the character of the material, all of the core and cuttings for each five feet of advance is retained as a sample until the ore boundary is reached. Sampling is begun anew with each change of material drilled.

In core drilling the core for each five feet of advance is kept separate from the cuttings. The core may then be split longitudinally into two halves. One half is retained to show the structure of the formation; the other half is analyzed separately, and this analysis is combined mathematically with the analysis of the sludge in the proportion that each represents of the volume of the material excavated from the drill hole.

The recovery of the sludge may be made either by passing the return water through a sluice or sludge box with suitable riffles to retain the sediment or by conducting it to barrels where the sediment is allowed to settle and the water is either drawn off or decanted.

Many errors are apt to creep into drill-hole sampling. In some drilling, there may be concentration of the valuable mineral; whereas in other instances, impurities may be washed out or lost. For instance, in the testing of gold placers by drilling, great care must be exercised to prevent a concentrating action from taking place at the bottom of the hole. In iron-ore prospecting, the gypsum may be dissolved out by the excess of water used in drilling, with a resulting incorrect sulphur determination in the laboratory. In drilling, soft or caving material from the upper part of the hole may slough off or be dislodged by the rods and contaminate the sample being taken below. This may be avoided by reaming and casing the hole after taking each five-foot sample.

When sludge boxes are used to collect the cuttings — as they were in all the earlier explorations for iron ore in the Lake Superior District — the analysis is often seriously affected by the impossibility of retaining all the fine, lighter material. In many cases, if not all, a loss of silica from the sample results in a higher analysis for iron than is actually contained in the ore body; and in one case, to the writers' knowledge, a marked reduction in phosphorus was apparently associated with the lighter material lost from the sample. This may be avoided by conducting all of the cuttings with the water to barrels, allowing them to settle until the water is clear, and then decanting off the water.

Grab Sampling and Decimating — The output of an operating mine may be tested by grab sampling, which may be applied to the freshly broken ore in the stope, to the ore in the tram cars, or to the ore in transit from the mines. The first procedure is objectionable in that the tonnage represented by the sample cannot be accurately estimated. In the last two the unit represented by the sample is approximately known. The method, which is the same in all cases, consists of taking from each pile, tram car or railroad car, according to some predetermined plan, a fixed number of equal-sized portions of each grade produced. Standard scoops may be used, to assure that the same amount of sample is taken from each point selected; and care must usually be exercised to have the sample contain the same proportion of fine and lump ore as the broken ore sampled.

When applied to units at selected intervals, as each fifth or tenth tram car, this method is usually called decimating. A fixed number of cars, or the day's or shift's output, may be combined and quartered down for analysis. In principle, both applications are entirely similar.

SAMPLING MATERIAL OF SEGREGATED SIZES — The sampling of stock piles usually presents a special problem because of the segregation of the coarse and fine material which occurs when a body of mixed material is dumped from an overhead point. Since the segregation is due to the ability of the lumps to roll down the slopes of the pile of fines, the particular disposition of the coarse and the fine material in any specific pile is dependent upon two factors:

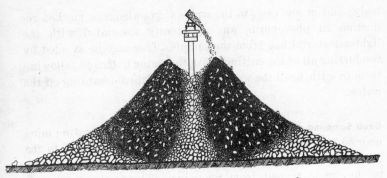

SIDE DUMP TRESTLE - EVENLY STOCKED ON BOTH SIDES

SIDE DUMP TRESTLE - STOCKED ONE SIDE FIRST   END DUMP TRESTLE

Sketches approximately to scale

Fig. 2. Segregation of sizes in stockpiling.

(a) Order or manner of piling.

(b) Percentage and relative size of lump in the mass.

Fig. 2 shows the probable segregation of mixed material for three common methods of stock-piling. The dimensions of the piles and the angles of repose are approximately those which are found in the storage of hematite iron ore. A pile 40 feet high usually has a top width of 10 feet and a bottom width of 110 feet, with sides slightly concave; thus approximately the upper two-thirds of the pile has a steeper angle of repose. These dimensions, of course, hold true only under normal conditions of weather and average moisture content in the ore. Ore stocked in freezing temperatures will assume a much steeper angle.

The upper sketch shows a cross section of a side-dumped stock pile in which the dumping has been regularly alternated from one side of the trestle to the other so that the two limbs of the pile have been kept at the same height throughout the entire piling process.

When a trestle car is dumped, the fine material stays about where it lands, whereas the lumps roll down the slope of the cone of fine material on whichever side they happen to fall. Some lumps are naturally prevented from rolling and remain in the pile of fine material, but the tendency is for the lumps to segregate from the fines, and so to form a center core of lumps between the two piles of fines and also a rimmed basin of lumps at the bottom upon which the pile of fines rests. There is also a tendency for the lumps to be more or less graded in size upward from the bottom of the pile.

In the lower left-hand corner of Fig. 2 is shown a cross section of an unevenly distributed side-dump stock pile. In this case, the trestle cars were first dumped continually on the right-hand side until the pile there was at nearly its full height and were then dumped on the left side, the left-hand pile thus being formed on top of the flank of the other. The probable segregation of the material according to size is decidedly different from the first case cited.

The lower right-hand sketch of Fig. 2 represents a longitudinal section through an end-dumped stock pile. Since all the material is dumped from a single line of overhead points, only one pile will be formed, and the tendency will be for the lumps to segregate entirely at the base of the pile.

The percentage of lumps contained in the run-of-mine product changes the relative size of the segregated piles but does not appreciably affect their location, whereas the relative size of the lumps probably affects slightly the location of the segregated piles because of the increased distance of roll of larger pieces.

From the foregoing it is apparent that each stock pile presents an individual sampling problem because, in sampling, accurate results can be attained only when the samples include the proper proportion of coarse and fine material. To secure this proportion, the choice of sampling method and the field procedure must be based on a thorough study of the pile in question and of the run-of-mine product in order to determine the order of piling and the percentage of lumps to be expected. Some ores disintegrate upon exposure to air, with the result that the stock-piled ore may vary considerably in consistency from the original run-of-mine. A certain amount of preliminary testing is often required before a proper sampling method can be determined. In this preliminary work, trenching, test-pitting, and drilling are sometimes resorted to. Complete cross-sectioning of the pile gives the most accurate results, but is ordinarily too expensive to be warranted.

SAMPLING ERRATIC ORES — When the values are so erratically distributed throughout an ore deposit that the usual methods of sampling fail, it may be necessary to take unusually large, or "bulk" samples of many tons or even hundreds or thousands of tons and run a mill test on each sample. This is found to be true particularly of ores of the metallic minerals, such as gold, silver, or copper. In the Lake Superior copper mines no method of sampling other than the mill test on a large tonnage has been found satisfactory.

Distribution and size of the individual metal particles in the gangue are the erratic factors that make sampling difficult. A high metal price, as with gold, accentuates the problem, since one or a few such particles in a small sample add greatly to the assay value per ton. Thin veinlets and rich streaks within them offer further difficulties, as the width of the veins is small compared with the width of the drift or stope face. In sampling such ores by the usual methods, as channel cuts or chips, it is often the number of samples taken that gives reliability to the results rather than the accuracy of each single sample.

SAMPLING RECORDS — In any method of sampling, the records kept are fully as important as the field practices used. Type of sample, length or size of sample, true thickness or width of vein, intervals between samples, location, date, and all other relevant data must be entered upon the records in order that the assays reported shall be of future value.

Field samples are usually put in individual canvas bags. A reference number or identifying symbol is assigned to each sample, marked on a tag and recorded in the notes. The tag is then placed inside the bag, which is often equipped with a locking device or seal. Tags must be resistant to moisture, dirt, and abrasion. Heavy paper, wood strips, or metal discs are commonly used for this purpose.

As a safeguard against loss, it is well to copy sampling field notes as soon as possible into a permanent office record, at which time the individual entries can be arranged according to field location and thus retained in more accessible form.

The best method of setting forth the results of sampling is by the use of assay maps. These may be tracings or white prints of the plans, longitudinal or cross sections of the mine. The location from which each sample is taken is indicated on the maps, and beside its location are noted the sample number and the value (or important constituents). The assay maps may also show the tonnage calculated for each block of ore and the average analysis.

This subject is discussed and illustrated in more detail in the first example of sampling practice given in Chapter 6.

ERRORS IN SAMPLING — Sampling results may go astray at any one of several points during the process of estimating ore values, and for one or more of the following reasons:

1. "Salted" or erroneous samples.
2. Insufficient number of samples.
3. Improper location of samples.
4. Improper or "salted" chemical analysis.
5. Incorrect weighting of assays.

"Salting" is the act of raising the value of the sample above that of the ore exposure from which it was taken. It may be intentional or unintentional. Intentional "salting" will not be dealt with in this text except for a warning that the examining engineer must be on his guard whenever the conditions surrounding the examination are in the least suspicious and must take every precaution against malicious tampering with the samples or containers. Samples should be handled promptly, storage avoided. Instances of "salting" schemes and their detection are to be found throughout mining literature, and afford interesting and worthwhile reading. One of the simplest and most practical precautions is for the engineer himself to take check samples at various points, guard them personally, and have them assayed by an impartial chemist.

Unintentional distortion of sample values should be closely watched for by an estimating engineer, as it can easily creep into the sampling method. Sampling an extensive property is a large task, and the actual labor of sample cutting must necessarily be detailed to hired help. Slovenly workers are, of course, always to be guarded against; but overconscientious workers are a source of trouble too, as they may alter the samples by their very attempts to do the job too well. The engineer can avoid this difficulty to a large extent by laying out the work in advance and making the operation as simple and mechanical as possible. He can so plan that most or all of the samples can be cut by following rules and he can himself mark the spots to be sampled. Thus he will minimize the chance of a workman's including in the sample extremely rich spots or extraneous material.

An insufficient number of samples (points sampled) for an orebody of given size and consistency will often yield erroneous results even though the samples are taken in a mechanical manner from points properly located. Each sample, as taken, represents an unduly large volume of ore and may not be a true specimen of the average values contained therein. In the location of points to be sampled, particular attention should be given to avoiding those at which the ore is obviously rich or spotty, for in valuable ores especially, a few specks of extremely high-grade material will appreciably alter the assay. Although it has been stated previously that sampling gives best results if done in a purely mechanical manner, this is true only when a large number of samples are taken at relatively close spacing. In taking fewer samples, the engineer must use his experience and common sense as a guide for the location of sample points.

An improper analysis by an impartial laboratory is a rare occurrence and can almost be eliminated as a source of error.

CHAPTER 5

SAMPLING CALCULATIONS

OUTLINING OF ORE — After the sampling has been completed and the analyses have been received from the laboratory, and before attempting to calculate the averages from groups of individual samples, the preliminary outlines of the orebodies should be determined. If several grades of ore are included in one orebody, the outlines of the ore by grades may be necessary. This may be done best from the sample maps, on which should be noted also all geological data on which the outline of the orebodies might depend. The boundaries of the ore may be property lines, contacts, or indefinite limits which depend entirely upon the sample assays. This preliminary outlining of the ore and grades is necessary at this point as a guide to the proper grouping of assays and for the determination of the weight that should be given to the individual assays of each group.

THEORY OF SAMPLE WEIGHTING — The calculation of averages from groups of individual sample assays is a problem of mathematical weighting. Fundamentally, the calculation is based upon a determination of the relative importance of each sample with respect to the other samples with which it is combined. A fairly taken sample is intended to be representative of the orebody or mineral mass at the point where it was taken. In practice, however, there is always an interval or distance spacing between the points tested and, therefore, each sample must be considered as representative of a certain surrounding volume, the size of which depends upon the location of the sample in question and upon its relation to adjacent samples or to ore limits.

Thus, when an orebody is systematically sampled at numerous points, each sample must be considered as representative of the ore not only at the point where it is taken, but outward in all directions from this point halfway to all adjacent sample locations. In other words, a sample must continue to be considered as representative of the ore until it is relieved of the responsibility by another sample. This can be shown best by citing the two extreme cases, as follows:

1. If the entire orebody is taken as a sample, the sample, of course, represents the exact assay of the ore, and each sample particle is held only to its own assay because there are no extra particles participating. The interval between points sampled is zero, and the influence of each sample particle is limited to its own volume.

2. If only one point in the entire orebody is sampled, the assay of the one sample must be assumed to represent the whole mass, and the influence of the sample must continue outward from the point tested to the ore limits in all directions. The volume attributable to the sample is the volume of the whole orebody.

In the first of these instances the relative value of each sample particle is the same as that of each other particle and the relative importance of each and all of the particles may be considered as unity, whereas in the second instance the value of the sample particle is a maximum and the relative importance may be considered as infinite.

Thus, the importance of sample weighting varies inversely with the number of samples taken for a given orebody or portion thereof. If a large enough number of samples is taken, a straight unweighted average will give a true result because the intervals between samples are correspondingly reduced and each sample is therefore representative of an insignificant volume as compared to the whole. In ordinary practice, samples are not taken at close enough intervals for this to hold true. As the interval between samples increases, each sample assumes a greater importance because of its increased volume of influence and, correspondingly, increases the importance of sample weighting.

WEIGHTING OF SAMPLES — The true weight of a sample is its "volume of influence"; hence, whenever feasible, sample weights should be assigned in ratio to the respective volumes. In grouping samples where three dimensions are being dealt with, the weight attached to each sample must be proportional to the volume of the block of ore at whose center the sample was taken.

In determining the assay value of a plane or warped surface such as a stope face or drift face, there are, of course, only two dimensions (length and breadth) to be considered and it will be impossible to attach volume weights to the samples. In this case, it is proper to weight the samples according to the "areas of influence" at whose centers the respective samples were taken.

Again, in the instance of a row of samples, where only one dimension (linear) is involved, it is appropriate to consider the "distance of influence" of each sample as its proper weight.

It must be borne in mind, however, that the ultimate aim in sampling is to determine the value of a volume of ore. Likewise, the ultimate purpose of weighting each sample that enters into the calculation of an average is to attribute to the sample its respective volume.

Although, in certain instances, weights may be computed on distance between samples (linear dimension only) or on areas of influence (two dimensions only), these are but preliminary steps toward the determination of true volume weights and are used either because the volume cannot be computed for lack of data or because the areas or distances are in proportion to volume.

When samples are taken equidistant from each other in one

dimension, the interval distance may be omitted from the calculations because it would factor out if included; when samples are taken equidistant from each other in two dimensions, both of these distances may be omitted from the calculations for the same reason; and if equal-sized samples are taken equidistant from each other in each of three dimensions, the samples may all be mixed to form a single composite sample because the dimensional intervals, if included, merely impute identical volumes to each sample.

DEGREE OF ACCURACY — The subject of "assay weighting," though discussed at length in the transactions of most of the mining societies and in mining literature in general, remains a debatable question when attempting an exact mathematical analysis. Fortunately, the refinements which have entailed the greatest amount of controversy are, in a sense, beyond the limits of practical application. Except by chance, a sample cannot be exact; in grouping sample assays, it is wasted effort to attempt a calculation that will be mathematically rigid, when the data upon which the calculation is based probably contain certain inherent errors. In all sampling calculations the probable degree of accuracy attainable should be borne in mind, so that the various phases of the calculations will be kept precise, relative to each other. The important point is that while being combined, the assays must be logically weighted according to what they represent. Any deviations from this plan must be based upon sound reasoning.

SPACING AND ARRANGEMENT — The purpose of this text in **OF SAMPLES** dealing with sampling calculations is to set forth the fundamental principles involved in grouping assays. Practically all sampling estimates are individual problems in some respect or another, but the theory remains the same. The following examples illustrate the theory; no attempt is made, however, to cover all possible cases.

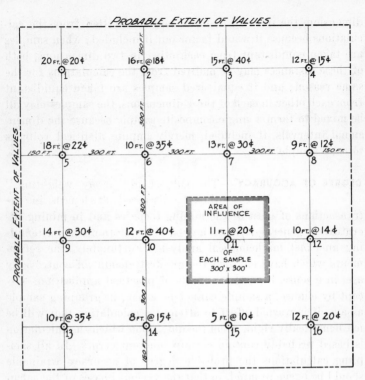

Fig. 3. Placer area sampled at regular intervals.

UNIFORM SPACING ON RECTANGULAR CO-ORDINATES

EXAMPLE 1.

Extended Area Fig. 3 is the plan assay map of a placer area which has been drilled and sampled at each 300-ft. intersection of a rectangular co-ordinate system. It is assumed that there are no property, assay, or other boundaries which limit the extent of the deposit, and that values extend one-half of the co-ordinate interval beyond the outside rows on each side. Each drill hole will lie at the center of a 300-ft. square of influence.

It will be apparent that, so far as area is concerned, each sample has equal influence and that if the depth (thickness) of the placer were equal at all intersections, a straight average of the sample assays would give the average analysis of the placer; but, in considering volume, the samples are not of equal importance, as the depths of the sampled holes vary. The samples are, therefore, weighted according to depth by taking the assay-foot product. Though not so stated, this gives a volume weight to each sample. The computations are as follows:

Sample Lengths		Assay Value		Foot-Assay Product
20 ft.	@	20¢ per cu. yd.		400
16	@	18	=	288
15	@	40	=	600
12	@	15	=	180
18	@	22	=	396
10	@	35	=	350
13	@	30	=	390
9	@	12	=	108
14	@	30	=	420
12	@	40	=	480
11	@	20	=	220
10	@	14	=	140
10	@	35	=	350
8	@	15	=	120
5	@	10	=	50
12	@	20	=	240
195				4732

$4732 \div 195 = 24.26$¢, average assay value per cubic yard.

$195 \div 16 = 12.18$ ft., average thickness of bed.

$= 4.06$ yd., thickness of bed.

As the ore values are assumed to extend one-half the co-ordinate interval beyond the outside rows of holes, the total area of probable values is a square 400 yards on a side, and therefore:

$400 \times 400 \times 4.06 = 649,600$ cu. yd. of gravel available.

$649,600 \times \$.2426 = \$157,600$, total values available.

EXAMPLE 2.

Included Area — Valence Weights If, in Example 1, the volume to be considered were limited to the area bounded by the drill holes, the situation would be as is shown in Fig. 4, where all samples do not have equal areas of influence. The average analysis of each volume inclosed between adjacent co-ordinate lines may be obtained by combining the assay-foot products of the four corners; the average depth of each unit is the arithmetical mean of the four corner-depths; and the several units may then be combined by the use of the depth-assay products, as tabulated on page 52.

It is apparent, however, in the calculation that the corner samples (No. 1, 4, 13, & 16) have entered into the computations only once, the intermediate side samples (No. 2, 3, 5, 8, 9, 12, 14, & 15) twice, and each of the interior samples (No. 6, 7, 10, & 11) four times. Therefore, the entire group of samples may be combined in a single operation by using weights of one,

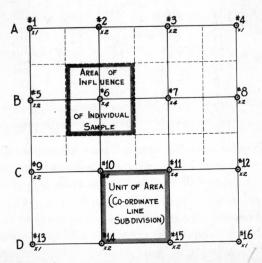

Fig. 4. Sampling at intersections of regular co-ordinates.

two, and four. This weighting is determined by the number of units — in this case squares — affected by each sample. This type of weighting has been aptly termed the "valence" of the sample, from the chemical term denoting the combining power of the elements.

Sample No.	Field Data Feet & Assay		Foot-Assay Product	Unit Areas Affected (Valence)	Valence -Foot Wt.	Valence-Foot-Assay Product
1	20' @	20¢	400	1	20	400
2	16	18	288	2	32	576
3	15	40	600	2	30	1200
4	12	15	180	1	12	180
5	18	22	396	2	36	792
6	10	35	350	4	40	1400
7	13	30	390	4	52	1560
8	9	12	108	2	18	216
9	14	30	420	2	28	840
10	12	40	480	4	48	1920
11	11	20	220	4	44	880
12	10	14	140	2	20	280
13	10	35	350	1	10	350
14	8	15	120	2	16	240
15	5	10	50	2	10	100
16	12	20	240	1	12	240
				36	428	11174

$11,174 \div 428 = 26.11¢$, average assay.

$428 \div 36 = 11.89$ ft., average thickness.

The same method may be used in determining the total volume or number of cubic yards in the deposit; i.e., each depth is given a valence or weight in proportion to the number of squares affected. It is apparent that this method of determining the volume is not mathematically exact unless the orebody is flat-lying and the depths are equal. Where conditions warrant, either a dip-factor or the prismoidal formula may be used to obtain the correct volume from the apparent depths shown by drilling. The computations are:

Unit Area No.	Samples No.	Field Data Feet & Assay		Foot-Assay Product	Average Thickness		Average Assay		Volume-Assay Product (Thickness × 1 × Assay)
1	1	20' @ 20¢		400					
	2	16	18	288	$\frac{64}{4}$ = 16.0'		$\frac{1434}{64}$ = 22.406¢		358.496
	5	18	22	396					
	6	10	35	350					
		64		1434					
2	2	16' @ 18¢		288					
	3	15	40	600	$\frac{54}{4}$ = 13.5'		$\frac{1628}{54}$ = 30.148¢		406.998
	6	10	35	350					
	7	13	30	390					
		54		1628					
3	3	15' @ 40¢		600					
	4	12	15	180	$\frac{49}{4}$ = 12.25'		$\frac{1278}{49}$ = 26.082¢		319.505
	7	13	30	390					
	8	9	12	108					
		49		1278					
4	5	18' @ 22¢		396					
	6	10	35	350	$\frac{54}{4}$ = 13.5'		$\frac{1646}{54}$ = 30.481¢		411.493
	9	14	30	420					
	10	12	40	480					
		54		1646					
5	6	10' @ 35¢		350					
	7	13	30	390	$\frac{46}{4}$ = 11.5'		$\frac{1440}{46}$ = 31.304¢		359.996
	10	12	40	480					
	11	11	20	220					
		46		1440					
6	7	13' @ 30¢		390					
	8	9	12	108	$\frac{43}{4}$ = 10.75'		$\frac{858}{43}$ = 19.953¢		214.495
	11	11	20	220					
	12	10	14	140					
		43		858					
7	9	14' @ 30¢		420					
	10	12	40	480	$\frac{44}{4}$ = 11.0'		$\frac{1370}{44}$ = 31.136¢		342.496
	13	10	35	350					
	14	8	15	120					
		44		1370					
8	10	12' @ 40¢		480					
	11	11	20	220	$\frac{36}{4}$ = 9.0'		$\frac{870}{36}$ = 24.167¢		217.503
	14	8	15	120					
	15	5	10	50					
		36		870					
9	11	11' @ 20¢		220					
	12	10	14	140	$\frac{38}{4}$ = 9.5'		$\frac{650}{38}$ = 17.105¢		162.498
	15	5	10	50					
	16	12	20	240					
		38		650		107.00			2793.480

2793.480 ÷ 107.00 = 26.11¢, average assay value per cu. yd.

107.00 ÷ 9 = 11.89 ft., average thickness.

Grouping into Rows The composite assay of the group may also be calculated by averaging each row of holes and then combining the several rows.[1] Since the distance between holes in any row (Fig. 4) is the same throughout the length of the row, the end samples should be given only half the weight of the intermediate samples when combining their foot-assay products. Likewise, when combining the row averages by their depth-assay products to obtain an average for the entire area, the end rows will carry only half the weight of the intermediate rows. If the weight attributable to the corner samples is taken as one, the intermediate side samples will again have weights of two, and the interior samples will again carry weights of four.

The final average result as to assay or thickness for a group of samples taken at the intersections of a regular co-ordinate system will be the same whether the averaging process is viewed from the standpoint of area of influence of individual samples, or of separation into unit areas, or of grouping by rows. In certain instances, when a definite allocation of values is desired, one of these methods would be used to the exclusion of the rest.

Equidistant Spacing on 60° Co-ordinates — Regularly spaced samples need not be on a rectangular co-ordinate system. Samples may be taken at the intersections of a 60° co-ordinate system, as shown in Fig. 5. The unit of area in this case is an equilateral triangle, and the areas of influence of all the points sampled are identical hexagons.

Semiregular Spacing — The samples may be regularly or irregularly spaced in rows, and the rows themselves may be regularly or irregularly spaced. In any combination of samples in rows, the average analysis of the plane or section through each row may be determined by weighing the samples in the row by their

---

[1] "Valuation of Dredging Ground"—C. S. Herzig.

respective lengths and distances of influence. The row sections
may then be combined to obtain an overall average by weighting
each section in proportion to its area and distance of influence.
In other words, the samples in a row may be combined by areas
of influence to obtain the average for the full section represented by the row and the rows may then be grouped in proportion to their volumes of influence. Fig. 6 shows an example of
regularly spaced samples in irregularly spaced rows.

Irregular Spacing — The exploratory drilling of an orebody is
seldom done in a consistently systematic manner, for a com-

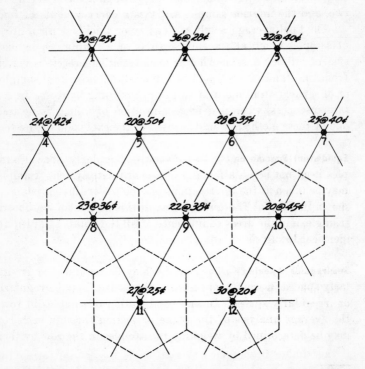

Fig. 5. Samples equidistant from each other on 60° co-ordinates.

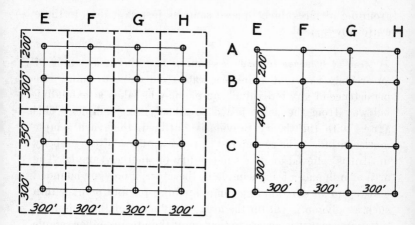

Fig. 6. Sampling at semiregular intervals.

plete program is justified only when preliminary work has roughly outlined the limits of the deposit and shown sufficient promise of values to warrant the necessary expenditure of capital. The engineer sent to examine a property will usually find that the previous work has resulted in a set of irregularly spaced samples, and unless he feels that the work should be done over, his best course is to adapt his program to the results at hand. Often this will mean a continuation of irregular drilling or sampling, with the locations determined by a study of the previous data. A clear understanding of the geology, in particular the structural relationship, may be critical to the effective planning of such a program.

When proper judgment is exercised in combining the several assays, a group of irregularly spaced samples which have been fairly taken should give just as accurate a composite result as samples in a symmetrical layout. Care must be taken to avoid giving undue prominence to rich spots by concentrating too many holes in such areas. The basic principle of weighting each sample according to its volume of influence applies to the grouping of irregularly spaced samples just as it does to those uniformly spaced.

Area of Influence Method   Assuming that the assay value of an orebody varies at a uniform rate from point to point,[1] the persistence of any individual sample may be taken as extending halfway from the point tested to all adjacent samples. This agrees with the theory previously outlined, that each sample must continue to be considered as representative of the orebody until it is relieved of its responsibility by another sample. The area of influence of any sample is, therefore, a polygon bounded midway to all surrounding sample points; for any point within such a polygon is within the area of influence of the sample in question, since it is nearer to that point than to any other sample point. In combining the group of assays, each sample is given its volume-of-influence weight by multiplying its area of influence by both the sample length (thickness or depth of bed) and the assay value to give a volume-assay product.

EXAMPLE 3.

To demonstrate the application of the method, take the hypothetical drilling plan shown in Fig. 7, in which the actual spacing of the holes (sample points) and their respective values are given for an area one-eighth mile square.

The problem is most readily solved graphically with the aid of a planimeter for scaling the respective platted areas, although as an alternative method each polygon may be subdivided into triangles and the area of each triangle computed from base and altitude measurements. The area of influence of any hole — for example, interior hole No. 10 — is defined by drawing the lines 10-5, 10-7, 10-11, 10-14, 10-13, and 10-9, con-

---

[1] "Mining Engineers' Handbook"—R. Peele. John Wiley & Sons, Inc., 2nd Ed., p. 475.

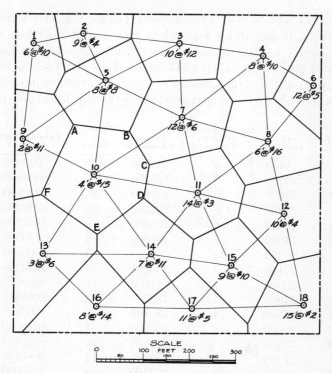

Fig. 7. Area of influence method of combining irregularly spaced assays.

necting hole No. 10 with each of the surrounding holes. Upon these radial lines the respective perpendicular bisectors AB, BC, CD, DE, EF, and FA are then erected to form the polygon ABCDEF, which bounds the area of influence of the hole in question. This process is then repeated for each of the other holes within the given area to produce a series of polygons such as are shown on the sketch. The respective areas of influence may then be scaled off with a planimeter accurately enough for most purposes. A tabulation of the data and computed results is given on page 58.

It is readily seen from an inspection of the plan sketch that polygons 13 and 16 are more likely than any of the others to be in error for lack of definite data. An additional drill hole located near the lower left-hand corner of the plat would either assure or disprove the presence of the wide variations in thickness and value that are now apparent between holes 13 and 16.

Hole No.	Area of Influence	Sample Length (Depth) (Thickness)	Volume Factor	Assay	Volume-Assay Product
1	15450	6′	92700	$10	927000
2	13900	9	125100	4	500400
3	24600	10	246000	12	2952000
4	27900	8	223200	10	2232000
5	26050	8	208400	8	1667200
6	14000	12	168000	5	840000
7	29250	12	351000	6	2106000
8	27700	6	166200	16	2659200
9	20900	2	41800	11	459800
10	34900	4	139600	15	2094000
11	27700	14	387800	3	1163400
12	26000	10	260000	4	1040000
13	32450	3	97350	6	584100
14	27100	7	189700	11	2086700
15	23500	9	211500	10	2115000
16	25700	8	205600	14	2878400
17	19600	11	215600	5	1078000
18	19150	15	287250	2	574500
	435850		3616800		27957700

3,616,800 ÷ 435,850 = 8.298 ft., average thickness.
27,957,700 ÷ 3,616,800 = $7.73 per ton, average value.

Assuming the specific gravity of the ore to be 3.0, would give

$$\frac{3,616,800 \times 3.0 \times 62.5}{2000} = 339,075 \text{ tons of ore available.}$$

339,075 × $7.73 = $2,621,050, total values.

EXAMPLE 4.

Triangular Grouping Possibly the simplest and most widely used method of combining irregularly spaced placer samples is by grouping into triangles. The area under consideration is subdivided into triangular blocks, with a drill hole or sample at each corner. An average assay for each block is computed by combining the three samples in proportion to their foot-assay products, and the volume-assay products of the individual triangular prismoids are then combined to give a final average assay value for the whole orebody.

The degree of irregularity of sample spacing, the uniformity of individual assays or the degree to which they are erratic, and the configuration of the body being sampled are the important factors to be considered in adapting this method to the sampling job. Particular care must be taken to avoid placing undue emphasis on any hole by centering too many triangles about it.

Fig. 8 is the assay map of a hypothetical placer deposit with samples grouped into triangles. A record of the computations is most readily kept by numbering each triangle and tabulating the data upon a form sheet, as on page 60.

It will be noted from the following calculations that the volume-assay product for each prismoid is, in reality, the value of the ore in the prismoid. By a tabulation of the results as given on the form sheet a direct allocation of values into individual prismoids is obtained in the process of arriving at the total value for the area and the average assay of the area.

The area of each triangle has been computed by two methods and the average result used to figure the volume of the prismoid. The first figure listed under triangle area is the product of the scaled base by one-half the scaled altitude; the second figure is the mean of two or more planimeter readings; the final figure is the average of the first two. It is obviously not necessary to use both these methods to compute the triangle

Δ No.	Sample Data	Foot-Assay Product	Average Assay	Average Thickness	Area of Triangle	Vol. of Prismoid Cu. Ft.	Cu. Yd.	Total Values in Prismoid
1	20'@33¢ 15 38 16 40 — 51	660 570 640 —— 1870	$\dfrac{1870}{51} =$ 36.67¢	$\dfrac{51}{3} =$ 17.00 ft.	21534 Bx½A 21600 Pl. 21570 Av.	366690	13581	$4980.20
2	20'@33¢ 18 45 15 38 — 53	660 810 570 —— 2040	$\dfrac{2040}{53} =$ 38.49¢	$\dfrac{53}{3} =$ 17.67 ft.	24990 25000 25000	441750	16361	6297.30
3	18'@45¢ 14 30 15 38 — 47	810 420 570 —— 1800	$\dfrac{1800}{47} =$ 38.30¢	$\dfrac{47}{3} =$ 15.67 ft.	35680 35900 35790	560830	20771	7955.30
4	16'@40¢ 15 38 13 60 — 44	640 570 780 —— 1990	$\dfrac{1990}{44} =$ 45.23¢	$\dfrac{44}{3} =$ 14.67 ft.	32175 32300 32240	472960	17517	7922.90
5	15'@38¢ 12 45 13 60 — 40	570 540 780 —— 1890	$\dfrac{1890}{40} =$ 47.25¢	$\dfrac{40}{3} =$ 13.33 ft.	32660 32900 32780	436957	16184	7646.90
6	15'@38¢ 14 30 12 45 — 41	570 420 540 —— 1530	$\dfrac{1530}{41} =$ 37.32¢	$\dfrac{41}{3} =$ 13.67 ft.	22400 22300 22350	305525	11316	4223.10
7	13'@60¢ 12 45 17 30 — 42	780 540 510 —— 1830	$\dfrac{1830}{42} =$ 43.57¢	$\dfrac{42}{3} =$ 14.00 ft.	30530 30600 30560	427840	15846	6904.10
8	12'@45¢ 19 50 17 30 — 48	540 950 510 —— 2000	$\dfrac{2000}{48} =$ 41.67¢	$\dfrac{48}{3} =$ 16.00 ft.	28512 28700 28600	457600	16948	7062.20
9	12'@45¢ 14 30 19 50 — 45	540 420 950 —— 1910	$\dfrac{1910}{45} =$ 42.44¢	$\dfrac{45}{3} =$ 15.00 ft.	28512 28700 28600	429000	15889	6743.30

Totals for Area = 144413   59735.30

$59,735.30 ÷ 144,413 cu. yd. = 41.36¢, average assay value per cubic yard

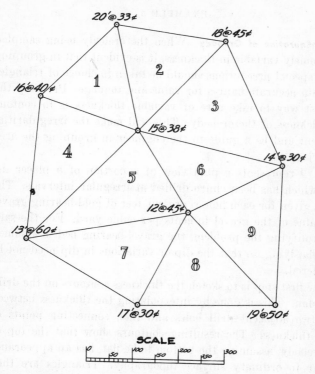

Fig. 8. Triangle grouping of irregularly spaced samples—arbitrary choice of triangles.

areas. They have been used here merely to show that comparable results may be obtained by the two types of mensuration; the final choice rests with the person who is performing the calculations. For extreme accuracy, the base and altitude of each triangle may be computed from totals of latitude and departure, or the area may be found by the double-meridian-distance method. No attempt has been made in these computations to carry the accuracy beyond the fourth figure; the field data are not sufficiently accurate to warrant such procedure.

EXAMPLE 5.

Configuration of Orebody   When the orebody being sampled is extremely variable in thickness, it is evident that in grouping assays special precautions should be taken in choice of triangles to obtain accurate figures for value and tonnage. Probably the simplest way to take care of variable thickness is to contour the thickness of the orebody. This will make the irregularities apparent and be a guide to the engineer in grouping the area into triangles.

Fig. 9 represents a plan view of a portion of a placer deposit which has been churn-drilled at irregular intervals. The values given for each hole represent feet of gold-bearing gravel and value of the gravel in cents per cubic yard. For the sake of simplifying the problem, the gravel-bearing bed is assumed to be flat-lying, so that the dip or variations in dip need not be considered.

The first step is to sketch the thickness contours on the drill-hole plan. This is done by interpolating the thickness between each two adjacent drill holes and then connecting points of equal thickness. The resulting contours show that the top of the orebody, assuming the bottom to be flat, has an appearance similar to ordinary surface topography. Triangles are then laid out between holes to include, as nearly as possible, a uniform slope throughout each triangle.

The mathematical calculation of assay averages is no different in this method from the calculation in that just outlined. Greater accuracy, however, should be attained, because a complete picture of the orebody is made available and the engineer can adapt the method to the orebody variations to a much greater extent.

In actual practice it is permissible to assume one surface (either top or bottom) of the orebody to be flat only when it is a plane surface or nearly so or when both surfaces vary symmetrically from the median. The dip, when regular, can be

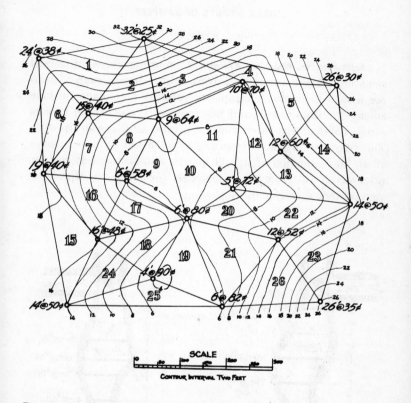

Fig. 9. Triangle grouping of irregularly spaced samples—based on thickness contours.

omitted from the contour map and from the immediate calculations and be applied as a general factor in computing the prismoid volumes. When both top and bottom contours (use colored inks to distinguish) are required to show the configuration of the orebody, the selection of triangles becomes doubly complicated because the samples must be grouped, if possible, so as to retain plane surfaces on both sides of the prismoids.

LINEAR GROUPS OF SAMPLES

EXAMPLE 6.

Arithmetic vs. Weighted Average Computing the arithmetical mean or straight unweighted average of a linear group of sample assays to obtain a composite value is a common mistake among the uninitiated, and has frequently resulted in serious error, particularly when rich or erratic ores are dealt with. This may be illustrated from the hypothetical group of assays of an 80-ft. portion of a gold quartz vein sampled at regular intervals of 10 feet by cross channels normal to the dip of the vein as shown in Fig. 10-A:

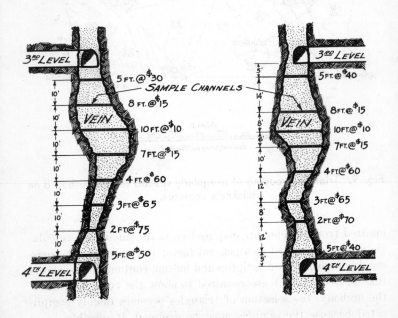

Fig. 10. Linear groups of channel samples.

Width	Assay
5 feet	$30 per ton
8	15
10	10
7	15
4	60
3	65
2	75
5	50
44 feet	$320

$44 \div 8 = 5\frac{1}{2}$ feet, average width of face.

$\$320 \div 8 = \$40$, arithmetical mean assay value of face.

Whereas the straight arithmetical mean appears to show $5\frac{1}{2}$ feet of ore averaging $40 per ton, yet if these samples are weighted according to the area of which each is representative, the result is entirely different, as follows:

Width	Assay	Assay-Foot Product
5	30	150
8	15	120
10	10	100
7	15	105
4	60	240
3	65	195
2	75	150
5	50	250
44 feet		1310 (ft. $)

$1,310 \div 44 = \$29.77$, average assay value of ore face, as contrasted with the higher figure of $40 per ton which was obtained by a straight arithmetical average of assay figures.

$44 \div 8 = 5\frac{1}{2}$ feet, average width of face.

$80 \times 5\frac{1}{2} = 440$ sq. ft., face area of vein.

EXAMPLE 7.

Distance of Influence A similar set of assays but with channels spaced at uneven measured distances is shown in Fig. 10-B. It is necessary, in this instance, to make some assumption in regard to extension of values in the vein beyond the end channels. This extension, as indicated, is taken as five feet, although from the given channel spacing, seven feet would be a reasonable assumption beyond the top channel and six feet below the bottom one. An extension of values for five feet assumes that the next channel beyond those shown on the sketch is 10 feet away.

This group of irregularly spaced samples would be averaged as follows:

Sample Width	Distance between Samples	Distance of Influence of Each Sample	Area of Influence of Each Sample	Assay of Sample	Area-Assay Product
	10 ft.				
5 ft.		12 ft.	60 sq. ft.	$40	2400
	14				
8		11	88	15	1320
	8				
10		7	70	10	700
	6				
7		8	56	15	840
	10				
4		11	44	60	2640
	12				
3		10	30	65	1950
	8				
2		10	20	70	1400
	12				
5		11	55	40	2200
	10		423 (sq. ft.)		13450 (sq. ft. $)

13,450 ÷ 423 = $31.80, average assay value of ore face.

Each assay, it will be noted, is multiplied by its length and by one-half the distance to the channels on each side, thus weighting each value by the area attributable to that value.

EXAMPLE 8.

Minimum Stoping Width In working narrow veins or thin seams the question of "minimum stoping width" complicates the mining problem and, in turn, affects the procedure of sampling such openings. By "minimum stoping width" is meant the narrowest stope opening that it is economical to drive in the regular course of mining. This can be shown most readily by taking the extreme case of a gold quartz vein which, in certain parts of the mine, has a normal width of three to four feet but which, at other points, thins down to a seam only six inches thick. It is obviously impossible to stope a six-inch seam without cutting out also a portion of the wall rock in order to make the stope large enough for the miners. The narrowest stope width in which it is possible for the miners to perform their work expeditiously is termed the "minimum stoping width."

In the sampling of a stope in which the vein is narrower than the stoped opening, the usual procedure is to cut the channels across the vein only and to record in the sampling notebook both the length of the channel and the full width of the stope at the same point. The sample is then assayed in the regular manner, but when it is combined with other assays to obtain the face average, its assay value is reduced to that fraction of the total stope width which is represented by the vein, and this reduced assay value is then weighted by the full stope width. In other words, the channel is assumed to extend the full stope width, and the assay of the vein itself is combined with a zero assay for the additional rock width to produce a discounted or diluted assay value for the full width.

A stope three feet wide is mined along a quartz vein. To obtain an estimate of values, the vein is cross-channelled at 10-ft. intervals. In one place the vein is only one foot wide. The assay of this particular sample is $90 per ton. In combining this sample with the others to calculate a face average, the value of $90 per ton for one foot of channel length must be averaged with that of two feet of barren rock because the stope is three feet wide. The assay of $90 for one foot would, therefore, be equivalent to one of $30 for three feet and would be so used. When there are evidences that the mineralizing solutions have so penetrated the country rock of one or both walls as to give irregular and minor assay values to this rock, the use of a sample channel the full width of the expected stope will give a more accurate total result.

To illustrate further, take the sampling data listed above for Fig. 10-A and assume that in working this deposit the minimum stoping width is five feet. The average assay value of the face would then be computed as follows:

Stope Width	Vein Width	Assay	Assay-Foot Product
5	5	30	150
8	8	15	120
10	10	10	100
7	7	15	105
5	4	60	240
5	3	65	195
5	2	75	150
5	5	50	250
50			1310

$1,310 \div 50 = \$26.20$, average assay value of the stope face.
$50 \div 8 = 6.25$ feet, average width of stope face.
$80 \times 6.25 = 500$ sq. ft., area of stope face.

It will be noted that in this instance the assays of all vein widths of less than the minimum stope width of five feet are diluted with zero assays to apportion their values over the required stoping face. This is most readily done by taking the assay-foot products in the regular manner and then dividing the total of the assay-foot products by the total of the face widths at the points sampled instead of by the total of the vein widths as in the previous problem.

In estimating ore values, it is sometimes advisable to sample only the orebody and apply to the values so found the cost of mining necessary to extract these values. In this way the rock dilution attendant upon thin-vein mining is applied as additional cost rather than as discounted assays. The final net result is the same in both cases. This procedure is especially applicable if sorting can be practiced underground and the waste material stowed in the openings as fill, so that only the ore is hoisted and treated.

BLOCKS OF ORE

EXAMPLE 9.

Combining Average Face Assays In order to demonstrate the combining of face assays so that the average assay of a block of ore may be obtained, assume a 30 × 40 ft. block of ore in a gold quartz vein which has been sampled on two sides at regular 10-ft. intervals by cross channels as shown in Fig. 11. The calculations are as follows:

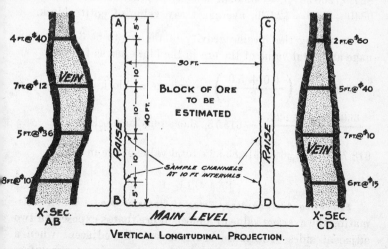

Fig. 11. Block of ore defined by sampled faces.

FACE AB			FACE CD		
Sample Width	Assay Value	Foot-Assay Product	Sample Width	Assay Value	Foot-Assay Product
4 ft. @	$40 =	160	2 ft. @	$60 =	120
7 @	12 =	84	5 @	40 =	200
5 @	36 =	180	7 @	10 =	70
8 @	10 =	80	6 @	15 =	90
24 ft.		504	20 ft.		480

504 ÷ 24 = $21, average assay value of face.

20 ÷ 4 = 5.0, average width of face.

24 ÷ 4 = 6.0, average width of face.

480 ÷ 20 = $24, average assay value of face.

40 × 6.0 = 240 sq. ft., area of face.

40 × 5.0 = 200 sq. ft., area of face.

$21 × 240 sq ft. = 5040, area-assay product of face AB.
$24 × 200 sq. ft. = 4800, area-assay product of face CD.
9840 ÷ 440 = $22.36, average assay value of entire block.

Assuming the specific gravity of the ore to be 3.0, the tonnage and total value of the ore in the block are as follows:

$$30 \times 40 \times \left(\frac{6.0 + 5.0}{2} \right) = \text{volume of block} = 6600 \text{ cu. ft.}$$

$$\frac{6600 \times 3 \times 62.5}{2000} = 618.75, \text{ short tons in block.}$$

618.75 × $22.36 = $13,835.25, total value of ore in block.

EXAMPLE 10.

Estimating Average Assay Value of Blocks of Ore   When estimating the average value of a block of ore that is exposed on two adjacent sides (two sides being necessarily adjacent when a block is exposed on three or four sides), the engineer encounters

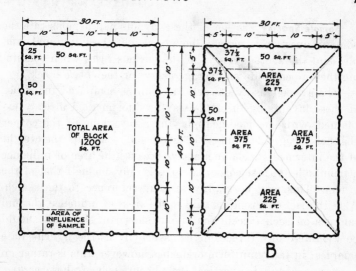

Fig. 12. Weighting of uniformly spaced samples.

a problem in weighting which belongs among the debatable refinements mentioned previously. To demonstrate this situation, take an example such as shown in Fig. 12, in which a rectangular block of ore 30 feet by 40 feet is bounded on all four sides by mine openings, with ore values visible on each exposed face. In order not to complicate the problem further, assume the block to be a portion of a uniform and relatively thin vein, so that the drifts and raises expose the whole thickness of the vein on each side. The problem is to sample this block by cross channels at 10-ft. intervals and to estimate the average assay value of each face, the tonnage available, the average assay of the entire block, and the total values available. As shown in the longitudinal section, the channels may be laid out in two ways — with the end channels of each face at the corners of the block or with the end channels of each face located at a half-interval (5 feet) from the corners so that there are no common channels.

Sample Spacing Either of these layouts will demonstrate the point in question — namely, how to weight the individual samples and the average assays of the various faces when combining them to compute an average assay for the entire block.

The average assay of each face can be computed for either of these layouts by the foot-assay-product method already explained, with one modification: the assay value of the corner channels (Fig. 12-A) must be given only one-half the weight of the intermediate channel assays because the area of influence attributable to these corner samples is only one-half that of the others. This may be readily seen by reference to the sketch. Also, if strict adherence is paid to the areas of influence, the end samples on each face in the layout shown in sketch B should be weighted only three-fourths as heavily as the intermediate samples; in fairly uniform orebodies, however, this is rather an unnecessary and impractical refinement, one of those controversial issues that continually crop out when sampling problems are under discussion. If the orebody is extremely rich or erratic, the channels will be spaced at closer intervals, and the end values will drop in relative importance because of the larger number of intermediate values with which they are combined.

Face Influence According to the methods already outlined, the average assay of each face is weighted according to its respective face area when combining to obtain a single average for the block. This, though a practical weighting, is not mathematically exact, as can be seen by referring to the dot-and-dash-lined (- . . . -) areas of sketch B, wherein, of a total of 1200 sq. ft. of area in the entire block, 375 sq. ft. are apparently attributable to each of the long sides, and 225 sq. ft. to each of the short faces. This gives a ratio of 3:5 for the ends to the sides instead of a 3:4 ratio based on the lengths of the sides and ends. Assuming uniform thickness of vein throughout, this difference would change the volume weights by 15 percent.

TREATMENT OF ABNORMAL ASSAYS — In the sampling of any orebody the purpose is to have the samples represent the ore at all points. An orebody necessarily fluctuates in value content from one point to another. It may have lean or barren spots; it may have rich spots. Sampling is intended to show these variations. Any cut-and-try procedure such as sampling, however, is liable to error; the samples may skip a lean or rich spot or they may, by chance, hit only the lean or only the rich spots. These eventualities give erroneous results and, since the results are seemingly consistent and the field data apparently normal, serious operating defects may exist until the truth is surmised and the error detected.

On the other hand, in the course of testing an orebody some few samples may vary from the mass in such a manner as to be conspicuously high or low. These are abnormal samples. They may, of course, be true ones; but the chances are that they just happened to have been taken at a rich or a lean spot in the ore. Unless they can be retaken in the field and their assays verified, the usual procedure is either to ignore them in computing averages or else to raise or reduce the conspicuous samples to the average of the surrounding points. This is obviously tampering with the data at hand, and such manipulation demands analysis of the situation on the part of the engineer. He must first of all be certain that the samples really are abnormal or erratic and then decide what, in all probability, they should have assayed. To be on the safe side, when only a few such values are involved, most engineers scale down the conspicuously high samples but seldom raise the low ones.

USE OF EXPERIENCE FACTORS — In most sampling situations, the estimation of tonnage and values can be handled adequately by the classical methods. These are the methods of sampling and weighting that have been described; they are fundamentally sound in principle, relatively simple to apply, and well understood by engineers and geologists.

Exceptional situations may call for special procedures in the combining of assays to give accurate results. These, generally, will relate to specific characteristics in the material being sampled, such as particle size and distribution, or loss by solubility of critical elements or contaminants. An example might be a placer gold deposit in which much of the gold occurs as fairly uniform, fine particles but with which are associated some amount of large particles and nuggets. The deposit is tested by drill holes. The larger particles, being much less in number in proportion to their value, have less chance of being included in a sample than the uniformly distributed small particles. Further, inclusion of a large particle, or two such particles, or a nugget in a sample will give higher than average to exceptionally high assays. These may appear to be erratic values. But if all the drill holes, by chance, missed large particles, the final result would be below the true value. In sampling and estimating a deposit of this type, some gauge is needed to bring the values into their true relationship, one with another. Analysis by grain count and probabilities[1] may offer a guide; so also may consideration of frequency distribution[2] of values among large groups of samples. More often, experience gained by operating companies through years of correlating daily field samples with final production will have developed suitable corrective measures to compensate for such troublesome values. The examiner will do well to seek out these experience factors whenever the situations that prompted their adoption are comparable to the conditions surrounding his problem. This is not to say that, carried to their ultimate, which often is impractical from the

[1] Swanson, C. O., "Probabilities in Estimating the Grade of Gold Deposits," C.I.M.M. Trans., Vol. 48, 1945, pp. 323-50.
[2] Truscott, S. J., "Mine Economics," Mining Pub., Ltd., London, 2nd Ed., 1947, Chap. 6.

standpoint of time and money, the classical methods would not reveal the true measure of the variables.

In the final analysis, mill recoveries or smelter returns, with due allowance for mining and treatment losses, will be the standard against which the field sampling and ensuing computations must be tested. Mathematical manipulation which attempts to improve on the accuracy of the original samples is to be avoided. Errors in the sampling can be corrected only in the field.

Much has been written on the mathematical theory of sampling. It would be futile here, in outlining the basic procedures for the sampling of mineral deposits, to digress into such theory which is widely applied to problems involving variables whose limits are either known or can be defined. The number of variables that affect the sampling and estimating of mineral deposits and the indeterminate nature of some of them prevent rigorous solution. The assumptions that must be made in regard to these variables, in large part at least, are not susceptible to rigid formulae, since they relate to the geologic nature of the problem.

CHAPTER 6

SAMPLING PRACTICE

Following are descriptions of sampling methods and procedures of the Anaconda Copper Mining Company at their Butte mines, of the Phelps Dodge Corporation at their New Cornelia property, and as generally followed by the Lake Superior iron ore industry. These have been selected as well-established practices, developed through years of use to meet conditions found in certain types of ore formation. Porphyry, vein, and bedded deposits are represented as well as single metal and complex ores. The practices outlined, though used primarily by the respective companies for control of mining operations, will serve as guides to the engineer confronted with the task of estimating mineral values and reserves. These selected examples are not intended to cover the entire field of sampling; to do so would be a comprehensive study in itself.

COMPLEX ORES — BUTTE DISTRICT [1] — The principal ores in the Butte mines are copper, zinc, zinc-lead, and manganese, with minor amounts of complex copper-zinc and zinc-lead-manganese ores. Each type of ore contains an appreciable amount of silver with a few cents in gold. All veins are sampled to obtain information necessary for control in mining operations and for estimating ore reserves.

---

[1] Digest of special report "Sampling Methods and Procedures in the Butte Mines of the Anaconda Copper Mining Company" prepared by Edward P. Shea, Mines Geologist, Butte, Montana, July 1947.

Representative samples are desired but the veins are not homogeneous and it is recognized that a single sample represents only a relatively small amount of material. Therefore, accuracy is restricted to practicability.

Veins Definite veins, where the ore minerals are confined within well-defined walls, are sampled from wall to wall and the country rock broken on either wall is measured and sampled for overbreak control. Where veins are composed of bands of different grade ore, the bands are sampled separately, and respective assays are combined by calculations to obtain a total width and average grade for the exposure.

Disseminated Deposits Disseminated deposits or deposits containing small veinlets or blebs of ore-bearing minerals are sampled in a manner similar to that for the definite vein deposits. The entire face is included and where it contains bands of ore of various grades the individual bands are sampled separately and the assays are combined mathematically to obtain the average grade of the exposure. Because of the irregular distribution of the ore-bearing minerals in such deposits, to obtain the most representative sample, cuts are made from top to bottom and across the entire face.

Car samples, or grab samples taken from the cars as the ore is being loaded from this type of deposit, are considered to be more representative than cut samples, as material from the entire excavation is represented rather than that from the face or outside edge. Also, car samples are weight samples and consequently differences in specific gravity are taken into account.

The grade of ore in disseminated deposits is difficult to estimate by observation and sampling is the only medium by which to obtain the value of the ore. As these deposits are not bounded by definite walls but gradually decrease in value from ore in the center to waste on the sides, sample results supply the only dependable mining control.

Low-Grade Deposits Because of the limited range between ore and waste, marginal low-grade deposits require more careful sampling than the good grade ores. To get a representative sample large sacks are used, and samples approximating five pounds per foot in width are cut. The specific gravity of each sample is determined and weighted averages are obtained by combining the width, grade, and specific gravity. The following example shows the effect of specific gravity on an average of three samples:

OMITTING SPECIFIC GRAVITY

Sample No.	Width	% Cu.	Oz. Ag.	W. × % Cu.	W. × Oz. Ag.
1	4.5′	1.2	0.3	5.40	1.35
2	0.5′	14.0	2.1	7.00	1.05
3	5.0′	1.2	0.4	6.00	2.00
Total & Average	10.0′	1.84	0.44	18.40	4.40

INCLUDING SPECIFIC GRAVITY

Sample No.	Width	% Cu.	Oz. Ag.	Specific Gravity	W. × S.G.	W. × S.G. × % Cu.	W. × S.G. × Oz. Ag.
1	4.5	1.2	0.3	2.80	12.60	15.12	3.78
2	0.5	14.0	2.1	4.16	2.08	29.12	4.37
3	5.0	1.2	0.4	2.80	14.00	16.80	5.60
Total & Average	10.0	2.13	0.48	2.87	28.68	61.04	13.75

Spotty ores, or those having wide differences in copper content, vary somewhat in specific gravity; therefore, the latter factor has more effect on ores of this type than on those having more uniform grade, especially if the gangue has a relatively high content of quartz.

Diamond Drilling Holes are diamond drilled to sample veins and an assay record is made of the cores and sludges. Where core recovery is good, core samples are used in preference to sludge samples. Good core sections through veins are considered to be more representative of the vein cut than the sludge because of losses entailed in slimes. Drillers pull the core when the cuttings indicate a change in the material being drilled, record the distance in the hole, and place a marker in the core box. Sampling of the core is done in a manner similar to crosscut sampling in that different types of material are sampled separately. The length of hole is determined from the driller's markers and the recovered core is measured in the core box. When cores are used to obtain a weighted average value of the material cut, recovered core is used and not length of hole. For example:

RECOVERED CORE

Dist. in Hole	Length of hole	Core Feet	% Cu.	Oz. Ag.	Length of Rec. Core × % Cu.	Length of Rec. Core × Oz. Ag.
101.0'-105.2'	4.2'	3.0	5.7	2.0	17.1	6.0
105.2'-110.6'	5.4'	3.8	3.0	1.0	11.4	3.8
101.0'-110.6' Av.	9.6'	6.8	4.2	1.4	28.5	9.8

Sludge samples are unsatisfactory and are not used except when core recovery is low. In these cases both core and sludge are saved, weighted, and assayed separately, and results are then combined to get an average. Sludge samples are unsatisfactory for the following reasons:

1. Sludge and heavy sulphide cuttings are lost in crevices in the hole.
2. In soft ground, caving from the walls of the hole contaminates the sample.
3. Source of sludge is not definitely known. (Soft material from any uncased location in the hole may contaminate the cuttings.)
4. Sulphides, because of their weight, are difficult to wash from the hole and salt cuttings beyond ore bands.

In addition to the above, the obtaining of sludge samples is impractical, as it slows the drilling and adds to the cost of the hole.

Face Sampling Before cutting samples, the face, sides and back of a working place are examined to determine if and where samples should be taken. Back samples are taken where face samples have been omitted or where the face samples do not represent the advance from the previous face tested. Drift faces are sampled after every blast and crosscuts are sampled on both sides wherever any vein material is exposed. In disseminated type ore deposits, crosscuts are sampled on both sides for the entire length. Raises are sampled on both ends of every floor in vein deposits and on ends and sides in disseminated ore bodies. Sidesets are sampled on every face that shows any mineralization, except those parallel to the structure.

In general, sample cuts are horizontal and horizontal widths are reported to supply proper data for ore reserve calculations as plotted on vertical plane longitudinal sections. In stopes and raises where the dip of a vein is flatter than 45°, samples are cut at right angles to the vein, and are so reported. In this case, slope distance is used in estimating ore reserves. This condition is illustrated in Fig. 11, where, on the first and second floor, with dip less than 45°, the samples are cut normal to the vein. These are reported as "true width" samples.

In sampling veins containing streaks of varying grade and hardness, it is difficult to cut a single sample composed of equal quantities per foot of the dissimilar streaks or layers. Therefore, each streak is sampled separately and the face average is calculated by combining the individual widths and assays of the several parts. This method gives a weighted average by volume only; specific gravity differences are not considered. Experience has shown that weighting by specific gravity is a refinement not necessary, generally, for operations control.

Streaks are sampled by starting at one edge and uniformly cutting or chipping small pieces continuously across to the other edge. This process is repeated until a sufficiently large sample, at least one pound per foot of width, is obtained. Sep-

DRIFTS & CROSSCUTS

SCALE: VARIOUS

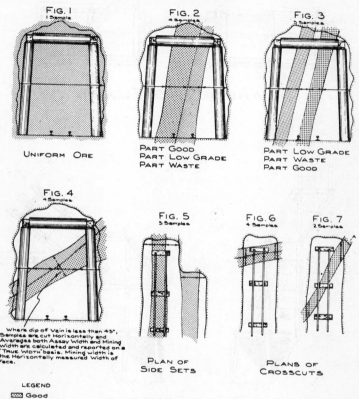

FIG. 1
1 Sample

UNIFORM ORE

FIG. 2
4 Samples

PART GOOD
PART LOW GRADE
PART WASTE

FIG. 3
3 Samples

PART LOW GRADE
PART WASTE
PART GOOD

FIG. 4
4 Samples

Where dip of Vein is less than 45°,
Samples are cut Horizontally and
Averages both Assay Width and Mining
Width are calculated and reported on a
"TRUE WIDTH" basis. Mining width is
the Horizontally measured Width of
Face.

FIG. 5
3 Samples

PLAN OF
SIDE SETS

FIG. 6
4 Samples

FIG. 7
2 Samples

PLANS OF
CROSSCUTS

LEGEND
▨ Good
▧ Low Grade
▨ Waste

Fig. 13. Sampling of drifts and crosscuts.

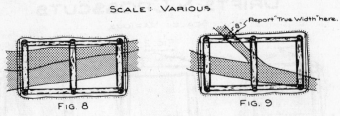

SCALE: VARIOUS

FIG. 8

FIG. 9 · "B" Report "True Width" here.

PLANS OF RAISE FLOORS

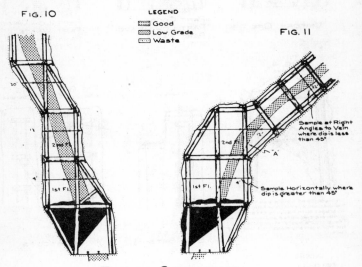

FIG. 10

LEGEND
▦ Good
▨ Low Grade
▧ Waste

FIG. 11

Sample at Right
Angles to Vein
where dip is less
than 45°

Sample Horizontally where
dip is greater than 45°

RAISE SECTIONS

Fig. 14. Sampling of raises.

arate sampling of streaks also gives specific data on location of high- and low-grade layers.

In special cases, where the ore is spotty and low-grade, larger samples of five pounds per foot of width are cut.

Ore samples are limited to five feet maximum width, or length of sample cut; in timbered workings to one set which is equivalent to 5.33 feet. The entire face is sampled in every case, as shown in sketches 1 to 5 and 8 to 11, inclusive, of Figures 13 and 14.

Any section of the face outside the walls of the vein is sampled to provide data for overbreak control even though it may be waste. The sampler checks his assay returns against his estimate of grades and where the difference is too great, the place is resampled.

Judgment, practical experience, and knowledge of principles dictate the sampler's procedure in obtaining representative samples. Where strict adherence to rules would not represent conditions truly, he deviates from prescribed procedure to cut the sample he judges best. For instance, if for some reason a decided change in grade occurs within a short distance, he will cut a sufficient number of samples to show the complete situation. In some cases, this may require separate samples across top and bottom of the face; in disseminated deposits, it may require chipping the entire face at regular intervals, wall to wall and top to bottom, instead of the usual horizontal sample cut four feet above the floor.

Stope Sampling Stopes are sampled at intervals of 10 feet. Ends of stopes are always sampled. In rill stopes the samples are cut across the back.

Silver determination is not made for stope samples. Development, sill, and raise samples are assayed for silver and the silver values in stopes are estimated from the copper-silver ratios in nearby development workings.

When a stope is stopped as unprofitable, the complete back

is sampled at intervals of five to ten feet to check the type of material remaining and to provide a full record for future reference.

Car Sampling   Mine car grab samples are taken in special cases. The procedure is to take one pound of "fines" from odd-numbered small (0.7 ton) cars and one pound of coarse material from even-numbered cars. This material is accumulated to form one sample from the total number of cars loaded from each working place during a shift.

When large cars (3.5 tons) are used, five pounds of "fines" and five pounds of coarse material are taken from alternate cars and combined for each working place. The five pounds of material from each of the large cars is composed of five one-pound grabs, one pound being obtained from each corner and one pound from the center of the top of each car.

At the zinc and manganese mines, in addition to the regular cut samples, a sample is also taken from the cars or skips as the ore is hoisted. Where cars are hoisted, approximately one pound per ton is obtained and accumulated until each sample represents 40 to 50 tons. At the mines where skips are used, a five-pound grab is taken from each six-ton skip and the grabs from each eight skips combined into one sample. At the manganese mines where the ore is hauled by truck to the railroad, a sample of about five pounds is taken from each 12-ton truck, and four such samples combined to represent one railroad carload.

Dump Sampling   Old mine dumps containing large tonnages are concentrator-tested in a preliminary way by using material obtained by grab sampling from numerous small pits located at regular intervals on the top and sides of the dump. If this sampling indicates profitable possibilities, a large-scale sampling program is inaugurated and power-shovel cuts are excavated at regular intervals. Generally, all material from such cuts to a maximum total of 25,000 tons is shipped, completely sampled and concentrator-tested, and from these results the advisability of shipping a portion or the entire remaining material is determined.

Calculations   To obtain the average of ore in the face of a drift or stope, assays of the respective samples are combined on an *assay-width* and *mining-width* basis. Except in special cases they are combined by volume only, with no regard to specific gravity, the results being sufficiently accurate for operating purposes. The assay-width average consists of a combination of the ore streaks and the included waste that cannot be sorted economically from the ore, assuming theoretically perfect mining. The mining-width average is made up from the assays of all the material in the face, that is, ore and waste combined. The assay-width average is made to show the width and grade of the ore in the face, regardless of the width of the mine working. This average is used in estimating ore reserves. The mining-width average shows how the mining is actually being done, thus a comparison of the assay-width average to the mining-width average furnishes a good control on mining operations.

The dividing line between ore and waste for the purpose of figuring assay width averages is 1.2% copper and 4.0% zinc. Streaks that assay under 4.0% zinc, but contain sufficient lead or silver to be the equivalent of 4.0% zinc, are considered to be ore. For this purpose 1.0% zinc is equivalent to 2.0 oz. silver and 1.0% lead is equivalent to 0.8% zinc. In figuring assay-width averages where waste occurs between two streaks of ore, the following rules apply:

1.   Include all waste less than 1.0 foot wide.
2.   Include ½ of the waste 1.0 foot to 2.9 feet wide.
3.   Exclude all waste 3.0 feet or more in width.

The following examples show comparisons of assay- and mining-width calculated averages, using the above rules.

	ASSAY-WIDTH AVERAGE			MINING-WIDTH AVERAGE		
	Width in Ft.	% Cu.	Oz. Ag.	Width in Ft.	% Cu.	Oz. Ag.
North	2.0	4.0	2.0	2.0	4.0	2.0
Center	0.9*	1.0*	0.5	0.9	1.0	0.5
South	2.0	4.0	2.0	2.0	4.0	2.0
Average	4.9	3.4	1.7	4.9	3.4	1.7

	ASSAY-WIDTH AVERAGE			MINING-WIDTH AVERAGE		
	Width in Ft.	% Cu.	Oz. Ag.	Width in Ft.	% Cu.	Oz. Ag.
North	2.0	4.0	0.2	2.0	4.0	0.2
Center	1.2†	1.0†	0.5	1.2	1.0	0.5
South	2.0	4.0	2.0	2.0	4.0	2.0
Average	4.6	3.6	1.0	5.2	3.3	1.0

	ASSAY-WIDTH AVERAGE			MINING-WIDTH AVERAGE		
	Width in Ft.	% Cu.	Oz. Ag.	Width in Ft.	% Cu.	Oz. Ag.
North	2.0	4.0	0.2	2.0	4.0	0.2
Center	3.5‡	1.1‡	0.1	3.5	1.1	0.1
Next	1.0	4.0	0.2	1.0	4.0	0.2
South	1.5§	0.8§	1.0	1.5	0.8	0.2
Average	3.0	4.0	0.2	8.0	2.1	0.2

---

* The center streak is waste, as it averages less than 1.2% copper, but this is included in the assay-width average because it is less than 1.0 foot wide. Therefore, the assay-width average and the mining-width average are the same.

† The center streak is waste and is between 1.0 foot and 3.0 feet wide, therefore ½ or 0.6 foot is included in the assay-width average.

‡ The center streak is waste and is over 3.0 feet wide, therefore it is excluded from the assay-width average.

§ The south streak is waste but it is not included, as it is located outside of the ore bands.

Both streaks are included in the mining-width average.

The following example shows the assay-width and mining-width average for a face of zinc ore:

Sample No.	Width in Ft.	% Zn	% Pb	Oz. Ag.
1 N.	3.1	18.5	3.0	15.1
2	0.8	3.0	2.0	1.0
3	3.1	0.2	0.1	0.4
4	4.2	16.5	2.0	10.0
5	3.8	1.6	1.0	8.1
6 S.	1.5	0.2	0.2	0.1
Assay Width Average	11.9	11.4	1.9	10.1
Mining Width Average	16.5	8.2	1.4	7.4

Sample No. 2 contains only 3.0% zinc, but the combined zinc, lead, and silver is the equivalent of 5.1% zinc, according to the rule; therefore, it is included in the assay-width average. Sample No. 3 is waste, over 3.0 feet wide, and is excluded. No. 5 contains the equivalent of 6.4% zinc and is included, but No. 6S is waste and is located outside of the ore bands. Therefore, it is not included. The mining-width average includes all the samples in the face.

Records Complete office records are kept on all sampling. These are for two purposes, (1) operational control, and (2) estimation of ore.

Of particular interest in connection with valuation are those forms and records used for estimation of ore. Form cards are made up for each stope; one for floor plan, one for vertical section, usually longitudinal. Cards are ruled in part with suitable co-ordinates for sketching the desired view to scale. Location of each sample is platted on the sketch of the stope or floor outline as of respective measurement dates. Each stope sketch is tied to mine co-ordinates for location.

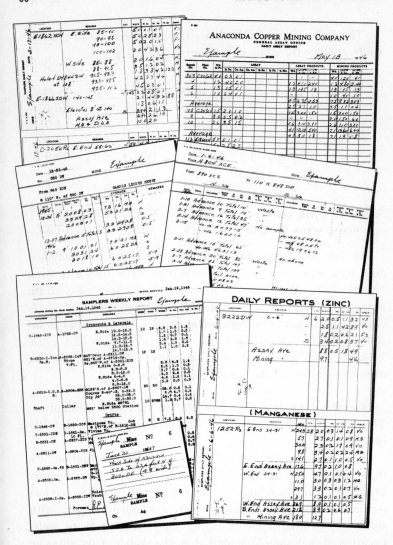

Fig. 15. Sampling records and computation forms.

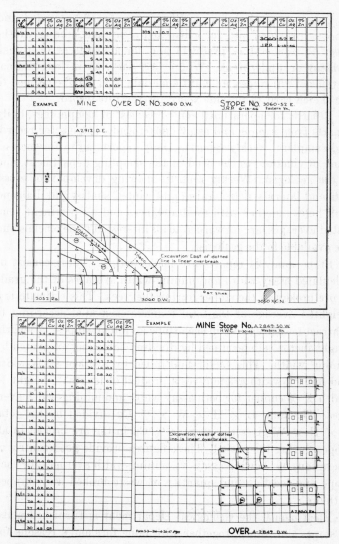

Fig. 16. Stope sampling and records.

Date, sample number, width, and assay are recorded and space is provided also for calculated assay and mining widths (feet × % metal = product) and for amounts of overbreak (waste) or underbreak. Where necessary, as in longitudinal sections of rill stopes, an additional data card may be clipped to the sketch card to provide space for the full record.

Records for operational control consist of sample tags, daily reports from sample and assay departments, ledgers for record, and samplers' weekly reports. Daily reports go to foremen on mine production, to the head of the sampling department, and to the geologist. Weekly reports, showing development, cross-cuts and laterals, drifts, raises and winzes, shafts, and diamond drill holes together with total advances and all pertinent computed averages, are forwarded to all interested mine officials and are available to the geologist.

Stope analysis reports are made weekly. These consist of calculated assay-width and mining-width averages of the grade of ore broken in the stopes during the week. This estimate is a weighted average of the total tonnage excavated according to contract measurements in each stope and in all stopes. A length-height factor is determined by dividing cubic feet excavated by mining width. This factor multiplied by average assay-width and mining-width grade gives a product of length × height × width × % copper for both assay-width and mining-width averages. The total L × H × W × % Cu divided by the total L × H × W gives the average % Cu in the ore broken in all stopes during the period. These figures provide good control of operations by showing assay- vs. mining-width averages for each stope and location and quantity of waste broken and shipped with ore.

Each month the Geological Department is furnished a list of stopes shut down, together with mine foreman's reasons for doing so. These are each analyzed against sampling and geological records as to ore possibilities.

DISSEMINATED ORES — ARIZONA [1]

Ore Occurrence   The major portion of the New Cornelia ore-body is composed of a hard quartz monzonite mineralized with finely disseminated veinlets and particles of primary chalcopyrite and bornite. A comparatively small amount of primary ore also occurs in diorite and rhyolite, and a thin blanket of secondary chalcocite ore lies along one side of the orebody. With the exception of the secondary chalcocite ore, the orebody is comparatively uniform in character.

The orebody was originally capped with from 20 to 190 feet of oxidized or carbonate ore containing malachite and azurite as the principal copper minerals, but this ore has now been removed by mining. The tenor of the carbonate ore was about the same as the underlying primary sulphide ore.

Prospect Drilling and Sampling   Prospect drilling or pit development is now carried on with churn drills exclusively. Earlier development was done with diamond drills, and the sampling practice connected therewith is described in U. S. Bureau of Mines Information Circular 6666.[2] Diamond drilling was attended by high carbon loss and relatively low core recovery (somewhat less than 50%), and churn drilling is now regarded as cheaper and just as reliable from a sampling standpoint.

Prospect drill hole assays are used for estimating ore reserves and for making long range mining estimates. In general, the holes are drilled vertically on the corners of 200 foot squares. Samples are taken at intervals of five feet, and each five-foot

---

[1] Digest of special report ''Mine Sampling Practice at New Cornelia Branch Phelps Dodge Corporation'' prepared by Alfred T. Barr, Mine Superintendent and John A. Lentz, Jr., Chief Engineer, Ajo, Arizona, May 1947.
[2] ''Mining Methods and Costs at the New Cornelia Branch,'' Phelps Dodge Corporation, Ajo, Arizona, by George R. Ingham and Alfred T. Barr.

sample is assayed. Assays are combined and averaged for larger intervals corresponding to present or future mining levels. Ore reserves are calculated by levels on the basis of the average assay for each hole and the criterion that each hole governs the tonnage included on the level for ½ the distance to its neighboring holes. Drill hole assays are accepted without correction, and it has been found that the extracted grade checks very closely with estimated reserves based on both churn drill and diamond drill holes. In estimating tonnages, a factor of 12½ cu. ft. per ton is used.

For deep holes a 13-inch bit is generally used until progress becomes slow or caving is encountered. In the latter case 10-inch casing is run if necessary. For short holes or the continuation of deep holes a 9-inch bit is used. As drilling advances the hole is bailed with a dart bailer. The bailer is emptied into a special splitter which is attached to the drill and takes a 1/16 sample from the center of the sludge stream through a ¾ inch throat. See Fig. 17.

CHURN DRILL SAMPLE CUTTER

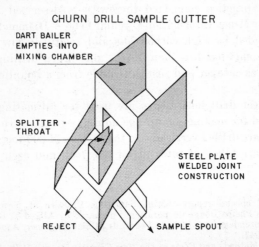

Fig. 17. Sample cutter for churn-drill sludge.

The sample is collected in a tub and is split with a Jones type splitter to a size that can be contained in a two-gallon can, which is equivalent to 10 pounds dry weight. The final field sample is sent to the sampling mill, where it is dried, pulverized, and prepared for assaying in the usual manner. The iodate method is used for copper determinations.

Records of the assays and geological information obtained from each hole are kept by the engineering department. The head sampler prepares a daily drill record listing the footage drilled, rock formation, mineralization, hardness of rock, and other pertinent information. He also collects small rock fragments from the sample rejects and these are glued to a sample board for a permanent geological record of each five-foot interval. Duplicate samples are obtained from the laboratory and filed, in case check assays are required later. The engineering department also prepares a complete log of each hole, listing the information obtained from the daily drill reports and assay reports. Chemical analyses, including gold and silver determinations obtained from composite samples of every 50 feet of hole, are also recorded. Average assays for each mining level are finally recorded on level maps and the ore outlines are drawn.

Blast Hole Sampling and Ore Control Daily and monthly ore estimates are based upon assays of samples taken from the cuttings of the regular blast holes. Normally these holes are drilled in a single line at intervals of 12 to 18 feet along the banks to be blasted and mined, and the assays of the samples taken from them afford an accurate means of determining the grade of the ore in the bank. Only one sample is taken for the total depth of each hole from the collar to the mining level below. The cutoffs between ore and waste are spotted from the locations of the holes, and before mining starts on a given section of a bank, targets are set along the loading track opposite these cutoff points. With a normal bank height of 40 feet, each hole controls from 1500 to 2600 tons of material.

Blast hole assays are accepted without correction. The difference between the average mill heads and mine grade (determined by blast hole assays) for a period covering the last 13 years is only 0.004% copper.

In blast hole drilling a nine-inch bit is used exclusively. The hole is bailed with a dart bailer at intervals depending on drilling requirements only. The bailer is emptied into the same type splitter described under prospect drilling, and the sample accumulates in a tub until the full mining level has been penetrated. After the sample depth has been reached, drilling advances from five to seven feet farther for blasting purposes. The drill crew attends to the collection of the tub sample, and a sample crew visits each drill once or twice a day to split the tub samples down to two-gallon size by means of a Jones type splitter. These samples are tagged and sent to the sample mill, where they are handled in the same manner as prospect drill samples.

Each hole drilled and sampled is numbered and located on a pit map. Assay values inserted for each hole are the basis for control of current operations. In conjunction with the shovel positions each day, they are used for determining the daily mine grade, which is computed and reported by the ore control engineer. At the end of each month the average grades for the various shovels and levels are corrected to the reported mill grade for the month by a percentage correction.

Accuracy Because of the comparative uniformity of the ore and the lack of large mineral veins, salting is a negligible factor in the drill holes. This is borne out by the close agreement between mill heads and the estimated mine grade based on either blast hole assays for short periods or prospect hole assays for long periods of production. Although a dart bailer does not remove all of the sludge from a hole, tests with a sand pump have failed to indicate any concentration of values at the bottom.

The special drill splitter described saves a great deal of labor, and tests have proven its $\frac{1}{16}$ sample to be fully as accurate as a sample obtained with four splits through a Jones splitter. This is no doubt due to the fact that the sludge is thoroughly mixed during bailing, and the sample is taken before any segregation can take place.

The largest piece of pure bornite found in a sludge sample passed a 0.263-inch screen. The copper content of larger rock fragments recovered from a churn drill hole diminishes so rapidly that the richest pieces have no greater effect on the final sample than a piece of bornite of the above size. This is accounted for by the finely disseminated mineralization and the brittleness of the ore minerals, and makes it possible to split to a relatively small size sample in the field without introducing large accidental errors.

Interval sampling helps to eliminate errors that would be caused by caving or loss of sample at a particular horizon and, as eight samples and assays are combined for a normal 40 foot level, it also reduces the accidental errors involved in splitting and assaying. Aside from these advantages it facilitates the calculation of the grade for any given mining level. In blast hole drilling this refinement is omitted because of the close spacing of the holes.

IRON ORES — LAKE SUPERIOR[1]

The Lake Superior region supplies the bulk of the iron ores consumed by domestic furnaces. It is customary for these ores to be contracted for a year or more in advance with a guarantee as to grade and with settlement to be based on sample analyses. Tonnages are large; allowable tolerances are relatively small. To provide the necessary control, sampling is done both at the mines and at the furnaces. In case of disagreement the furnace, or Lower Lake, assays govern settlement.

---

[1] Adapted from report prepared by Franklin G. Pardee, 1947.

Importance of Sampling   In addition to affording the basis for sale of ore and control of mining operations, sampling is also relied upon for exploration and development of the mines. It has been said [1] that — "there is probably no other single operation connected with the handling of iron or manganese ores that is more difficult, on many occasions at least, or more important at all times, than proper sampling."

Iron Ores   Iron ores are not uniform, physically or chemically. They range, in physical characteristics, from soft, earthy limonites and hematites, which crumble in the hand, to hard dense magnetites and specular hematites. Chemically, there is broad variation in content, particularly among the minor constituents and in moisture content.

Silica is the most evident impurity. It may be united with the iron as a silicate, or free. The iron silicates are usually harder and more resistant than the ore itself and form layers in the ore, complicating both mining and sampling. Phosphorous and sulphur are critical impurities but appear in such small amounts as to have no effect on sampling. Other common constituents may be alumina and manganese.

Open Pit Development   An open pit iron deposit is first tested by drilling. All samples from the drills are analyzed carefully by standard procedures. When opened, the mine is cross-sectioned by the engineers. Drill holes put down for blasting purposes are sampled and the results plotted on the cross sections along with the information from the original drilling. Test pits are often put in as aids to exploration. These are sampled and results recorded. After stripping, samples are usually taken from the surface of the orebody. All this is prior to any ore shipment.

---

1 "Methods of the Chemists of the U. S. Steel Corp. for the Sampling and Analysis of Iron and Manganese Ores," Carnegie Steel Co., 3rd Ed., 1926, p. 10.

Additional information on the grade or grades of ore is obtained from samples taken along the sides and breasts of the cuts as the power shovels open up the pit. These analyses are added to the data on the cross sections.

Underground Development In underground mining, the first information on grade of ore comes from diamond drill holes, followed by sampling of drifts and crosscuts. A check on the accuracy of this sampling is made both by sampling tram cars from individual areas in the mine and by sampling the mine output as it is hoisted. If the ore is put in stock pile, it is often desirable to sample the stock pile by one of the standard methods to check the grade of the pile.

Ore Grading The Lake Superior ores vary from range to range, from mine to mine, and within a mine. The ores are generally mixed, or graded, to shipment specifications, which involves scheduling of mine output not only in accord with a plan for mining but also in line with assay requirements.

It is recognized practice, at the open pits, to plan operations in detail well in advance of mining, on the basis of the analysis data already referred to. A common unit for such planning is a "block" of ore containing, say, 5000 to 10,000 tons. Block dimensions are adapted to the cut and swing of the power shovels in use at the mine. Average analysis of each block is determined and recorded on the mining plan. Blocks, or portions of blocks, are then combined, as needed, to meet shipment requirements. Final grading to bring a cargo to guarantee is done at the docks upon receipt of composite analysis of the rail shipment or shipments comprising the boat cargo. Thus pit operations are frequently detailed, on an analysis basis, down to the individual shovel cut.

Underground mining is planned, insofar as physical conditions permit, to have the analysis of the daily hoist conform with the grade or grades of the ore produced from the mine.

This procedure is especially necessary when the mines are loading directly into railroad cars for shipment to the dock. This means that mining operations must be laid out far enough in advance so that the daily hoist will approximate the correct grade or grades. This is not always possible because of the many variations found in most orebodies and some adjustments can be made from stock pile or by mixing of railroad cars in such a way as to obtain a uniform grade at the dock.

Classification of Ores   Lake Superior iron ores are generally classified as Bessemer, Non-Bessemer, or High-Phosphorous. Separate Lake Erie base prices are established for each group. Bessemer ores receive a premium for phosphorous content below .045 per cent, dry analysis. Iron content is penalized below 50 per cent, natural basis. Moisture lowers natural iron content. Silica may be penalized above a certain amount. Manganese is classified as iron up to the point where an ore can be sold as manganiferous. Hard ores and silicious ores are generally contracted for aside from the regular Lake Erie schedule. Structure affects the desirability of an ore, fine or dusty ores being subject to flue loss.

Accuracy of Grading   Tolerances allowed in analyses of iron ores are comparatively small, although large tonnages are involved. For the iron content, analyses based on sampling at the mines and again at the furnaces are expected to check within $\frac{5}{10}$ of 1% of the guaranteed figure. The same tolerance is allowed for silica and manganese. For Bessemer ore the phosphorous content is watched closely. A variation of more than .002% is considered too much. For non-Bessemer ore this figure is not checked so closely. Moisture sampling is the most difficult, as laboratory analysis is on dry material whereas the ores are sold on natural iron, moisture included. Tolerance of about ½ per cent is allowable for moisture.

The Sampling Problem The combination of physical and chemical variables, together with the large tonnages involved, constitute, in the main, the problem of sampling iron ore. Conditions under which sampling must be done are variable, requiring proper techniques. Time factor may also have an important bearing on procedure, as in the instance of open pits, where only a few hours are available for final grade determination between mining of ore and cargo clearance.

Procedures and techniques have been developed during the many years that the Lake Superior mines have supplied ore to the furnaces. Attainment of progressively closer tolerances has been achieved.

At first, the only analysis required was for iron; later, ores were graded on iron and phosphorous content; now many cargoes are graded on iron, phosphorous, silica, and manganese.

Conditions of Sampling To accomplish the aforementioned purposes, ores are sampled (a) in place, (b) in transit, and (c) in stock pile.

Sampling in place includes diamond and churn-drill holes, test pits, and underground faces of all types.

Sampling in transit refers to railroad and boat cargoes.

Stock piles may be sampled during stocking, during shipment, or as completed stocks.

Principles Sampling practices, described in brief detail below, recognize the fundamental principles of sampling. Each sample is composed, within practicable limits, of a sufficient number of equal-sized portions taken at uniform intervals so that the portions may be combined, without weighting, and yet be representative of the tonnage involved. The number of such portions depends upon the circumstances.

Samples are combined to represent larger tonnages either by weighting the components or by mixture of a sufficient number of samples.

Diamond Drilling When full core is recovered, it is split lengthwise; one half is labeled and filed for geologic study or reference, the other half taken as sample. Each five feet of ore depth is usually assigned a separate sample.

When the ore crumbles and core is not obtained, the cuttings are washed from the hole and recovered for each five feet, or less, of advance.

Churn Drilling Holes are usually cased to prevent contamination. Casing is carried as close as practicable to the bottom of the hole. Water flow is regulated to prevent scouring. Each advance of five feet or less is sampled separately by collecting all sludge in barrels fitted with stoppered holes, some 10 inches from the bottom, for draining or decanting off the clear water after settlement of the cuttings.

Test Pits Test pits, usually about $2\frac{1}{2} \times 3\frac{1}{2}$ feet in size, are sampled by cutting channels or grooves in the walls. Each five feet of depth in ore is sampled separately. When the ore is unstratified or in more or less horizontal layers, the channels run continuously down the center of two or four sides. When strata are inclined, the channels on each five feet of depth are cut across the formation as a series of diagonals on opposite walls. If the strata are vertical, each five feet of advance is sampled in the middle by horizontal channels on opposite walls.

Drifts and Crosscuts Sides of drifts and crosscuts are sampled by channels at right angles to the formation. It is customary to have one sample represent about 25 feet of linear opening and be made up of four cuts, two on each wall, uniformly spaced within this length.

Working Places In soft ore, breasts are sampled by three equally spaced parallel channels, about $1\frac{1}{2}$ inches wide by one inch deep, normal to the formation.

Hard ore faces are chip sampled from numerous points, uniformly spaced. Equal-sized chips are taken, as nearly as possible, at each point. Usual spacing is 1½ to 2½ feet, horizontally and vertically.

Stopes, top-, and sub-slice workings are tested by sampling the cut after blasting. Portions are taken from 20 to 30 points, uniformly spaced on the surface of the pile to make up the sample.

Car Sampling Iron ore loaded into railroad cars either at open pit or underground mines is sampled in the cars; usually three to five and even up to 10 cars being sampled as a unit. Sample portions are taken from the top surface of the ore in each car and ready methods have been devised for insuring proper spacing of the 20 to 35 points tested on each car. One method, for example, uses ropes with knots at specified intervals laid on top of the standard ore car. If the rope is laid along the top of the car, lengthwise, three times (along centerline and at specified parallel spacing on either side) and there are eight knots in the rope, this means that the sampler will take portions of ore at 24 points.

The sampler is usually provided with a standard scoop which holds about three cubic inches of material. A scoop of ore is taken at each knot. If the point falls on a lump of a volume greater than half the volume of a scoop of fine ore, one or more pieces are broken from the lump sufficient to fill the scoop. If the point falls beside a lump, a small piece of the lump is taken with enough fine to fill the scoop, each being in proper proportion.

The complete sample taken from three, five, or 10 cars, or whatever number may make up the group, is sent to the laboratory and the resultant analysis represents the grade of ore in these cars.

In theory, this method of top sampling is not suited to the testing of a single body of ore, as the points are not uniformly distributed throughout the body. As applied, however, each car is a standard unit or portion of a larger mass, the cargo. All units are thoroughly mixed in loading and unloading the boat. The points sampled, 20 to 35 for each car, should be points uniformly distributed throughout the cargo mass.

Boat Sampling   At the furnace docks, the ore is sampled during removal from the vessel by taking scoops of ore at designated points on both sides of the cuts or trenches made in the ore beneath the hatches by the unloading machines. Points are usually spaced about a foot apart in vertical rows about four feet apart. The scoop used holds about seven cubic inches of material. Other procedures are similar to those for car sampling.

Moisture Samples   Each railroad car is usually tested for moisture at three points along the top centerline. Holes are dug three to ten inches deep and a scoopful of ore taken from the bottom of each hole. Metal containers with tight lids are used to collect the material.

A single moisture sample may represent 10 to 20 cars, unless separate grades or ownerships are involved.

CHAPTER 7

ORE ESTIMATION

BASIC FACTORS — Estimation of ore tonnage involves two factors: weight of ore and volume of ore.

The weight of the ore is found by a specific gravity-porosity determination.

The volume is computed from plan and section maps by the use of planimetered areas or by arithmetical calculation.

SPECIFIC GRAVITY, POROSITY, — "Specific gravity" and "den-
AND TONNAGE FACTOR sity" are synonymous terms used to express the weights of substances relative to that of pure water at 4°C. The term "porosity" refers to the voids or pore space within a material and is expressed as a percentage of the total volume. These voids may be free from moisture, partially filled, or saturated. Thus, the actual weight of a given volume of any substance is dependent upon the densities of the elements of which the substance is composed as corrected for porosity and moisture.

Ores are composed of minerals, voids, and moisture. To clarify the terminology, the density of solid ore (no voids, no moisture) is spoken of as the "mineral specific gravity" in contrast to the "rock specific gravity-dried" in which the pore space is included but not the moisture, and in further contrast to the "rock specific gravity-natural" in which both the voids and moisture are considered.

The relations of these three different densities, one to another, are readily stated by equations, as follows:

Let G_m = mineral specific gravity

G_d = rock specific gravity-dried

G_n = rock specific gravity-natural

P. = porosity — in terms of percentage of total volume occupied by the voids or pore space

M = moisture — in terms of percentage loss in total weight upon drying at 100° C for 12 hrs. or until weight becomes constant.

Since the effect of porosity is to increase the volume without any addition in weight, the "mineral specific gravity" and the "rock specific gravity-dried" may each be expressed in terms of the other as

$$G_m = \frac{G_d}{(1-P)}$$

or

$$G_d = G_m(1-P)$$

From these equations,

$$P = 1 - \frac{G_d}{G_m}$$

Similarly, since the effect of moisture is to increase the weight of the ore with no increase in volume (the moisture occupies the pore space), the "rock specific gravities — dried and natural" may be equated, each to the other, as follows:

$$G_d = G_n(1-M)$$

or

$$G_n = \frac{G_d}{(1-M)},$$

and, by substitution,

$$G_n = \frac{G_m(1-P)}{(1-M)}$$

or

$$G_m = \frac{G_n(1-M)}{(1-P)}$$

To illustrate with an example, assume a block of natural rock, one cubic foot in size, to weigh 150 lb. When dried, the moisture loss is found to be 25 lb., or $16\frac{2}{3}\%$ of the original weight. Upon immersion and complete saturation, the block absorbs 31.25 lb. or .5 cu. ft. of water, thus showing the porosity of the rock to be 50 per cent.

From the above data the following calculations may be made:

$$\text{Rock specific gravity-natural} = G_n = \frac{150}{62.5} = 2.4$$

$$\begin{aligned}
\text{Rock specific gravity-dried} &= G_d = G_n(1\text{-}M) \\
&= 2.4(1\text{-}.16\tfrac{2}{3}) \\
&= 2.4 \times .83\tfrac{1}{3} = 2.0
\end{aligned}$$

or
$$G_d = \frac{150\text{-}25}{62.5} = 2.0$$

$$\begin{aligned}
\text{Mineral specific gravity} = G_m &= \frac{G_n(1\text{-}M)}{(1\text{-}P)} \\
\\
&= \frac{2.4(1\text{-}.16\tfrac{2}{3})}{(1\text{-}.5)} \\
\\
&= \frac{2.4 \times .83\tfrac{1}{3}}{.5} = 4.0
\end{aligned}$$

or
$$G_m = \frac{150\text{-}25}{62.5 \times .5} = 4.0$$

Porosity as such is not ordinarily determined by laboratory methods because of the difficulty of obtaining complete evacuation and complete saturation of the pore space. This is especially true of meduim- to fine-grained rocks. The most satisfactory figures for porosity are those computed from laboratory determinations of mineral gravity, natural rock gravity, and moisture content of the sample or specimen of the ore.

Mineral Specific Gravity — The densities of the elements, common minerals, certain of the less complex ores, and some of the common rocks are well known and are to be found in tabulated form[1] in mining and geology handbooks. The density of a complex ore, however, is usually an unknown which must be determined before ore volumes can be translated into tonnage. The orebody in question must be sampled for specific gravity in much the same manner as it is sampled for values. The number of such samples required to attain an accurate figure for ore density depends upon the character of the formation, but it is always advisable to test the orebody at as many points as possible in order to assure the accuracy of the final tonnage factor figure.

There are two common methods of determining the mineral specific gravity of an ore:

1. On certain less complex ores a mineralogical or chemical examination will give the relative percentages of the various minerals which have combined to form the ore. Inasmuch as the specific gravity of each mineral is known, a simple arithmetical calculation will give the gravity of the combination.

2. An average crushed and dried sample of the ore may be tested with a narrow-neck bottle by weighing the bottle when it has been filled to a definite mark with distilled water at $4°C$, introducing into the bottle a weighed amount of the sample, restoring the level of the water to the mark, and finally weighing again. The specific gravity then equals the weight of the sample used divided by the difference between the combined weight of the sample plus the original bottle of water and the final weight of the bottle with the sample in it. The difficulty of picking an average sample of the ore is the most serious drawback to the use of this method.

1 "Mining Engineer's Handbook"—R. Peele. John Wiley & Sons, Inc., 3rd Ed., pp. 25-21.

In the practical application to an orebody of the mineral specific gravities determined by either of the above-mentioned methods, it is most important to include a proper factor to cover porosity and moisture. This factor may be computed from test results or, if only an approximation is desired, may be estimated by one familiar with the ore.

Rock Specific Gravity-Natural — The "rock specific gravity-natural" of an ore may be determined as follows:

1. A hole (1 to 2 cubic feet in size) is dug in the face of the orebody and all of the material so removed is caught and weighed. It is important that the ore shall not dry out before weighing, because it would not then be in its natural condition. It is customary to place the sample immediately in a moisture-proof can. The hole is then filled to the original surface with shot (or some other material which does not readily pack, such as beans, oats, or plaster of Paris). The shot have been previously measured in a rectangular wooden box of known cross section so that the remaining volume of shot can be readily computed, thus giving the volume which has been emptied into the excavation in the ore face. When the volume of ore removed and its weight are known, the specific gravity can be found by dividing the weight of the ore by the weight of the same volume of distilled water at 4°C.

This method is highly practical for use on complex ores and on ores which vary in character; an appreciable quantity of the ore is represented in each test and the body may be tested at frequent intervals, just as in sampling. The average of a number of such tests should give a reliable figure for the natural rock density. Of the several measuring materials listed, plaster of Paris is the most accurate, because each of the other materials (shot, beans, oats, etc.) is capable of being "close packed," "loose packed," or packed to any intermediate degree, although with proper care this source of error can be reduced to a minimum. When plaster of Paris is used, the cast, after removal from the hole, is coated with paraffin and its volume determined by water displacement.

2. When weighing it separately is possible, the entire product of a stope or large room may be used to determine natural specific gravity. This method requires accurate measurement of the opening from which the ore is taken and also requires care to see that only the ore removed from the opening is weighed. A modification only slightly less accurate is to weigh carefully the product from a drift or crosscut (preferably a crosscut because it gives a better section of the ore) and later measure the volume of the opening.

Apparent disadvantages of this method are two: (a) a great amount of labor and care is involved in its proper execution, and (b) the ore of the stope or drift used in the test may not be representative of the entire orebody. However, if several such large openings, in different parts of the orebody, can conveniently be tested, this method gives a high degree of accuracy because of the large amounts of ore included.

Porosity — Porosity may be determined by performing upon an average sample of the ore or upon each of a group of ore specimens the following operations:

a. Determine the mineral specific gravity by either of the methods outlined above.

b. Determine the natural specific gravity by either of the methods given.

c. Determine the moisture by noting the percentage loss of the weight of the wet ore upon drying at 100°C for 12 hours or until weight becomes constant.

d. Calculate the "rock specific gravity-dried."

e. Calculate the porosity on a dry-ore basis by dividing the difference between the mineral and dried specific gravities by the mineral gravity according to the formula given above:

$$P = 1 - \frac{G_d}{G_m}$$

The porosity of a uniform ore formation may be found by saturating one or more completely dry hand specimens with water and noting the weight absorbed. In drying, the heat should not be so intense as to drive off any molecular moisture. In certain instances both heat and pressure may be required to obtain complete absorption.

Laboratory technique for this determination has been published in a U. S. Bureau of Mines Report.[1]

Tonnage Factor — In estimating total values, the specific gravity figure for an ore is not ordinarily used as such, but is converted into a figure representing cubic feet of ore per ton, called the "tonnage factor." In the calculation of tonnage factors the unit customarily used for various ores is an item which must be considered. Iron ore is sold on a long ton (2240 lb.) basis; coal, particularly anthracite, is estimated and sold on both the long and the short ton (2000 lb.) basis; whereas the short ton is generally used as the unit for other minerals. The foreign unit is the metric ton (2204.6 lb). The tonnage factor of a given ore, of course, varies for each of these units.

The diagram of Fig. 18, showing graphically the relative effects of density, porosity, and moisture upon the cubic feet per ton,[2] is here given to facilitate the proper correlation of the various items.

---

[1] "Method for Measuring Voids in Porous Material"—Dep't. of Commerce, U. S. Bureau of Mines, R. I. 3047, Oct. 1930 by J. D. Sullivan, G. L. Oldright, and W. E. Keck.

[2] After "Economic Geology," Vol. III, No. 4, 1908, by Warren J. Mead. Also given in U. S. G. S. Monograph 52, p. 482.

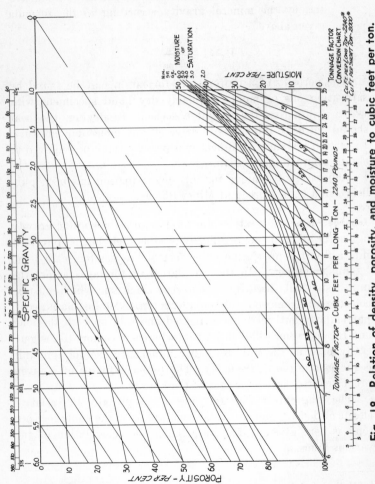

Fig. 18. Relation of density, porosity, and moisture to cubic feet per ton.

Construction and Use of the Diagram. "The top and bottom lines of the diagram proper, labeled respectively, 'specific gravity', and 'cubic feet per ton', and connected by parallel vertical lines, constitute a transformation table by means of which the number of cubic feet per ton of a material of a given density may be at once determined (or vice versa) by moving vertically between the upper and lower edges of the diagram. Immediately above the edge of the diagram proper is a scale of pounds per cubic foot, which may be used by moving vertically upward from any point on the 'specific gravity' or 'cubic feet per ton' scales.

"The effect of porosity is to decrease the density of a substance, hence, rock specific gravity is less than mineral specific gravity. To introduce the factor of porosity in the diagram, the upper line extends to the right to the point indicating a specific gravity of zero. The line at the left edge of the diagram is perpendicular to the upper edge and divided into 100 equal divisions, representing percentages of pore-space. Each tenth point of the vertical 'porosity' line is connected with the point indicating a specific gravity of zero. Hence, on moving vertically downward from any point on the 'specific gravity' line, a succession of equally spaced lines are crossed indicating percentages of pore space. To show the change in specific gravity resulting from a given porosity of a substance of known mineral specific gravity, a set of parallel lines connect points on the 'porosity' and 'specific gravity' lines. These lines are of steeper inclination than the porosity lines and are all parallel to the line connecting 100 per cent porosity with zero specific gravity. The diagram thus automatically shows the relation between mineral specific gravity, porosity, and cubic feet per ton.

"So far, the diagram takes no account of moisture, and hence is applicable only to perfectly dry material. Moisture, when present in an ore or similar substance, occupies the pore-space. When the pore-space is filled with moisture, the material is said to be saturated. As the moisture occupies the natural openings in the ore, its presence affects the weight of the ore and not its volume, hence its effect is to increase the density and decrease the number of cubic feet per ton.

Let G_d = density as affected by porosity

$$\text{Cu. ft. per ton} = \frac{2240}{G_d \times 62.5} \, .$$

When moisture (M) is present, the above equation becomes

$$\text{Cu. ft. per ton} = \frac{2240(1-M)}{G_d \times 62.5} \, .$$

The lower part of the diagram is crossed by a set of parallel horizontal lines indicating percentages of moisture, as shown at the right-hand edge of the diagram. Following the above equation, a set of inclined lines connect points on the 'moisture' and 'cubic feet per ton' lines. Given the number of cubic feet occupied by a ton of any porous material when dry, the effect of any percentage of moisture is indicated automatically by the diagram."

Mineral specific gravity and porosity determine the percentage of moisture which it is possible for an ore to hold. This maximum, or moisture of saturation, may be calculated as follows:

Let M_s = moisture of saturation.

The moisture of saturation percentage is the weight of the water which will fully occupy the pore-space divided by the total weight of the rock with the pores completely filled with water. Omitting the actual weight in pounds or grams, this resolves into:

$$M_s = \frac{P}{G_m(1\text{-}P) + P} \, ,$$

and, substituting for P its value $1 - \dfrac{G_d}{G_m}$, gives

$$M_s = \frac{1 - \dfrac{G_d}{G_m}}{G_d + 1 - \dfrac{G_d}{G_m}}$$

"By substitution of values for G_d and G_m in the preceding equations, the moisture-of-saturation curves are obtained. The curves enable one to determine at once the moisture of saturation of any material, given the specific gravity and porosity. Each curve corresponds to a certain mineral specific gravity, and the moisture of saturation is found by moving vertically from the point indicating the number of cubic feet per ton of the dry material to the proper moisture-of-saturation curve."[1]

The use of the diagram is most readily explained by an example. Assume an ore with mineral specific gravity of 4.8, porosity of 35 per cent, and moisture 8 per cent. Starting from the given specific gravity (4.8) on the upper line of the diagram, move vertically downward to the flatly inclined line representing the given porosity (35 per cent); thence upward to the right, parallel to the steeply inclined set of lines to the top edge of the diagram, where the rock specific gravity of the dry material (mineral density corrected for porosity) is found to be approximately 3.1; thence directly downward to the lower edge of the diagram, where the cubic feet per long ton corresponding to this dry, porous density is given as 11.5. Since the water occupies the pore-space, the effect of moisture is to increase the weight of the material without changing the volume. To correct the cubic feet per ton for moisture, move directly upward from this last point to the horizontal line representing the given moisture content (8 per cent); thence down the steeply inclined line to the left to the bottom of the diagram, where the final tonnage factor figure is shown to be 10.6. From the moisture-of-saturation curve it is apparent that an ore of 4.8 mineral density and 35 per cent porosity is capable of holding approximately 10.5 per cent moisture. Thus the ore, as assumed, has approximately 76 per cent of the pore space filled with moisture.

---

[1] After "Economic Geology," Vol. III, No. 4, 1908, by Warren J. Mead. Also given in U. S. G. S. Monograph 52, p. 482.

Below the diagram proper is a conversion chart which compares, at sight, tonnage factors for the two common units, the long and the short ton. For example, 10.6 cubic feet per long ton is equivalent to 9.45 cubic feet per short ton.

It is easy to see how a large error can be introduced into tonnage calculations if a factor of 12 cu. ft. per ton is used in a place where 11 or 13 cubic feet of ore are required to make a ton. This figure should never be taken for granted by an engineer in ore estimations. He should at least check the figure that is being used at the mine under investigation.

DESIGNATION OF ORE PROBABILITY — In estimating the value of a mineral deposit and in forecasting its future development and prospects, the terms *ore in sight, proven ore, probable ore,* and *possible ore* have often been used rather loosely, especially in prospectuses distributed in connection with the unregulated financing of new properties. In the literal sense of these terms, there is no such thing as "ore in sight" or "proven ore" because in a mine the ore values beyond the rock walls cannot actually be seen. The whole interpretation of these terms hinges on the question: "When ore values can be seen on a rock exposure or are known in drill holes, how far into the rock mass can the values be safely assumed to extend?" Much, of course, depends upon the type of deposit — whether rich and spotty, or uniform in content; also upon the number of visible sides of the block and upon the size of the block relative to the openings from which it is viewed. It is evident that a small block showing ore on four sides is more certain than a large block showing ore on four sides and, of two blocks of like size, one blocked out on four sides is more sure than one visible from only three or two sides or one side. The extent to which invisible material may be classed as ore is a matter of judgment based on geologic and other evidence. In every case where terms such as the above are used to describe conditional ore, a full explanation of each term should be included in the report submitted by the examiner.

C. K. Leith,[1] in preparing estimates of iron ore reserves, has defined terms used to designate respective classes of ore as follows:

" 'Assured' ore is defined to cover principally the ore blocked out in three dimensions by actual underground mining operations and drill holes, where the geological factors which limit the orebody are definitely known and where the chance of failure of the ore to reach these limits is so remote as not to be a factor in the practical planning of mine operations.

" 'Prospective' ore covers further extensions near at hand, where the conditions are such that ore will almost certainly be found but where the extent and limiting conditions cannot be so precisely defined.

"Ore is classed as 'possible' where the relation of the land to adjacent orebodies and to geological structures warrants the presumption that ore will be found but where the lack of exploration and development data precludes anything like certainty of its actual location or extent."

The U. S. Bureau of Mines and the U. S. Geological Survey, in recent estimates of mineral reserves, have agreed upon and defined [2] the following terms to signify relative dependability of information:

" 'Measured ore' is ore for which tonnage is computed from dimensions revealed in outcrops, trenches, workings, and drill holes and for which the grade is computed from the results of detailed sampling. The sites for inspection, sampling, and measurement are so closely spaced and the geological character is so well defined that the size, shape, and mineral content are well established. The computed tonnage and grade are judged to be accurate within limits

---

[1] Prospectus, The Cleveland-Cliffs Iron Co., Dec. 10, 1935, Lehman Bros., Field, Glore & Co., Hayden, Stone & Co., p. 9.
[2] "Investigation of National Resources," Subcommittee Hearings, U. S. Senate Committee on Public Lands, May 15-20, 1947; pp. 119-20.

which are stated, and no such limit is judged to differ from the computed tonnage or grade by more than 20 per cent.

" 'Indicated ore' is ore for which tonnage and grade are computed partly from specific measurements, samples, or production data and partly from projection for a reasonable distance on geologic evidence. The sites available for inspection, measurement, and sampling are too widely or otherwise inappropriately spaced to outline the ore completely or to establish its grade throughout.

" 'Inferred ore' is ore for which quantitative estimates are based largely on broad knowledge of the geologic character of the deposit and for which there are few, if any, samples or measurements. The estimates are based on an assumed continuity or repetition for which there is geologic evidence; this evidence may include comparison with deposits of similar type. Bodies that are completely concealed may be included if there is specific geologic evidence of their presence. Estimates of inferred ore should include a statement of the special limits within which the inferred ore may lie."

These definitions of parallel terms are useful to the engineer and geologist in helping to clarify the overlapping terminology in this field. Terms used in regional estimates will necessarily be defined somewhat less definitely than those used for a particular orebody.

METHOD OF ESTIMATING — In a broad way, the basic factors of a mine valuation are reserve, unit profit, and life. These items are used in estimating and with appropriate interest rates, in discounting future earnings to present worth. It is obvious that these factors are not susceptible to rigorous determination. In the usual case, each of these factors has an interdependent range of values affected by economic conditions.

Tonnage of ore in the deposit, apparently a rigid problem in measurement — so much volume, therefore, so many tons — depends on determining what grade is ore at the time and hence on the cost-price relationship for the projected method of mining and rate of output under economic conditions as forecast. This cost-price relationship, that is, the cost of production vs. market price per unit, establishes the grade of material above which profit can be realized. Material of a grade above this dividing line, or assay cutoff, may be classed as ore; material below the line is not ore, since it is not profitable to mine it under the conditions as estimated and forecast.

In estimating ore, three related tonnage figures will be under consideration; total tons of mineral-bearing material in the deposit, total tons that can be classed as ore, and tons of ore that can be recovered, or produced. Part of the job of estimating is done in the laboratory, determining tonnage factors; part in the drafting room, measuring block volumes from the maps and converting them to tonnages of such grade as the assays give; part is the consideration of the other factors entering into the cost-price relationship and the decision as to methods, rates, costs, and prices that will distinguish ore from rock.

In addition, there are uncertainties in the measurement problem that must be evaluated. These will be related to the degree to which the deposit is developed at the time of examination. These uncertainties have been mentioned in the discussion of ore terminology and, in general, are the reason for the classifying of tentative ores into groups defined by degree of observation and strength of geologic evidence.

The porphyry coppers, for instance, use a cutoff grade somewhat below 1% copper content, a drop in grade of about the order of one magnitude from previously mined vein and complex ore deposits. This was brought about by the development of block-caving, a low-cost, large-scale method of mining, the successful application of which brought these massive deposits in as ore whereas by other methods of underground mining they would have been unprofitable. Large-scale open-cut mining of these deposits has had a similar influence.

Experience has shown that the tonnage of ore that is very

likely present in a mining district is probably greater than that which is shown up by the exploration and development, but because of incomplete geologic data, or some other cause, it cannot be allocated definitely to the individual property.

Such deposits as undisturbed coal beds and gold-bearing placer gravels, when of uniform thickness and broad extent, are susceptible to much more accurate forecasts of reserve tonnage than are deformed deposits of complex ores.

Estimators handle these problems in different ways but with the same objective, namely, to arrive at a figure for total recoverable ore. Fitzhugh[1], in referring to specific deposits, speaks of "the appraisal of ore expectancies"; Lasky[2], on the broader aspects, of "the concept of ore reserves"; others in similar terms in outlining the variables in the problem. In any case, the estimator will apply certain discounts to some of the measurements.

Some engineers make their estimates by computing the tonnage of assured ore, or ore blocked out, the probable ore, or that which may reasonably be expected to be present, and the possible ore, or that which may be present but is so doubtful as to carry little weight, and make discounts on each item — for instance, a small amount on the developed ore, and larger discounts on the probable and prospective ores. Some estimate the tonnage of developed, probable, and possible ore in full, add them together, and discount the total result by some percentage. This discount expresses the judgment of the engineer on the possibility of recovering these tonnages.

. It is reasonable to make these deductions when measuring the tonnage in an orebody that is fairly well blocked out, but to do so in cases where much of the computation is based on estimates does not appear to be well-founded. In the case of pros-

---

[1] E. F. Fitzhugh, Jr., "The Appraisal of Ore Expectancies," A.I.M.E. Tech. Pub. No. 2090, 1948.

[2] S. G. Lasky, "The Concept of Ore Reserves," Mining and Met., Oct. 1945, pp. 471-4.

pective or possible tonnage, where even the existence of the ore is doubtful, the making of an estimate followed by detailed deductions for various hazards would appear to be similar to assuming the length of a base line to be so many feet and then proceeding to measure the angles to seconds of arc.

In this connection it is well to remember that orebodies are usually not free from barren stretches. Some clue to this condition can be given by the exploration of the orebody, but no development can be made extensive enough to locate all the unproductive areas. Most engineers make some allowance for this possible lack of uniformity in the ore by subtracting a percentage of the final computed tonnage figure.

Certain other considerations may be related to ore estimation. One of these is the choice between including a large quantity of subgrade material to increase the overall tonnage and scaling down the volume to make the product more valuable per ton. Another consideration is the question of subsidence and ultimate cost of destroying the ground surface.

MINING LOSS— Except under unusual circumstances and in relatively small areas, there is bound to be some loss under any mining system. This loss may be pillars left in place to support the ground; pillars crushed before they can be recovered; pockets or extensions of ore made inaccessible for some reason; or a continuing, daily loss through ore becoming mixed with waste for one reason or another. As in the case of barren areas in the deposit, permanent pillars may be deducted by specific measurement. Other losses, continuing and unpredictable in nature, are accounted for better by discounting the overall tonnage figures than by attempting detailed deduction or by the use of a higher cubic foot per ton factor.

Dilution, the additional tonnage mined in winning a previously estimated quantity of metal, is common to all caving methods of mining with the possible exception of top-slicing under most favorable conditions. This term ''dilution'' is to be distinguished from "recovery," the percentage of previously estimated economic metal content in the orebody actually extracted by the mining operations. When the ore limits within a mineral deposit are defined by an economic assay boundary, it is entirely possible, in mining, to recover 75%, 90%, 100%, or 110% of the metal previously estimated, depending upon the dilution incurred. Dilution, in this case, merely brings in added tonnage of material of less than the estimated cutoff grade but, nevertheless, tonnage containing metal. Thus the metal recovered may not all be the identical metal on which the estimates were made.

In some cases, an apparent recovery of 100% may be attained but at a lower grade. A recovery of 100% with zero dilution represents maximum efficiency of operations. Dilution affects not only the mining costs, but also the selling price of the ore. This effect is most evident when barren waste comes in during mining to dilute the product. Dilution is a factor that should be considered carefully in estimating the value of an orebody adaptable to a caving system of mining.[1]

---

[1] "Stope Control, Dilution, and Recovery with Caving Methods" — C. A. Mitke — E. & M. J. Vol. 126, p. 246.

"Mining Methods" — C. A. Mitke. McGraw-Hill Book Co., Inc. 1930, Chapter X.

CHAPTER 8

ASSETS OTHER THAN ORE

Given a deposit of ore of quantity and quality that can be exploited at a profit, capital and labor must be added in order to place the property on a producing basis. The returns from the property must be sufficient not only to redeem the purchase price of the land with interest commensurate with the risk involved, but also to return all capital required to put the property on a producing basis together with a fair rate of interest.

PLANT AND EQUIPMENT — The plant and equipment of a mine are of value only in proportion to their ability to produce ore. If ore cannot be mined, plant and equipment are worth practically nothing, as they have very limited resale value when their usefulness for ore production is finished. The engineer, in estimating the value of an operating property, must determine whether or not the plant is adequate to produce the desired quantities of ore at the required cost per unit. In mining, as in every other business, there is a determinable point of equilibrium between the plant investment and the rate of production at which the greatest net profit may be realized. The engineer is concerned, therefore, with the estimate of the cost of all new processes and equipment necessary to convert the existing plant into one which will produce a maximum of ore values at a minimum cost. This cost represents money which must be spent on revision of plant and practice prior to production and, therefore, like other development costs, must be deducted from the valuation of the property in arriving at a fair purchase price.

DEVELOPMENT — Development includes shafts, crosscuts, drifts, and other access openings needed for production, as distinguished generally from similar openings made for purposes of exploration, although there is no sharp line of demarcation between the two.

Money spent for development of a property is even more intimately tied up with the ore than that spent for plant and equipment. Although sometimes a market may be found for items of mine equipment which may be moved after the mineral is exhausted or a property proved valueless, it is rare indeed for the development work done for one property to have any value to another property.

As will be noted later in outlining the relation of the royalty interest to valuation, the irretrievable association of development moneys with the orebody is recognized by law, wherein the operator of a property on a lease basis is considered, in some cases at least, to acquire an interest in the ore by the expenditure for development openings, though title to the ore rests with the fee owner, the other party to the contract.

VALUE TO FUTURE OWNER — Although money spent for development will seldom be assigned much value in the case of a forced sale of an unprofitable operation, it is readily conceivable, providing the deposit does contain mineral values, that the difference between the actual development cost and its transfer asset value may be sufficient to convert the operation to a profitable business. In any case of transfer, this capital loss by the first owner represents a gain to the new purchaser, providing the development openings are located advantageously and are usable.

To illustrate this point, suppose that A, the present operator of a mine has spent, say, $500,000 in sinking shafts and developing levels, only to find that the grade of the deposit is not quite high enough to net a profit over and above capital and operating costs. Having reached his financial limit, A offers the property for sale. B has the property appraised and buys it at a figure that allows very little for plant, equipment, and development already in place. With reduced overhead, B finds that the grade of ore is sufficient for him to show a profit.

WORKING CAPITAL — In addition to the capital necessary for plant, equipment, and development, money must also be provided to keep the business functioning on a production basis. This is known as working capital. Supplies have to be purchased in an amount dependent on the size and nature of the property, and kept on hand to avoid delays; labor must be paid and other running expenses met until such time as the ore or mineral is marketed and cash is being received in a quantity sufficient to meet current expenses. If the market for the product is seasonal (as it is with Lake Superior iron ores or with coal) or if, in order to get the best price for the product, it is necessary to withhold it from the market at times so that inventories are built up, there may be a considerable variation in the amount of working capital required at different times of the year or from year to year. There should be sufficient moneys provided in the capital or surplus of the company to cover the minimum requirements for working capital; money for seasonal needs or to carry unusual inventories may, under normal conditions, be obtained by commercial loans. But whether these requirements are met by owned or borrowed money, the interest on this money is a proper and necessary charge against the business.

Since working capital is intimately tied to the production process, it is subject to the same risks as capital invested in real property unless provided under separate guarantee. Companies operating several mines may be able to finance their working capital needs on the basis of a combined pool more cheaply than the individual who can borrow only on the assets of a single property.

The minimum amount of working capital may generally be

computed by taking the total cash outlay of the operation from the time the ore is broken until the cash is received in payment for that ore.

MISCELLANEOUS ASSETS — In examining any mining property, **AND CIRCUMSTANCES**   the engineer should take into consideration such assets as timber holdings, land, and potential and actual power sites and water supplies, not so much for their cash value as for their possible economic advantage in making the business more self-sufficient. The actual cash worth of these various items is usually added to the mineral valuation of the property to obtain the purchase price, except when these outside assets are disproportionately high with respect to the mineral worth.

Water is essential for milling by gravity and flotation methods. Whether or not any substantial value is assigned to this asset in the case of a mine and mill, it must be recognized that the adequacy of the water supply may well be critical to the business. Whereas the removal of water from mine openings is a cost item and may, at times, become difficult to handle, a good supply of water on surface for milling is distinctly an asset. Thorough investigation of the water supply is an important part of the examination whenever the ore is to be milled at the property. If water has to be brought from any distance, pipeline (or flume) construction and transmission may call for heavy capital expense. The alternative may be a transportation charge of similar magnitude for hauling the mine ore to the mill.

Timber holdings, likewise, may be an important asset to a mining property, particularly in sparsely timbered areas where freight from the nearest lumbering center is a considerable cost item. With selective logging, a moderate area of forest can yield a continuing supply of timber sufficient for all underground support and other construction about the mine.

In remote localities water power, when available and developed, is an advantage to mine operation and to community facilities; in more populated areas water-power development for a mine may well expand into a stable subsidiary business selling power to nearby communities. Power development, usually at considerable capital outlay and not often critical to mine operation in view of the availability of fuels, is an asset in appraisal.

Other less tangible assets of a mine will include its labor force and community. An established community, with housing, schools, sanitary and other public facilities, is important to the welfare of a mining business, though difficult to assess in money value. For a new property more than a few miles from towns or other settlements, the assembling of a labor force and the provision of housing and community facilities will be a cost of the operation. For an established property under examination for transfer or consolidation, these adjuncts must likewise be given consideration.

CHAPTER 9

ECONOMIC CONSIDERATIONS

EARNING POWER — BASIS FOR VALUE — Earning power is the customary basis for valuation of any producing industry. Earning power is dependent not only upon natural resources, plant, equipment, and efficiency of operation, but also upon all of the critical economic factors which influence marketing, supply and demand, and the purchasing power of the dollar.

Transportation — Transportation, in many instances, is of great importance to the mining industry and may be the controlling factor, particularly in the case of low-value minerals such as coal, iron ore, and even petroleum. The coal deposits of Alaska and the iron deposits of Brazil are pointed examples. Oil fields at a distance from consuming centers and lacking pipe lines or water transport, such as those in the Rocky Mountain area, are likewise affected.

Sale of Product — Another factor of considerable importance which affects all commodities except gold, and possibly uranium at the present time, is the marketing of the product. Some companies sell their ores, some sell a partly refined product, and some a refined one. Some companies contract with selling agencies to dispose of their product, while others have their own selling organizations. In any case, the success of the enterprise is largely dependent upon the sale of a satisfactory amount of the commodity.

It would be absurd to compute the value of a mine on the basis of the most efficient production, if the market will absorb only half this amount. The market for the product is often determined by the business connections of the owners or management. The extension of liberal credit, which of course depends upon the financial ability of the company, is often necessary in order to sell the product. The terms of sale are sometimes determined by custom, as the following example shows.

Lake Superior iron ores are generally sold on contract covering deliveries during the season of navigation on the Great Lakes. Contracts are generally closed prior to the opening of navigation. The customary contract provides for payment to be made in twelve equal monthly installments beginning May 1 of the year of shipment and ending April 1 of the following year. The navigation season opens about the middle of April and closes about the middle of December but, because of late-season storms, high marine insurance rates, and trouble with ore freezing in the railroad cars and docks, very little ore is shipped after November 15. The average date of shipment is August 1, and of payment, October 15. On November 15 the mine has shipped all the ore contracted for, but has received only 58% of the contract price and must wait four and one-half months for the final payment. As Lake Superior iron ore is usually sold f.o.b. Lower Lakes, the mine must be prepared to finance not only the mining of the ore but also the rail and lake freight charges to the point of delivery, and these may be as much or more than the mining cost.

The value of ores or metals held in stock for any considerable period waiting for a favorable market may be very soon eaten up by interest and taxes. Before a price of $3.00 f.o.b. mine is refused for an iron ore, it should be realized that if money is costing 6% and general property taxes on stockpile ore are 10¢ a ton, the price will have to be $3.28 the following year in order for the company to break even, and $3.57 if the ore is held for two years.

Mining produces raw materials, and the industry is, therefore, subject to more extreme fluctuations than are the manufacturing industries. Possible exceptions to this are the producers of the monetary metals, gold and silver, and to some extent the producers of such necessities as coal, salt, sulphur, etc. All producers of raw materials are subject to more frequent and greater business changes, primarily because of the large amounts of raw material supplies in transit and in stock. At the first indication of a slackening demand, the producer of finished products cuts off his raw material purchases and starts to use up his stock. He continues to operate, while the raw material producer must stop. When demand for finished products revives, the manufacturer not only orders the necessary raw materials for current production but builds up his supply for future use. Thus, raw materials are the first to be curtailed and may be the last to be drawn upon in the cycle of business activity.

Depletion and Increasing Costs — Mineral production differs from ordinary business, as manufacturing, in three respects:

1. Depletion — the stock in trade of a mineral producer (mine, oil well, quarry, etc.) is not replenishable; when the warehouse has been emptied, the mine is finished. In lumbering, depletion can be overcome by selective logging to allow time for new growth.

2. Grade of Ore — the quality of the raw material processed at one mine, by natural endowment, is not necessarily comparable, even within trade limits, with similar raw material at another mine. For instance, one mine may be working a gold quartz vein containing two ounces of values ($70) per ton while a similar vein at another mine may run only one ounce ($35) per ton, whereas white pine logs going to two sawmills, though widely separated, may be graded so that one mill receives about the same raw material as the other. Or, on the other hand, the raw material of two mineral producers may be

identical, as with two adjoining coal mines working the same seam or two oil properties draining the same pool.

3. Increasing Cost with Depth — mining becomes more difficult with depth, adding to the cost of support of workings, ventilation, hoisting, etc. Capital outlays for improved equipment and efficient management may offset the normal increase temporarily. Open pits encounter similar problems in haulage and maintenance of walls. An old rule says that 90% of the profits of mining come from the first 1000 feet.

These characteristics of mineral production will affect earning power and must be kept in mind while considering the usual economic influences. A specific mine has a relatively short life and cannot be classed with perpetual utilities or long-lived manufacturing industries. It is true that a few of the world's great mines have been operating for centuries, but it is likewise certain that even these will someday be worked out. It is not to be concluded that the production has been uniform throughout this period. For the mineral industry as a whole, more mineral has been produced since 1900 than for all previous centuries. The mining industry must be perpetual, as it is the foundation of our industrial life, but the average life of individual mines is relatively short. With few exceptions, mines are located in isolated regions unsuited geographically and otherwise for commercial centers and manufacturing activity. A mining town is usually dependent for its existence upon a single industry and, as a result, the mines bear the larger part of the community tax burden.

The earning power of a mining enterprise is thus a highly variable quantity, sensitive to a great number of economic influences as well as subject to its own peculiar burdens and difficulties.

PROFIT SPREAD — ''Profit spread'' in mining, as in all business, is the difference between the total cost of the commodity produced and its selling price. Neither the cost nor the selling price remains constant. Even though no change in methods of production be assumed, there still remain two variables that affect both: (a) the value or purchasing power of money; and (b) the exchange value of the commodity — that is, its relative price as compared with the prices of other commodities.

Assuming for the present no change in (b), both unit cost and unit sales price tend to vary with the general commodity price index. Of the four general productive agents — land, labor, capital, and management — land, being determined by the price paid for the property, will remain fixed, as will also that portion of capital which is invested in fixed assets, equipment, and development at the time of purchase; the cost of other capital, labor, and management will vary with the commodity price index, as will also the price of the commodity produced. It is found, therefore, that during the life of a property there is a smaller variation in the profit as expressed in money (profit spread) than there is in the cost per unit or in the selling price, although the percentage of variation is somewhat greater.

Commodity Price Index — For example, assume that at a commodity price index of 100, the cost per unit is 10¢, selling price 14¢, and profit 4¢; that the land factor is 12½% of the initial cost of production (equivalent to a royalty of ⅛ or 12½%) and the cost of that portion of capital tied up in fixed assets is 7½% (covered by depreciation), making a total of 20% of the cost that will not be affected by a change in general commodity prices. Let the price index go up to 150 and allow sufficient time for costs of labor, supplies, and circulating capital, and for the price of the commodity produced, to adjust themselves to this index, and we have

	Index 100	Index 150	Difference Money	%
Selling price	14¢	$14 \times 1.5 =$ 21¢	7¢	50
Cost	10	$2 + 8 \times 1.5 =$ 14	4	40
Profit	4	7	3¢	75

Under the same conditions, let the general index of commodity price go down to 75, and we have

	Index 100	Index 75	Difference Money	%
Selling price	14¢	14 × .75 = 10.5¢	3.5¢	25
Cost	10	2 + 8 × .75 = 8.0	2.0	20
Profit	4	2.5	1.5¢	37.5

In the first instance, although the selling price has increased 50% because of the increase in the price index, the cost price has also increased 40% from the same cause, and instead of an apparent increase of 7¢ in profit the real increase is only 3¢.

In the second instance the selling price has decreased 3.5¢, an amount which almost wipes out the profit if the cost price had remained the same; but the change in price index has also decreased the cost, and there is still a profit of 2.5¢.

Management Policy — There are at least three other factors which tend to further reduce the amount of variation in profit.

(1) In times of prosperity there is a tendency toward inefficiency. Management tends to be satisfied with conditions, this attitude has its effect on labor, and small economies seem to be of little importance. If labor is scarce, as is usually the case during periods of high prices, it is inefficient because a lower class of labor is employed and because men cannot be driven at top speed when jobs are plentiful. In times of low profit, or when the price of the commodity produced has dropped below cost and employment is scarce, the management is keenly interested in any method or change of method to effect economies, and there is a marked increase in the efficiency of labor.

(2) In times of high prices and profits, it will pay to mine lower-grade ore than can be profitably mined during times of normal or low prices. Under these conditions, the output and

total profit may be increased but the unit profit may be de-creased. In times of low prices, mining is often confined to that ore which will produce a profit at the current market. This increases the unit profit at the expense of the reserves of high-grade ore.

(3) In times of low profits there is a tendency to defer all expense items that are not immediately necessary — the repairs and maintenance of buildings and structures, miners' cottages, etc.; these needs which must be cared for eventually are mainte-nance items and are a charge to operating expense during pros-perous times. The purchase of minor items of equipment, such as rails, mine cars, drilling machines, and scraper hoists, which are usually charged to operation and not to a plant account, is apt to be made to a greater extent during prosperous times than in times of low profits.

Commodity Exchange Value — It was noted above that the profit in mining might be affected also by another variable, (b), the exchange value of the commodity produced. This can be illus-trated by a few examples:

(1) In 1915 butter sold for an average price of 30¢ per pound and in 1920 it sold for 67¢. According to the Wholesale Price Index (U. S. Dept. of Labor) shown in Fig. 19, the average commodity price level based on 1926 as 100 was 69.5 in 1915 and 154.4 in 1920. Ex-pressed in terms of 1926 dollars, the price of butter for each of the years given is

$$30 \div .695 = 43.2¢ = \text{1915 price in 1926 dollars.}$$
$$67 \div 1.544 = 43.3¢ = \text{1920 price in 1926 dollars.}$$

This shows that butter, as a commodity, did not change in relative importance between 1915 and 1920; the dif-ference in butter price was wholly due to a change in the price level of all commodities or in the purchasing power of the dollar.

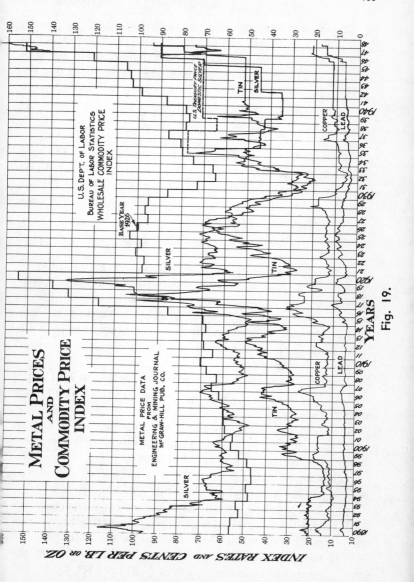

METAL PRICES AND COMMODITY PRICE INDEX

METAL PRICE DATA FROM ENGINEERING & MINING JOURNAL McGRAW-HILL PUB. CO.

U.S. DEPT. of LABOR BUREAU OF LABOR STATISTICS WHOLESALE COMMODITY PRICE INDEX

BASE YEAR 1926

U.S. TREASURY PRICE DOMESTIC SILVER

SILVER
TIN
COPPER
LEAD

YEARS

INDEX RATES AND CENTS PER LB. or OZ.

Fig. 19.

(2) The average price of silver in 1909 was 54.2¢ per ounce, while in 1919 it was $1.12 per ounce. In these two years the wholesale commodity index figures based on 1926 as 100 were respectively 67.6 and 138.6. What was the silver price in terms of 1926 dollars for the two years given?

$$54.2 \div .678 = 80.0¢$$
$$112 \div 1.386 = 80.7¢$$

(3) Copper averaged 13.2¢ per pound in 1909 and 27.4¢ per pound in 1919. Index prices for these two years based on 1926 as 100 were respectively 67.6 and 138.6. If these copper prices are expressed in terms of the 1926 base, they are

$$13.2 \div .676 = 19.5¢$$
$$27.4 \div 1.386 = 19.7¢$$

The preceding examples are of individual commodities which did not change in relative supply and demand for the two years cited, and whose changes in price have been entirely due to changes in the price levels. The following instances show cases in which the price change of the given commodity has been due to a change both in price level and also in the relative importance of the commodity:

Referring to example (2) above, we find that in 1931 silver sold for 30¢ an ounce with the commodity index at 70, thus giving

$30 \div .70 = 42.9¢$ as the equivalent price per ounce at 1926 levels and showing that silver dropped considerably in relative importance during the period 1919 to 1931.

Likewise, referring to example (3) cited above, we find that copper sold down to 6½¢ per pound in 1931, thus giving

$6½ \div .70 = 9.3¢$ per pound as the equivalent price at the 1926 base level. Copper thus dropped in relative importance (governed by supply and demand) from 1919 to 1931.

(4) Slate roofing (No. 1 Sea green) sold in 1919 at the quarry at an average price of $7.875 per 100 sq. ft., and

in 1927 for $14.00 per square.[1] The wholesale commodity index based on 1926 as 100 gave price levels in 1919 as 138.6, and in 1927 as 95.4. Comparing these prices in terms of the 1926 dollar, gives

$$7.875 \div 1.38 = \$ 5.68$$
$$14.00 \div .954 = \$14.70$$

(5) The average price of a Ford automobile in 1914 was $637.50, and in 1925 the price of the same model was $390.90. Index prices in 1914 showed an average value of 68.1 as compared with an average of 100 in 1926 and 103.5 in 1925. Expressing the prices of this item in terms of 1926 dollars, gives

$$637.50 \div .681 = \$935$$
$$390.90 \div 1.035 = \$378$$

This shows a decided drop in the price of the article in question, in spite of a rise in the general commodity level. This change apparently was not due to lack of demand but rather to cost reduction made possible by greater demand.

It is evident that if the price of the ore or metal produced changes relative to other commodities and if the profit is based on the current relation between prices, the latter will be either increased or decreased. This rule also applies to gold. When the price index is low, gold mining is very profitable, but when the index is high, the profits of gold mining are greatly reduced because of the increased cost of production. It is too much to expect the engineer to foretell with any degree of accuracy the price of the commodity produced in relation to that of other commodities, but he can at least note the trends in relative prices. A large potential supply of the commodity may fore-

---

[1] U. S. Dept. of Labor, Bureau of Statistics.

warn of lower prices in the future, as was the case in copper when the African deposits were under development. The development of new oil fields promises increased competition for anthracite and even bituminous coal, and the development of improved internal combustion engines increases the gravity of the coal producer's situation.

THE BUSINESS CYCLE — The trends of business and economic conditions are most readily visualized for comparative purposes when set forth in the form of graphs. Most investment houses and many business, statistical, and economic groups keep periodic records of trade activity either for private reasons or for the purpose of keeping the public informed in regard to commercial conditions. In this text a few of the more general business graphs are given and their sources noted.

Fig. 19 is a chart showing graphically the fluctuations in the prices at New York of silver, tin, copper, and lead metal,[1] together with the U. S. Dept. of Labor price index of wholesale commodities.[2] These curves, or similar ones plotted for other metals or commodities, show the trend of prices during the last four decades and may be used to determine the average selling price of a metal in past years as a basis for predicting future price levels. A single quotation on a certain metal is not of much value by itself, but the complete record of prices for the last forty years gives a rather firm foundation upon which to base an estimate of future average prices, because several complete business cycles have occurred within this period and the time interval is long enough to include a number of major industrial advancements.

On the chart of business cycles, Fig. 20, are shown nine index and trend curves relating to business, prices, and values

---

1 "Engineering and Mining Journal," McGraw-Hill Pub. Co.
2 U. S. Dept. of Labor, Bureau of Statistics.

Fig. 20. Chs

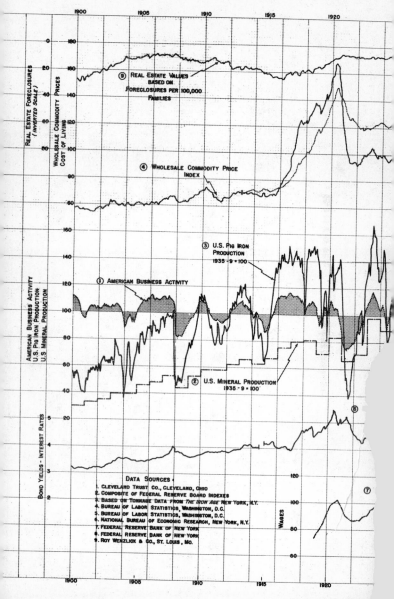

Fig. 20. Cha

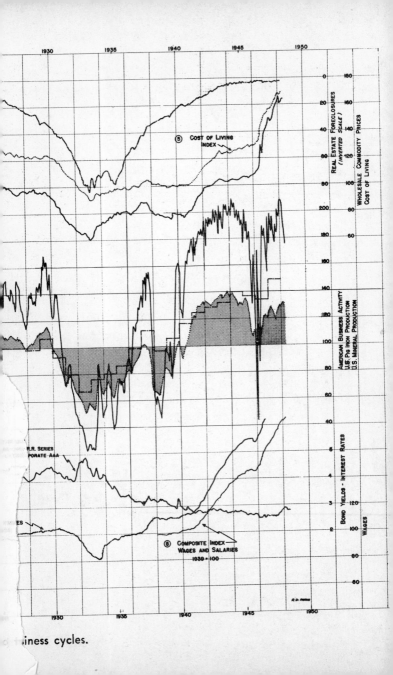

CoST OF LIVING INDEX ⑤

RR. SERIES
PORATE-AAA

⑥ COMPOSITE INDEX
WAGES AND SALARIES
1939·100

R.D. PARIS

REAL ESTATE FORECLOSURES *(INVERTED SCALE)*
WHOLESALE COMMODITY PRICES
COST OF LIVING

AMERICAN BUSINESS ACTIVITY
U.S. PIG IRON PRODUCTION
U.S. MINERAL PRODUCTION

BOND YIELDS · INTEREST RATES
WAGES

...iness cycles.

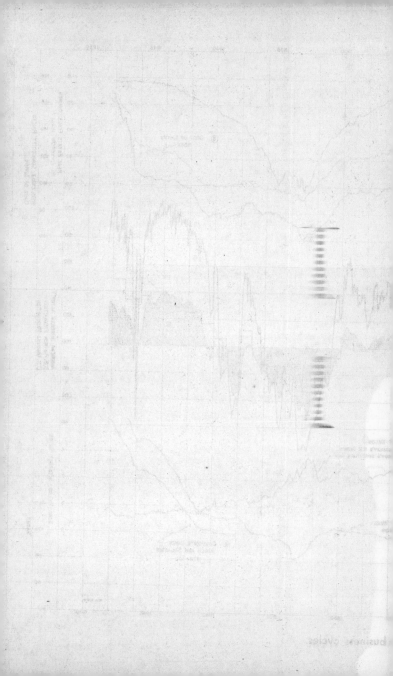

for the period since 1900. In order of reference, these are curves of American business activity[1], total U. S. production of minerals[2], U. S. pig-iron output[3], wholesale commodity prices[4], consumers' prices[5] (formerly called the cost of living index), bond interest yields[6], wages[7], combined wages and salaries[8], and the value of real estate as indicated by the rate of mortgage foreclosures[9] for nonfarm families.

The index of total U. S. mineral production was prepared by adjusting data prior to 1919 to the 1935-9 base; the pig-iron index was calculated by the author from published figures for monthly production, using the average monthly output during the period 1935-9 as the base. The curve of bond interest yields is a combination of two series; the Macaulay series of high-grade railroad bonds from 1900 through 1936 and Moody's Aaa corporate series from 1937. The rate of mortgage foreclosures has been plotted to an inverted scale to indicate trend of real estate values.

With these as a model, an examining engineer may prepare special charts related to the circumstances of a particular property. When maintained up to date, Figs. 19 and 20 will indicate in general the current phase of the business cycle and thus offer the examiner a guide to his forecasts. Although such prediction may be only partly accurate, because business cycles are not uniform in time or intensity, nevertheless a study of the statistical record will permit wiser decisions than will an utter disregard of such evidence.

To be swayed in judgment by the spirit of the times is

---

[1] The Cleveland Trust Co., Cleveland, Ohio.
[2] The Federal Reserve Board, Washington, D.C.
[3] The Iron Age, New York, N.Y.
[4] Bureau of Labor Statistics, Washington, D.C.
[5] Bureau of Labor Statistics, Washington, D.C.
[6] National Bureau of Economic Research, New York, N.Y.
[7] Federal Reserve Bank of New York.
[8] Federal Reserve Bank of New York.
[9] Roy Wenzlick & Co., St. Louis, Mo.

easy. For instance, when copper metal was quoted above 20¢ a pound in 1929, the earning capacity of a normally sub-marginal property was high and would lead an unscrupulous or unobservant estimator to place a high valuation on the property; whereas a study of the problem would have shown that the price for copper which could normally be expected over an appreciable period of years would be only about 14¢ or 15¢, a price which would result in a lower valuation for the mine. To take the reverse of the situation, with copper at 7¢ a pound, as it was in 1931, a normally profitable mine was showing an operating loss, and to base a valuation on the financial status of the company at that time would likewise be grossly unfair.

To aid the engineer in making a detailed study of business conditions at any point in the swing of activity, the relative status of the more prominent industries involved and the criteria at the breaking points of an extreme business cycle [1] are shown in Fig. 21. No individual cycle is exactly normal, but all cycles are actuated by certain factors and result in similar effects. Exact prediction of conditions is impossible, but sound, logical reasoning by a person who understands the funda-mentals governing trade fluctuations and crises can result in deductions which are close enough for practical purposes and accurate as to trend, and which will ward off heavy financial loss to the engineer's client. No attempt will be made here to discuss individually all of the factors which affect, directly or indi-rectly, the value of a mining enterprise. The subject has been covered in a general manner, and the itemized analysis must be made by the estimator.

The phase of the business cycle during which the sale of a mining property is being effected materially alters the tactics of the two parties engaged in the deal. To illustrate this point,

---

[1] Data from Alexander Hamilton Institute text on ''Investments'' by A. W. Taylor, pp. 237-244.

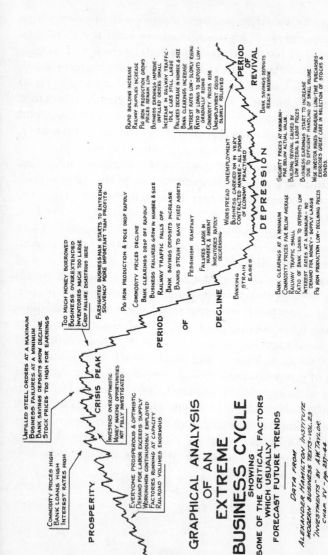

Fig. 21.

GRAPHICAL ANALYSIS
OF AN
EXTREME
BUSINESS CYCLE
SHOWING
SOME OF THE CRITICAL FACTORS
WHICH USUALLY
FORECAST FUTURE TRENDS

Data from
ALEXANDER HAMILTON INSTITUTE
MODERN BUSINESS TEXTS-VOL.23
"INVESTMENTS" BY A.W.TAYLOR
CHAP XV - pp. 237-44
1925 EDITION

PROSPERITY

Commodity prices high
Bank loans high
Interest rates high

Everyone prosperous & optimistic
Demand for labor exceeds supply
Workingmen continuously employed
Factories running at capacity
Railroad volumes enormous

Investors overoptimistic
Money making opportunities
not fully investigated

CRISIS PEAK

Unfilled steel orders at a maximum
Business failures at a minimum
Bank savings deposits show decline
Stock prices too high for earnings

Too much money borrowed
Business overextended
Inventories much too large
Crop failure disastrous here

Farsighted businessman starts to entrench
Solvency more important than profits

PERIOD

Pig iron production & price drop rapidly
Commodity prices decline
Bank clearings drop off rapidly
Business failures grow in number & size
Railway traffic falls off
Bank savings deposits increase
Banks strain to save fixed assets

Pessimism rampant

Failures large in
number & amount
Inventories rapidly
decreasing

OF

DECLINE

Banking
strain
eases

Widespread unemployment
Business carried on in very
contracted manner - all forms
of economy practised

DEPRESSION

Bank clearings at a minimum
Commodity prices far below average
Railway traffic small
Ratio of bank loans to deposits low
Interest rates at a minimum - no
demand for money - supply large
Pig iron production low- declining prices

Security prices at minimum-
far below actual value.
Building revival caused by
low material & labor prices
Business earnings start to increase
due to efficient handling of small volume
Wise investor makes favorable long-time purchases-
exercises great care in selection of stocks &
bonds.

Rapid building increase
Railway supplies increase
Pig iron production grows
prices remain low
Business earnings improve-
unfilled orders small
Increase in railway traffic-
idle cars still large
Bank clearings increase
Failures decrease in number & size
Interest rates low- slowly rising
Ratio of loans to deposits low-
gradually rising
Commodity prices rise
Unemployment crisis
slowly relieved

PERIOD
OF
REVIVAL

Bank savings deposits
reach maximum

suppose a fair valuation has been placed on the property by a reputable engineer. With this estimate on hand the seller, during a period of prosperity and high metal prices, will bargain from his own inflated figure downward to the engineer's estimate; whereas, during a depression, with the same estimate at hand, the bargaining will proceed from a greatly discounted figure upward toward the estimated value. It will be apparent that the best time to sell a mine is during a period of prosperity, and the best time to buy a mine is during a depression.

The chief interest of the examining engineer in cyclical changes in prices is to avoid overemphasis of the current price level by recognition of the fact that such changes exist. The products of our mines are necessary commodities. In the long run the price of any commodity will equal the economist's cost of production, which includes payment for land, labor, capital, and management. Regardless of the current price level and of profits earned under present conditions, the engineer should compare the property being examined with competing properties. If the property presents about the average conditions under which the producers of the bulk of the commodity operate, it should make a fair profit in normal times, should make a good profit in good times, and should be able to ride out a depression if properly financed. If the examination shows the property to be superior to its principal competitors, the results of operation should be proportionately more favorable, but if it does not compare favorably with its competitors, even though it may make a profit during a period of high prices, it will be unable to compete in periods of low prices and may be a poor investment at any price.

CHAPTER 10

ESTIMATING FUTURE COSTS AND PROFITS

As already outlined, the simplest and most accurate method of estimating future earnings is to use "profit spread" as a basis. There are, however, numerous instances in which estimates of future costs and future selling prices are desired. An operating company usually makes cost setups one, two, or even five years ahead of actual operations. A client, in purchasing a property, is interested not only in the profit to be expected but also in the operating cost required to produce this net return.

BUILDING UP FUTURE COST SHEET— In making an estimate of the costs of production, the engineer must understand the whole operation, divide it into functions, and then estimate the labor and supply costs entering into each function; that is, he must build up a cost sheet in advance of operation. His first step is, therefore, the preparation of an outline for the cost sheet. The construction of a labor statement is a convenient intermediary step toward preparation of labor estimates for the cost sheet. This statement will list the number of men in each classification, the wages paid per man, and the total wages for each class. It will also show the "tons per man per day" for each occupation. The unit cost can be computed from the labor statement and transferred to the cost sheet under the proper headings. Next, the supplies for each account are entered, and finally the overhead accounts, administration, sales, freight, etc. The engineer is in exactly the same position as a contractor making an estimate of the cost of construction of a building. The contractor has never built one exactly like it, but from past experience and records of costs he can assemble estimates of unit costs into an estimate for the cost of the entire structure.

It will be apparent that if the property is in operation, or if there are available the history of previous operations and accurate cost records, the situation is much simplified. In this case it may be advisable to use the outlines of the cost system which have been in use, and to adjust the actual costs obtained in the past to future conditions.

The following are some of the items which must be considered in an adjustment of previous costs to future operation :

(1) Any change in output will change the cost of production.

(2) If costs are figured per pound of metal produced, a change in the grade of the ore will change the costs per unit.

(3) A change in the character of the ore may require a change in treatment. Harder ore will usually increase not only the labor cost, but also the cost of steel and explosives. This change may, however, permit a change in method of mining that will economize on timber consumption.

(4) An increase in depth may necessitate a change in mining methods, the use of more timber, the installation of artificial ventilation, or an increase in the amount of development per ton, and may cause an increase in hoisting and pumping charges and a decrease in output.

In computing the value of a mining property in the ensuing part of this text, the redemption of the purchase price is provided for in the formula. For this reason no depreciation, depletion, or other deferred charges are to be included in the estimated cost of production. However, provision must be made in the cost estimate for any new items of plant, equipment, and development which are not provided for by a direct deduction from the purchase price. For example: The company which has been operating the property may include in its cost a charge of 20¢ per ton which is concurrently credited to a capital account covering stripping the overburden from the orebody. The purchasing company is buying the property stripped and developed. The expense incurred in this stripping is included in the purchase price and, as a redemption of the purchase price is provided for by the formula used, it should not be duplicated as a cost of mining. This matter will be more evident after a study of the valuation formulas.

In recent years, more particularly since 1913 when the U. S. federal government required all mines to set up valuations for taxation purposes, the tax situation has become relatively more important with regard to mines because of the increased attention paid by most states to this source of revenue. There are, in general, three types of taxes, (1) state and local taxes, (2) privilege taxes, and (3) federal taxes. Privilege taxes, such as the tax on the corporation operating the mine, are usually determined readily and seldom show great variation. The amount of federal income tax depends, of course, on the profit obtained by the operation of the property. This item cannot be computed until the estimate of future profits has been made and must, therefore, be left out of the calculation until the last. The same condition is true of state income taxes wherever applied.

The rates, methods of assessments, classes of property, etc., that are part of the machinery for gathering the state and local taxes can be easily determined from local information and records. It is sometimes difficult to predict the future needs of the locality in which the mine is located and the effect these will have on mine taxes. The following are a few of the factors that would make changes of importance in the tax cost of any mine: (1) the percentage of tax paid by the mine in relation to the other property in the assessing district; (2) the number of mines and prospects in the district, and the length of life of these properties in relation to the mine being valued; (3) the possible need of the local assessing district for improvements, such as schools, roads, etc.; (4) the bonded indebtedness of the assessing district.

The average future price of the product should be different from that shown by the past record, if (1) the grade of ore remaining in the mine is different from that produced in the past, (2) the ore impurities or material associated with the remaining ore has a tendency to lower or raise the selling price, (3) the future mining operations will be such that dilution or contamination of the ore will take place, with a resultant lowering of grade and selling price, (4) economic conditions are such that changes in price received for the product are to be expected. It is this last question which is so difficult to answer. The spread between the cost and the selling price, except in unusual cases, offers the best solution to this particular phase of the problem whenever it can be used.

In arriving at both cost and sales price per ton, it must be remembered that these should be computed for the same locality. The sales price of the ore at the collar of the shaft must be compared with the cost of production to that point. If a transportation system, a mill, and a smelter are part of the operation, the costs are taken up to the point at which the ore is sold. The cost of transportation, milling, and smelting must be analyzed in the same manner in which the mine costs are examined. Familiarity with ore transportation problems and with milling and smelting questions is essential for the proper handling of the costs and the adjustments that are to be made in these instances. The influence of new milling and smelting practice, the effects of new machinery and equipment, and the possibility of a change in grade and quality of the ore are only three items out of the many that must be considered.

ESTIMATING LIFE — The value of the mine is a function of the rapidity with which the reserves can be exhausted. In general, the shorter the period for mining a given reserve, the greater will be the specialization and therefore the greater the economy in production, the lower will be the fixed charges per unit, and the sooner the profit to be derived will be realized.

Hoover's statement[1], "The economic and advisable ore reserve will be equal in volume to the annual output multiplied by a number of years just under that needed by the increment of profits to equalize the amortization required to construct increased treatment units," applies only to gold mines, but may be used in planning the production of base metals and ores to the extent that the market permits.

Some of the factors limiting production are (1) rapidity with which development work is extended, (2) size and shape of orebody, (3) mining conditions, (4) method of mining, (5) labor supply, (6) capacity of shaft, hoist, haulage equipment, etc., (7) mill, transportation, and smelter capacity, and (8) the market for the product.

With modern methods of shaft sinking and drifting, the speed of development within practical limits is largely a matter of expense. In firm ground, shafts can be deepened from 50 to 70 feet a month, depending upon size and the nature of ground, and drifts can be driven from 300 to 400 feet a month without a material increase in the expense. These figures can be doubled if conditions warrant the extra cost.

The size and shape of an orebody determine the number of openings, and usually the amount of ore that can be produced in a given time depends upon the number of working places. The mining conditions, such as ventilation, amount of water,

---

[1] "Engineering & Mining Journal," March 24, 1904 — H. C. Hoover. Also reprinted in "The Economics of Mining" — Hill Pub. Co. 1905-1907.

character of the ore, grade of the ore, etc., are so interrelated with the size and shape of the orebody and the mining method selected that one condition cannot be considered without some attention being given to the others. The labor supply relates to the quality as well as to the amount of the labor available. The productive capacity often bears a direct ratio to the wage system employed and the quality of management.

The capacity of the various ore-handling equipment needs no discussion. Under some conditions, slight changes are often made, with resulting increase in amount of ore handled. It is well to remember at all times that the equipment will be called upon to handle a certain amount of waste. The mill, transportation, or smelter capacity can usually be estimated within narrow limits, but this is also subject to adjustment by the engineer.

The possible future sales and demand for the product are the stumbling blocks that have wrecked many otherwise able attempts to predict the future value of a mine. The physical capacity of the mine estimated at near its top limit is often used, under the assumption that all that can be produced can be sold, but this is true only in the case of a gold mine. For the other mines the demand for the product must be taken into account.

How to determine the average future production for any mine can not be answered here, nor is it possible to lay down any definite rules of guidance. A study of the past demand may be of some help. An examination of future tendencies is necessary, but where to draw the line is problematical. The use of curves to predict future tendencies is often helpful, but they must be used with discretion. The prediction made by Andrew Carnegie is a classical example of this statement. After drawing up a curve showing the increasing demand for iron ore, Carnegie made the statement that the production of ore from the Lake Superior District would be doubled every ten years. This had been the case prior to the time he made his prediction, and the same ratio held for some time afterward. However, the curve has flattened out since 1910 in a marked degree, largely because of one item which Carnegie did not think about when making his calculations. Formerly, iron and steel were made almost entirely from iron ore. Scrap iron and steel have gradually replaced some of the iron ore in the furnaces, and at the present time the percentage of scrap in steel is apparently increasing. In some open hearth plants the amount of scrap melted amounts to over fifty per cent. The original theory was correct, but a new factor entered which made a big difference in the demand for the product. Further, in regard to iron, the demand for ore also fluctuates with the need for various grades at the furnaces and with changing metallurgical processes.

The age of the mine at the time of the valuation must also be kept in mind throughout the examination. If the property is young, is only partly explored, and has a long life ahead, one interpretation can be put on the past results. If the mine is in the full flush of production, has large reserves ahead, and is making excellent costs, it is probably in its maturity, and the past results must be looked at from that angle. Another change in viewpoint is needed for a mine that has entered its decline, that is marked by gradually rising cost of operation, and that has a harder struggle each year to maintain ore reserves.

These periods in the life of a mine are quite definite, but they are difficult to recognize. A change in management often throws an entirely new light on conditions. An exploratory campaign may show that instead of being on the decline, the property has just started to produce. In any event, the age of the mine is a determining factor in the valuation, no matter whether it is considered as a definite item or made use of indirectly in connection with some part of the computation.

REVIEW OF ESTIMATE — Evaluation of mineral property is necessarily an estimate of future earning power. It requires that the estimator set up a schedule of operations which he considers best suited to the physical and economic conditions surrounding the property. This schedule may or may not be adhered to later on if and when the property is acquired by his client or otherwise disposed of pursuant to recommendations. But the schedule remains the basis for the valuation and setting it up necessarily involves assumptions as to rate of mining, costs, selling prices, efficiencies, and resultant profit spread. Some of these factors, particularly forecasting of costs and markets, are not subject to accurate determination. A method, previously noted, of guarding against serious error may be applied in some instances. If the estimated cost per pound of metal, or per unit of production, for the property in question is at the approximate level or below that of low-cost producers in the particular field, the accuracy of forward predictions as to prices becomes relatively less important to the assurance of success in the venture. This yard stick should be resorted to whenever reliable cost data on similar current operations is available. Conversely, if the estimated costs fall within the range of less efficient to marginal producers, data should be scrutinized carefully as assurance of success is less evident.

FINANCIAL REQUIREMENTS — The amount of money required to properly finance a mining enterprise is such a widely variable quantity and is so dependent upon many individual and local conditions that any general figure is of no value. A separate cost setup must be made for each property, and, even when dealing with an individual property, the financial requirements will vary for different rates of production, intensities of mining, various adaptable methods of mining, size of surface plant, etc.

However, the things which the financial structure of a

mining enterprise must accomplish are more or less the same, whether the mine be small or large, young or old. These may be listed as follows:

1. Any mine, to be a profitable venture, must have a reasonable expectancy of ore available to amortize the estimated investment and still leave a dividend surplus. This reserve, sufficient to last the required number of years at the calculated rate of mining, must be of developed and ''probable'' ore, or else the venture becomes too highly speculative for safe investment.

    In case sufficient ore is not reasonably assured to satisfy the amortization requirements, a preliminary exploration program can be separately financed to prove up new ore.

2. Enough money must be available to properly develop and equip the mine so that low operating costs may be maintained and safe operation be assured.

3. There must be sufficient working capital to operate and provide for all ordinary emergencies.

4. An extra sum must be provided to finance the underwriting of the stock sale and cover all legal expenses.

SUMMARY OF EXAMINATION

REPORT WRITING — A good report is clear, complete, and definite. Its purpose is to present a set of facts or determinations to the reader. In expressing the writer's views, the report reflects not only his understanding of the problem, but also his ability to organize the results of his work so as to present them in logical, concise form. It is a gauge of the orderliness and efficiency with which the background work was done. The report is an important part of an investigation; no less so for a mine examination.

Correct grammar is essential. Short sentences are better than long ones. Unnecessary words should be avoided. Although considerable latitude is permitted in ordinary expression, choice of words for technical terms should be precise.

Careful selection of subject matter is important. Only relevant material should be included and this must then be outlined systematically in order to develop the argument in logical sequence. Each part of the survey should follow along naturally, with easy transitions from one part to the next. Clear thinking and careful organization on the part of the writer will result in a report that is easy to read.

Style and appearance of the report are important. A good piece of work deserves to be set up attractively. The expense of dressing up a report proportional to the importance of the work is trivial when compared with the time, effort, and expense of making the examination and the deductions from it. Detailed suggestions for report writing may be found in various texts on the subject of technical writing and in some mining handbooks.

THE REPORT — The object of a mine examination report is to set forth the decision of the engineer with regard to the property in question. It is good practice at the beginning of the report to summarize the important factors in the situation and present the conclusions reached. This digest, however, should never be written until the full report has been prepared. By this form of presentation, the reader gets the meat of the situation quickly and may then look into the details, if interested.

In cases where a definite decision cannot be reached, it is often advisable to reverse the order of the report and lead up to the conclusions through sequential discussion of the situation. This keeps the reader's perspective aligned with that of the writer.

A report of any considerable length, to be readily usable, should include a table of contents and an index. The addition of marginal notes summarizing long sections of information and paralleling the text is an aid to quick reference and reading.

Photographs of the property, buildings, and equipment not only add to the appearance of the report, but often portray conditions more clearly than any written description. Photostat reductions of maps bound in the report are preferable to loose maps whenever sufficient detail can be shown in this manner. If larger maps are necessary, they may be put in a pocket in the report. Extensive reports should be bound in permanent form. Loose-leaf binders, such as are used for college theses, are satisfactory for less important reports.

The engineer should retain a duplicate copy of the report, together with all notebook and original data for his files. It often happens that even though any given examination does not result in a purchase or sale for his client, the same property will come up for his consideration again, and the information at hand may prove of value. A report should always be dated and signed.

PART II

MINE VALUATION

Open Pit Mine.

INTRODUCTION

Basic Data — In estimating the value of a mining enterprise, the work leading to the final result may be divided into two parts.

The first of these is the examination of the property in order to determine ore reserves, mining costs and profits, financial requirements, and future prospects, as already discussed in the preceding chapters. Whatever conclusions are reached in this phase of the work are dependent upon the experience, thoroughness, and integrity of the examining engineers. Based upon the results of the examination are the mathematical calculations to determine the value of the property in dollars and cents. In the following discussion only this second phase of mine valuation will be treated — the calculations pursuant to the field examination.

In order to understand the problem involved and to formulate equations for valuations under various conditions, it is advisable to lead up to the final forms through a logical study of the fundamentals.

Definitions and Theory — The mathematical premises set forth here to determine simple annuity values are those which are customarily used in interest calculations. The final forms, as applied to uniform annual income, were first set forth in 1877 by H. D. Hoskold in his treatise entitled "The Engineer's Valuing Assistant."[1] In these the application is directly to mining or some other industry of depleting reserves and by them a replacement of the original capital investment is allowed at the expiration of the annuity life at either the same or a different rate of interest than the dividend on the capital itself.

---

[1] H. D. Hoskold—"Engineer's Valuing Assistant."
Longmans, Green & Co., 1st Ed. 1877, 2nd Ed. 1905.

This same principle of capital replacement has been discussed also in other treatises of mine valuation, among the most prominent of which are "Principles of Mining" by Herbert C. Hoover (McGraw-Hill Book Co., 1st Ed. 1909) and "Cost of Mining" by James R. Finlay (McGraw-Hill Book Co., 1st Ed. 1909).

The following quotations define terms used in this discussion:

> "Value is the quality in anything which fits it to be given and received in exchange. The value of all exchangeable articles of utility must, however, be determined by the money worth set upon each commodity when brought into the market."[1]
>
> Interest is "the price or rate of premium per unit of time paid by a borrower for the use of what he borrows," or, it is "the rate percent of money paid for the use of money."[2]
>
> "An annuity is a series of payments usually equal in amount, made at equal intervals of time."[3]

The fact that the interval of time generally taken is a year accounts for the name "annuity."

> "Every beneficial interest or sum of money accruing, or to accrue, and to be paid at the end of a year, or portion of a year, may be considered as an 'annuity,' and may be either terminable with the life of an individual or perpetual. Any sum of money left unpaid for a certain number of years is called an 'annuity in arrears,' and when not payable until after a fixed

---

[1] H. D. Hoskold—"Engineer's Valuing Assistant."
   Longmans, Green & Co., 1st Ed. 1877, 2nd Ed. 1905.
[2] Webster's New International Dictionary.
   G. & C. Merriam Co., Springfield, Mass.
[3] E. B. Skinner, "Mathematical Theory of Investment," Ginn & Co., 1924.

number of years it is said to be a 'reversionary' or 'deferred annuity'."[1]

An annuity of indefinite, unlimited, or perpetual life is termed a "perpetuity."

"In either case the annuity is transferable, and may be purchased on certain agreed terms; each class of annuities must, however, receive a particular mode of treatment, adapted to and peculiar to the nature of the circumstances connected with each particular case."[2]

A mining property has a definite value only by virtue of its ability to produce a profit over a term of years.

"The money value of a mine is that sum which the exploitation of the mineral will return, together with a fair rate of interest, besides paying operating expenses, taxes, etc., the same fair rate of interest on the required working capital, and redeeming with a fair rate of interest the capital required for equipment and development."[3]

"Present value" and "present worth" are synonymous terms used to designate the capital which must be invested immediately (or at a given date of valuation) to be equivalent to the future income to be received in exchange therefor. Or, in other words, "present value" is the immediate (or valuation-date) worth of a future receivable income whether that income be an annuity extending over a period of time or a principal sum payable at a specified time.

---

[1] H. D. Hoskold—"Engineer's Valuing Assistant."
   Longmans, Green & Co., 1st Ed. 1877, 2nd Ed. 1905.
[2] H. D. Hoskold—"The Engineer's Valuing Assistant."
[3] F. W. Sperr—"Mining Engineering Notes," Mich. Coll. of Mines.
   1909, 4th Ed. 1924.

It should be understood, in considering the accrual or discount of money values, that reckonings may be made at any time during the life of a series of payments. The time of such reckoning is a valuation date, the choice of which is not dependent upon the mathematics but probably is determined by economic or engineering reasons. Whatever mathematics may be involved can be accommodated to any valuation date so chosen.

The annual profit or income from a mine can be considered as an annuity. This annuity has a value which can be computed. The transfer of a mine merely represents the transfer of the annuity or income from the mine. To determine the figure at which the exchange of annuity or income should take place, it is necessary to compute the present value of this annuity or income.

> "If money could not be employed and a marketable rate of interest obtained for its use, the value of any income or annuity would be equal to that paid at the end of one year multiplied by the number of years the annuity has to run."[1]

Since, however, money does command a certain wage or interest, the problem of compound interest must enter into all transactions extending over a number of years. It is evident, then, that if A desires to sell to B an annuity that has a certain number of years to run at a certain rate of interest, the exchange will take place only when A and B have agreed on the interest to be added to the arithmetical sum of the annual payments throughout the annuity or the discounts to be subtracted from it. This same thought expressed in another way is simply that any exchange into which the element of time enters must take into consideration the earning power of, or interest rate on, the money involved over the life of the transaction.

---

[1] H. D. Hoskold—"The Engineer's Valuing Assistant."

CHAPTER 11

MATHEMATICAL PREMISES — COMPOUND INTEREST

Payment Dates — All receivable income payments, unless otherwise specified, are assumed to be paid at the end of a year or of the period between payments, whereas principal sums set aside to improve at compound interest start earning at once.

An annuity payable at the end of each year, or period between payments, is termed an *immediate annuity,* whereas one payable at the beginning of the year, or period, is called an *annuity due.* Mathematical derivations of equations for the sum and the present value are given for both types of annuity. Attention, however, is directed to the tables included in the text wherein unit factors are listed for various rates per cent and for annual periods of time up to 50 years. As regards annuities (Tables 3, 4, 5, and 6) the factors listed are all for immediate annuities, although the method of converting these factors to the required amounts for annuities due is shown in each case. These factors are of assistance in the solution of specific problems dealing with interest accruals, discounts, and annuity purchases. The tables are frequently referred to in the solutions of the examples used to illustrate the various premises discussed in the text, and it is recommended that immediately upon completion of the mathematical analysis of each premise the reader study the derivation and use of the corresponding table factors.

The basis for all these computations is compound interest. The discussion of compound interest and of the various types of annuities and their values under any and all conditions is facilitated by the use of symbols.

Symbols —

Let S = Sum, or amount; an accumulation

P = Principal, or purchase price

r = rate of interest, or interest on \$1 for 1 year

R = amount of \$1 with one year's interest = $1+r$

> When different rates of interest are involved they may be designated by r', r'', etc., and the amount of \$1 improved at these respective rates for 1 year may be represented by

$$R' = (1 + r')$$
$$R'' = (1 + r'') \text{ etc.}$$

n = any integral number of years—active life

m = any integral number of years to be distinguished from n years—deferment period

M_n = amount of \$1 per year for n years at r rate of compound interest

V_p = present value of an amount due in the future.

PRINCIPAL SUMS AND DISCOUNTS

Premise 1. Increase of Principal at Compound Interest — \$1 at r rate of interest for 1 year amounts to

$$1(1 + r) = R.$$

In n years the amount of this accumulation is

$$1(1 + r)^n = R^n.$$

Therefore, the increase of any principal sum at compound interest may be represented by

$$PR^n \text{ or } P(1 + r)^n.$$

The improvement due to interest may be found by subtracting the original principal from the sum to which this principal amounts in the given period at the given rate.

$$S = PR^n$$

and I, the interest accrual, $= S - P$
$$= PR^n - P$$
$$= P(R^n - 1).$$

Example 1.

To what sum will \$1 amount in 8 years at 10% compound interest?

$$S = 1(1 + r)^n = R^n$$

$$= \overline{1.10}^8 = \underline{\underline{\$2.14}}$$

or, from Table 1, under 10% for 8 years,

$$S = \underline{\underline{\$2.1436}}.$$

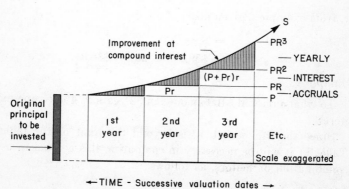

Fig. 22. Increase of a principal at compound interest.

Example 2.

To what sum will $25 amount in 15 years at 6% compound interest?

$$S = PR^n$$
$$= 25 \times \overline{1.06}^{15} = \underline{\$59.91}$$

or, from Table 1, under 6% for 15 years,

$$S = 25 \times 2.3966$$
$$= \underline{\$59.91.}$$

Example 3.

What interest accumulation will $25 earn if invested for 15 years at 6% compound interest?

$$I = P(R^n - 1)$$
$$= 25(\overline{1.06}^{15} - 1)$$

The value of $\overline{1.06}^{15}$ may be taken directly from Table 1 under 6% for 15 years.

$$= 25(2.3966 - 1)$$
$$= 25 \times 1.3966 = \underline{\$34.91}$$

or, from example 2 given above,

$$I = S - P$$
$$= \$59.91 - 25 = \underline{\$34.91.}$$

Example 4.

To what sum will $100 amount in 92 years at 4% compound interest?

Since the life period, n, is beyond the limit of the tables (Table 1) it will be necessary in computing this accrual to use a combination of factors, as follows:

Let $a + b + c = n$.
Then $R^n = R^a \times R^b \times R^c$,
and $S = P(R^a \times R^b \times R^c)$.

If a, b, and c are chosen as 50, 40, and 2 years, respectively, the calculation, using factors from Table 1, will be

$$S = 100 \times 7.1067 \times 4.8010 \times 1.0816$$
$$= 100 \times 36.9034$$
$$= \$3690.34$$

Premise 2. Present Value of a Principal at Compound Interest — The present value of $1 due n years hence at r rate compound interest is the amount which, if set aside now at the given rate percent, would improve to $1 at the end of the n year period.

$$V_p = \frac{1}{R^n} \text{ because } V_p R^n = 1.$$

[handwritten:] $S = PR^n$ $\quad \frac{1}{R^n} = PR^n \quad \frac{1}{R^n} = V_p$

Thus, the present value of $1 due n years hence at r rate is the reciprocal of the sum to which $1 would improve at r rate in n years.

For any amount other than $1 the present value under the conditions specified would be

$$V_p = \frac{P}{R^n} .$$

Example 5.

What is the present value of $1 due 10 years hence at 10% compound interest?

$$V_p = \frac{1}{(1+r)^n} = \frac{1}{R^n}$$

$$= \frac{1}{1.10^{10}} = \frac{1}{2.594} = \$.3855$$

or, from Table 2, under 10% for 10 years,

$$V_p = \$.3855.$$

Example 6.

What is the present value of $25 due 15 years hence at 6% compound interest?

$$V_p = \frac{P}{R^n}$$

$$= \frac{25}{1.06^{15}} = \frac{25}{2.3966} = \$10.43$$

or, from Table 2, under 6% for 15 years,

$$V_p = 25 \times .41727 = \$10.43.$$

Example 7.

At the age of 21, A will receive $10,000 from his father's estate. A is 16 years old today and wishes to sell this legacy to B. They agree on a 7% interest rate. What sum will B pay to A for his legacy?

$$V_p = \frac{P}{R^n}$$

$$= \frac{10,000}{1.07^{5}}$$

$$= \frac{10,000}{1.4026} = \$7129.62,$$

because this purchase price will improve to $10,000 in 5 years at 7% compound interest.

Or, from Table 2, under 7% for 5 years,

$$V_p = 10,000 \times .71299$$
$$= \$7129.90.$$

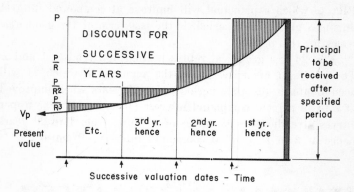

Fig. 23. Present value of a principal at compound interest.

Example 8.

What is the present value of $100 due 78 years hence at 3% compound interest?

The life period, n, in this instance, is beyond the limit of the tables (Table 2), and a combination of factors may be used as was done in Example 4, above:

Let $a + b = n$
Then $R^n = R^a \times R^b$

and $V_p = \dfrac{P}{R^a \times R^b} = P \left(\dfrac{1}{R^a} \times \dfrac{1}{R^b} \right)$

If a and b are chosen as 40 and 38 years, respectively, the calculation, using factors from Table 2, will be

$$V_p = 100 \times .30656 \times .32523$$
$$= 100 \times .09970$$
$$= \$9.97.$$

Graphs of Compound Interest— A graph of simple interest is a straight line. Compound interest, being a geometric series, gives an exponential curve of the type $y = e^x$ to infinity. The amount

PR^n, to which a principal will improve at compound interest during a given finite period, is the last term of the geometric series for this period.

Fig. 24 is a graphical representation of Premises 1 and 2. The lower set of curves shows the amounts to which \$1 will accumulate in any time period up to 20 years when improved at 2 to 12 percent compound interest (Premise 1). The upper curves give the present values of \$10 due from 1 to 20 years hence at 2 to 12 percent compound interest (Premise 2). It

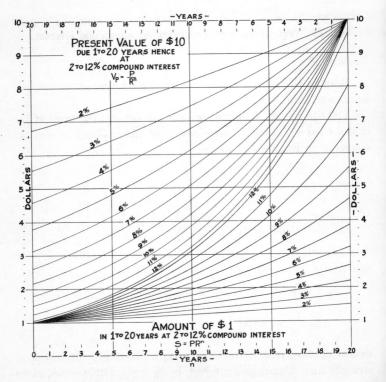

Fig. 24. Compound interest curves.

will be noted that for the same principal and rate both curves would be identical in every way. This is to be expected, since the lower curves represent values of R^n, while the upper ones are the plotted values of $1/R^n$.

Although these graphs are shown primarily to enable the reader to obtain a more vivid picture of interest accumulations and discounts, they also serve a practical purpose in that values of R^n and $1/R^n$ may be read directly from the curves to an accuracy of three places and may be estimated fairly closely for fractional percentages and fractional years. The ordinates of both sets of curves are dollars, and the abscissas are years. Values may be read directly for principal sums of $1, $10, $100, $1000, etc., and the factor thus read from the curves may be applied to any principal sum according to the formulas

$$S = PR^n \quad \text{and} \quad V_p = P \times \frac{1}{R^n}.$$

$S = PR^n$ **ANNUITIES** $AR^{(n-1)} + AR^{n-2} \cdots$

Premise 3. Amount of an Annuity at Compound Interest — An annuity accruing for n years at compound interest is a simple geometric progression. Representing the annuity payment by A and its sum by S gives, for an immediate annuity:

$$S = AR^{n-1} + AR^{n-2} + \ldots + AR^2 + AR + A.$$

Multiplying both sides of the above equation by R, gives

$$RS = AR^n + AR^{n-1} + AR^{n-2} + \ldots + AR^2 + AR.$$

Subtracting the first equation from the second gives

$$RS - S = AR^n - A,$$
$$S(R-1) = A(R^n - 1),$$
$$S = \frac{A(R^n - 1)}{R-1} = \frac{A(R^n - 1)}{r}.$$

The amount of an immediate annuity of \$1 per year for n years at r rate compound interest is, therefore,

$$M_n = \frac{R^n - 1}{r} \quad (\textit{Immediate annuity})$$

and it is these values which are listed as unit factors in Table 3.

Example 9.

To what sum will payments of \$1 per year amount in 15 years at 6% compound interest?

$$M_n = \frac{R^n - 1}{r}$$

$$= \frac{\overline{1.06}^{15} - 1}{.06}$$

$$= \frac{2.3966 - 1}{.06} = \$23.276$$

or, from Table 3, under 6% for 15 years,

$$M_n = \$23.276.$$

Example 10.

What will be the amount of an annuity of \$25 per year for 15 years at 6% compound interest?

$$S = \frac{A(R^n - 1)}{r}$$

$$= \frac{25(\overline{1.06}^{15} - 1)}{.06} = \$581.92,$$

or, from example given above,

$$S = AM_n = 25 \times 23.276 = \$581.90,$$

or, from Table 3,

$$S = 25 \times 23.276 = \$581.90.$$

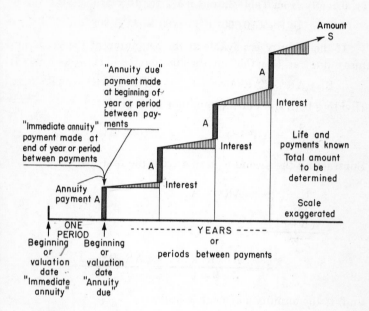

Fig. 25. Amount of an annuity at compound interest.

Example 11.

A mining company decides to prolong its life by purchasing new properties. It is apparent that present orebodies will start to play out in 10 more years. The company decides to invest $10,000 annually from earnings in 6% bonds to finance this exploratory program. What sum will be available at the end of the 10-year period?

$$S = \frac{A(R^n - 1)}{r} = \frac{10,000(\overline{1.06}^{10} - 1)}{.06}$$

$$= \frac{10,000(1.7908 - 1)}{.06} = \frac{10,000 \times .7908}{.06} = \frac{7908}{.06}$$

$$= \$131,800$$

or, directly from Table 3, under 6% for 10 years,

$$S = 10,000 \times 13.1808 = \$131,808$$

If the annuity is payable at the beginning of the year (annuity due) an equation for its sum may be derived as follows:

$$S = AR^n + AR^{n-1} + \ldots + AR^3 + AR^2 + AR.$$

Dividing both sides of the equation by R gives

$$\frac{S}{R} = AR^{n-1} + \ldots + AR^2 + AR + A.$$

Subtracting the second equation from the first gives

$$S - \frac{S}{R} = AR^n - A,$$

$$\frac{S(R-1)}{R} = A(R^n - 1),$$

$$S = \frac{AR(R^n - 1)}{R-1} = \frac{AR(R^n - 1)}{r},$$

and, if the annuity payment is unity

$$M_n = \frac{R(R^n - 1)}{r} \qquad (\textit{Annuity due})$$

Unit factors for annuities due may be taken from Table 3 by the simple conversion of using the factor listed for $n + 1$ years and subtracting 1 from it.

Example 12.

What will be the amount of an annuity due of \$100 per year for 20 years at 5% compound interest?

$$S = \frac{AR(R^n - 1)}{r}$$

$$= \frac{100 \times 1.05\,(\overline{1.05}^{20} - 1)}{.05} = \$3471.93$$

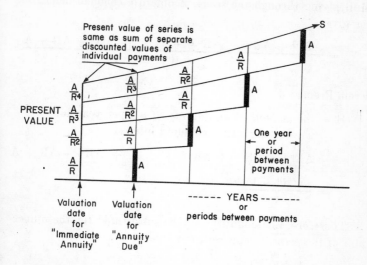

Fig. 26. Present value of an annuity at compound interest.

or, directly from Table 3 by taking the factor for n + 1 years and subtracting one,

$$S = 100 \times (35.7193 - 1) = \underline{\$3471.93}.$$

Premise 4. Present Value of an Annuity at Compound Interest — The present value of an annuity is the sum of the separate present values of all of the individual annuity payments. It may also be considered as the present value of the sum to which the annuity will amount in the given life period at the specified rate of interest.

Thus, the present value of an immediate annuity (payable at the end of the year, or period between payments) of $A per year for n years at r rate compound interest is:

$$V_p = \frac{A}{R} + \frac{A}{R^2} + \frac{A}{R^3} + \cdots + \frac{A}{R^{n-2}} + \frac{A}{R^{n-1}} + \frac{A}{R^n}.$$

Multiplying through the series to obtain a common denominator gives

$$V_p = \frac{AR^{n-1} + AR^{n-2} + AR^{n-3} + \dots + AR^2 + AR + A}{R^n}.$$

From Premise 3

S = the amount of an annuity of \$A per year for n years at r rate compound interest

$$= AR^{n-1} + AR^{n-2} + AR^{n-3} + \dots + AR^2 + AR + A$$

$$= \frac{A(R^n - 1)}{r}.$$

Therefore, this quantity may be substituted for the numerator of the present-value series to give

$$V_p = \frac{\dfrac{A(R^n - 1)}{r}}{R^n} = \frac{A(R^n - 1)}{R^n r},$$

or, if the annuity is of unit amount per year

$$V_p = \frac{R^n - 1}{R^n r} \quad (\textit{Immediate annuity})$$

and it is these unit values which are listed as factors in Table 4.

Example 13.

What is the present value of an annuity of \$1 per year for 20 years at 6% compound interest?

$$V_p = \frac{\overline{1.06}^{20} - 1}{\overline{1.06}^{20} \times .06} \qquad \begin{array}{l}\text{From Table 1} \\ \overline{1.06}^{20} = 3.2071\end{array}$$

$$= \frac{3.2071 - 1}{3.2071 \times .06} = \frac{2.2071}{.1924} = \underline{\underline{\$11.47}}$$

or, from Table 4, under 6% for 20 years,

$$V_p = \underline{\underline{\$11.4699}}.$$

Example 14

What is the present value of an annuity of \$25 per year for 20 years at 6% compound interest?

$$V_p = \frac{AM_n}{R^n} = \frac{25(\overline{1.06}^{20} - 1)}{\overline{1.06}^{20} \times .06} = \underline{\underline{\$286.75}},$$

or, from example given above,

$$V_p = 25 \times 11.47 = \underline{\underline{\$286.75}}$$

or, from Table 4,

$$V_p = 25 \times 11.4699 = \underline{\underline{\$286.75}}.$$

Example 15.

A has an income of \$100 a year from a mine that will run for 10 years. This income or annuity is offered for sale to B. If B purchases the annuity, he will receive \$1000 from the mine but he will not obtain possession of the full amount until the end of the tenth year. Obviously, the annuity will not be worth the full \$1000 to B but must be discounted. If A and B decide that 6% is a fair rate of interest in this transaction, the value of the first year's installment will be \$94.34 (Table 2). The reason for this is that \$94.34 put into a bank paying 6% interest would amount to \$100 at the end of the year. The second year's installment of this annuity is worth at present \$89.00, the third year's installment \$83.96, etc. The ten installments combined would amount to \$736, the price B would be willing to pay for the annuity.

Or, substituting in the formula

$$V_p = \frac{A(R^n - 1)}{R^n r} = \frac{A(\overline{1.06}^{10} - 1)}{\overline{1.06}^{10} \times .06},$$

which from Table 1 gives the values

$$= \frac{A(1.7908 - 1)}{1.7908 \times .06} = \frac{A(.7908)}{.10745} = A(7.3597)$$

$$= 100 \times 7.3597 = \underline{\$735.97},$$

or, directly from Table 4,

$$V_p = \underline{\$736.01}.$$

Example 16.

A mining property is sold for $70,000 in payments of $20,000 cash and $5000 per year for 10 years. If money is worth 6% what would be the equivalent total cash price for the mine?

Here the problem is to determine the present value of an annuity of $5000 per year for 10 years at 6% compound interest.

$$V_p = \frac{A(R^n - 1)}{R^n r}$$

$$= \frac{5000(\overline{1.06}^{10} - 1)}{\overline{1.06}^{10} \times .06} = \frac{5000(1.7908 - 1)}{1.7908 \times .06}$$

$$= \frac{5000 \times .7908}{.10745} = \frac{3954}{.10745} = \$36798.$$

Cash Price $= 36798 + 20000 = \underline{\$56798},$

or, from Table 4,

$$V_p = 5000 \times 7.3601 = 36800,$$

which gives a cash price of $\underline{\$56800}.$

If the annuity is payable at the beginning of each year (or period between payments) it is an annuity due. Its present value may be derived in a manner similar to that above by setting up the series to give

$$V_p = A + \frac{A}{R} + \frac{A}{R^2} + \cdots + \frac{A}{R^{n-3}} + \frac{A}{R^{n-2}} + \frac{A}{R^{n-1}},$$

which, reduced to a common denominator, will give

$$V_p = \frac{AR^{n-1} + AR^{n-2} + AR^{n-3} + \cdots + AR^2 + AR + A}{R^{n-1}}.$$

$$= \frac{A\left(\dfrac{R^n - 1}{r}\right)}{R^{n-1}} = \frac{A(R^n - 1)}{R^{n-1}r},$$

or it may be taken directly from Premise 3 as the present value of the sum to which an annuity of this type will amount, as follows:

$$V_p = \frac{\dfrac{AR(R^n - 1)}{r}}{R^n} = \frac{AR(R^n - 1)}{R^n r} = \frac{A(R^n - 1)}{R^{n-1}r},$$

or, if the annuity payments are each of unit amount

$$V_p = \frac{R^n - 1}{R^{n-1}r}. \quad (Annuity\ due)$$

Here again the factors of Table 4 which are unit values for immediate annuities may be converted to annuity due factors by choosing the table factor for $n - 1$ years and adding 1 to it.

Example 17.

What is the present value of an annuity due of $50 per year for 16 years at 4% compound interest?

$$V_p = \frac{50(\overline{1.04^{16} - 1})}{1.04^{15} \times .04}$$

$$= 50 \times (11.1184 + 1) = 50 \times 12.1184$$

$$= \$605.92.$$

Annuity Graphs — All types of annuities are capable of graphical as well as analytical solution. Plotting an annuity as a graph or curve, although less accurate, gives a much clearer picture of the characteristics of the particular annuity than can be

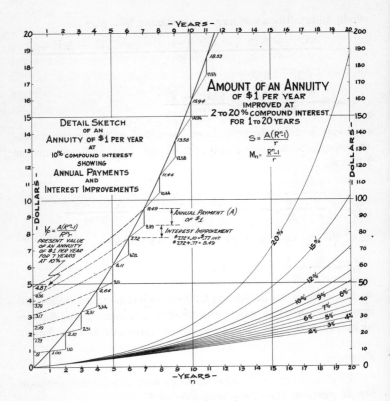

Fig. 27. Annuity curves.

gained from a study of the formula or from the tabulated values of the annuity for varying rates percent and years. In order to obtain a perfect picture of the characteristics of an annuity, the curve would have to be plotted to infinity for both of the co-ordinate units used. Such a procedure is impossible and also obviously unnecessary, since for all practical purposes the trends of an annuity can be pictured by curves representing the improvements resulting from customary rates percent for relatively short periods of time.

The general trends of annuity accumulations at compound interest are shown in Fig. 27 by a series of curves giving the sums to which an immediate annuity of $1 per year will amount in from 1 to 20 years when improved at rates of 2, 3, 4, 5, 6, 7, 8, 9, 10, 12, 15, and 20 percent. The effect of compound interest is clearly shown by this series of curves because they are all based upon a single set of annuity payments. For instance, at the end of 20 years the actual annuity payments have totaled $20, and any surplus accumulation above this figure has been due to compound interest. Thus, when the annuity is improved at 2% there is only $4.30 interest on the annuity in the 20-year period; whereas at 20% the interest accrual alone amounts to $166.69, or over 8 times the actual money invested.

A detailed analysis of an immediate annuity of $1 per year at 10% interest is plotted on the left-hand side of Fig. 27. The ordinate scale is enlarged ten times (each small unit representing 10¢ instead of $1) in order to show more distinctly each yearly payment of $1 and each yearly interest accrual. Thus, in the stepped curve, the vertical projections, or the rate of slope of the inclined curve segments, show the constantly increasing interest improvements. As may be seen from a study of the itemized sketch, the annual payments of $1 are made at the end of each year, and during each year the total sum in the accumulation at the beginning of the year is increased by 10% because of interest. Thus, at the beginning of the seventh year the annuity total is $7.72, and during the seventh year 10%, or $.77, is added for interest, the total thus being brought to $8.49 at the end of the year. The yearly payment of $1 then increases the total amount to $9.49 at the beginning of the eighth year. This typical cycle is repeated each year as long as the annuity runs. The smooth curve connecting the upper angles of the stepped analytical graph is the limit which the stepped curve will approach as the annuity continues to infinity. It is drawn through the plotted points representing the successive yearly amounts of the annuity.

In the lower left-hand corner of the detail graph just mentioned (Fig. 27), there are shown curves giving the present value, or purchase price, of the annuity for each of the first seven years of its life. It will be noted that each curve is merely a backward continuation of the inclined interest segments of the stepped annuity improvement graph. When each successive present-value curve is sketched in, it can be clearly seen that the present value of the annuity at any time is merely the sum of the individual present values of each of the yearly payments as stated in the discussion of Premise 4.

AMORTIZATION OF CAPITAL

Premise 5. **Redemption Fund Amounts** — To amortize is to extinguish by periodically charging off a portion, or to liquidate, usually by a sinking fund. A redemption, or sinking fund, is an account to which yearly or periodic payments are made for the purpose of replacing a capital investment. The payments are made from earnings, and the account is improved at a safe

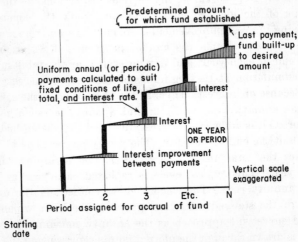

Fig. 28. Sinking or redemption fund accrual.

rate of compound interest so that in the given period of time allowed for redemption the actual payments plus the accrued interest will equal the capital invested.

A redemption fund is an annuity (a geometric progression), since it is periodic (usually consisting of annual payments) and is improved at compound interest. The formula, then, for the amount of an annuity may be used to determine the size of the series of payments that will be needed to accomplish a given accrual. These payments plus interest constitute the redemption fund. The amount to be amortized, the time allowed for amortization, and the interest rate determine the size of the individual payment.

Thus $\quad S = \dfrac{A(R^n - 1)}{r} \quad$ is the amount to which an annuity will accrue,

and $\quad A = \dfrac{Sr}{R^n - 1} \quad$ is the annual payment needed to amount to S in n years at r rate compound interest.

This annuity A is, in effect, the periodic sinking-fund payment which, for purposes of distinction, will be designated as s.

(Note that s, the annual sinking-fund payment or remittance, is a lower case letter and is to be distinguished from the capital letter S used to represent a sum or amount.)

Then, substituting s, the annual sinking-fund payment, for A, the annuity payment, gives

$$s = \frac{Sr}{R^n - 1}$$

and, if the amount to be replaced is $1,

$$s = \frac{r}{R^n - 1} \, .$$

Example 18.

What annual redemption-fund payment will amount to $1 in 10 years at 3% compound interest?

$$s = \frac{r}{R^n - 1}$$

$$= \frac{.03}{1.03^{10} - 1} = \frac{.03}{1.3439 - 1}$$

$$= \frac{.03}{.3439} = \underline{\$.087},$$

or, from Table 6, under 3% for 10 years,

$$s = \underline{\$.08723}.$$

Example 19.

What annual payments, improved at 4% compound interest, will amount to $20,000 in 20 years?

$$s = \frac{Sr}{R^n - 1}$$

$$= \frac{20,000 \times .04}{1.04^{20} - 1}$$

$$= \frac{800}{2.1911 - 1}$$

$$= \frac{800}{1.1911} = \$671.65$$

or, from Table 6, under 4% for 20 years,

$$s = 20,000 \times .03358$$
$$= \underline{\$671.60}.$$

Example 20.

A mine installs a new hoisting plant at a cost of $100,000. It is estimated that the equipment will become obsolete in 10 years. What sinking fund must be set aside annually at 4%

compound interest to replace the hoist investment at the end of the period?

$$s = \frac{Sr}{R^n - 1}$$

$$= \frac{100,000 \times .04}{\overline{1.04}^{10} - 1}$$

$$= \frac{4000}{1.4802 - 1} = \frac{4000}{.4802}$$

$$= \$8329.86, \text{ annual redemption amount.}$$

Or, from Table 6,

$$s = 100,000 \times .08329$$

$$= \$8329.$$

Premise 6. Diminishing Annuities — It is frequently necessary, in conducting a business, to borrow a sum of money with which to improve a plant or a process and then to repay this borrowed sum from the increased earnings which the improvement permits. This procedure is the reverse of a sinking-fund accumulation in that it makes the total sum available at the beginning instead of at the end of a certain period of years.

When a sinking fund is set aside to accumulate, the interest accruals help to build up the total in the account so that the payments together with the accrued interest become equal to the required total at the termination of the period.

In the case of the diminishing annuity the unpaid balance of the total loan is drawing interest until the whole of the loan is extinguished by the periodic payments. If the payments are made regularly, as specified, the interest is simple interest, whereas if the payments are neglected at any time, the interest automatically changes to compound interest until the payments are resumed.

Thus, each payment is called upon to satisfy two demands— first, to pay whatever interest charges may be due at the date of the payment and, second, to apply the balance of the payment toward a reduction of the principal.

On this basis, the time required for a definite annual payment to repay or extinguish a given principal sum, with interest, may be determined as follows:

Let P = Principal sum borrowed or to be paid off,
    r = rate of interest on principal,
    R = $1 + r$,
    A = annual payment,
    n = years required to extinguish the principal

The process of diminishing the principal is equivalent to

$$PR - A \qquad\qquad \text{for the 1st year}$$
$$(PR - A)R - A \qquad \text{'' '' first 2 years}$$
$$(PR^2 - AR - A)R - A \qquad \text{'' '' '' 3 years}$$
$$PR^n - AR^{n-1} - AR^{n-2} - \ldots - AR^2 - AR - A$$
$$\text{for the n-year period.}$$

Therefore, $PR^n - [AR^{n-1} + AR^{n-2} + \ldots + AR^2 + AR + A] = 0$

or, from Premise 3, $PR^n - \dfrac{A(R^n - 1)}{r} = 0$

$$PR^n = \frac{A(R^n - 1)}{r}$$
$$PR^n r = AR^n - A$$
$$PR^n r - AR^n = -A$$
$$AR^n - PR^n r = A$$
$$R^n (A - Pr) = A$$
$$R^n = \frac{A}{A - Pr}$$

and $n = \log \left(\dfrac{A}{A - Pr} \right) \div \log R.$

Table 1 may be used to convert (approximately) R^n directly into years n for any given rate r and known values of P and A.

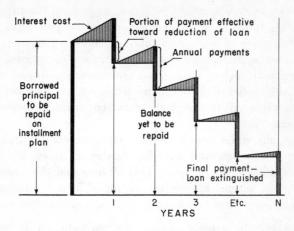

Interest cost

Portion of payment effective toward reduction of loan

Annual payments

Borrowed principal to be repaid on installment plan

Balance yet to be repaid

Final payment— loan extinguished

I 2 3 Etc. N
YEARS

Fig. 29. A diminishing annuity.

Example 21.

A mining company borrows \$50,000 at 6% interest in order to modernize its plant. A direct saving of \$6000 per year will result, and the plan is to apply this sum annually against the loan. How long will it take to repay the borrowed money?

$$R^n = \frac{A}{A-Pr},$$

$$\overline{1.06}^n = \frac{6000}{6000-50000 \times .06} = \frac{6000}{3000} = 2,$$

$$n = \frac{\log 2}{\log 1.06} = \underline{\underline{12 \text{ years.}}}$$

FREQUENCY OF INTEREST CONVERSION

Interest Compounded Semiannually, Quarterly, and Monthly — No reference has been made heretofore to other than annually compounded interest. In business transactions, interest is frequently compounded at semiannual periods and occasionally at quarterly or even monthly intervals, as it is to the investor's advantage to have interest compounded as frequently as possible. This phase of interest calculation has been purposely postponed because inclusion of discussions of these conditional modifications with each of the previous premises would tend to confound the reader with too many formulas. A brief summary will be given of the methods ordinarily used to solve such problems.

The only differences between interest accrual at fractional and at yearly intervals are the number of times interest is accounted for in any given period of time and the amount of the interest accrual at each accounting. Thus, if interest is to be reckoned t times in a year, the rate of interest must be proportionately reduced to $\frac{r}{t}$, and the value of R becomes $\left(1 + \frac{r}{t}\right)^{t}$. This change can be readily applied whenever necessary to any of the formulas previously derived for the various premises.

Premise 1.

The increase of principal at compound interest may be stated generally as $S = P\left(1 + \frac{r}{t}\right)^{tn}$.

(a) If interest is compounded annually, $S = P(1 + r)^{n} = PR^{n}$.

(b) ” ” ” ” semiannually, $S = P\left(1 + \frac{r}{2}\right)^{2n}$.

(c) ” ” ” ” quarterly, $S = P\left(1 + \frac{r}{4}\right)^{4n}$.

(d) ” ” ” ” monthly, $S = P\left(1 + \frac{r}{12}\right)^{12n}$.

Example 22.

To what sums will \$1 amount in 10 years at 8%, if interest is compounded annually, semiannually, quarterly, monthly?

(a) $S = R^n = \overline{1.08}^{10} = \underline{\$2.1589}$ (annually) (Table 1).

(b) $S = \left(1 + \dfrac{r}{2}\right)^{2n} = \left(1 + \dfrac{.08}{2}\right)^{2 \times 10} = (1 + .04)^{20} = \overline{1.04}^{20}$

$= \underline{\$2.1911}$ (semiannually) (Table 1)

(c) $S = \left(1 + \dfrac{r}{4}\right)^{4n} = \left(1 + \dfrac{.08}{4}\right)^{4 \times 10} = (1 + .02)^{40} = \overline{1.02}^{40}$

$= \underline{\$2.2080}$ (quarterly) (Table 1)

(d) $S = \left(1 + \dfrac{r}{12}\right)^{12n} = \left(1 + \dfrac{.08}{12}\right)^{12 \times 10} = \overline{1.00667}^{120}$

This is beyond the capacity of Table 1, so logarithms will have to be used, as follows:

$$\log 1.00667 = 0.002887,$$
$$.002887 \times 120 = 0.346440,$$
$$\text{antilog } 0.346440 = \underline{\$2.2205} \text{ (monthly)}.$$

Example 23.

To what sum will \$50 amount in 6 years at 6% semiannually compounded interest?

$$S = P \left(1 + \frac{r}{2}\right)^{2n} = 50 \left(1 + \frac{.06}{2}\right)^{2 \times 6} = 50 \times \overline{1.03}^{12}$$

$$= 50 \times 1.4258 = \underline{\$71.29} \text{ (Table 1).}$$

Premise 2.

The present value of a principal sum due n years hence at r rate of interest when the interest is to be realized more frequently than at yearly intervals may likewise be stated as

$$V_p = \frac{P}{\left(1 + \dfrac{r}{t}\right)^{tn}}.$$

Example 24.

What is the present value of $50 due 8 years hence at 8% interest compounded quarterly?

$$V_p = \frac{P}{\left(1 + \dfrac{r}{t}\right)^{tn}} = \frac{50}{\left(1 + \dfrac{.08}{4}\right)^{4 \times 8}} = \frac{50}{1.02^{32}}$$

$$= \frac{50}{1.8845} = \underline{\underline{\$26.53}} \text{ (Table 1),}$$

or $\qquad = 50 \times .53063 = \underline{\underline{\$26.53}} \text{ (Table 2).}$

Premise 3.

The amount of an annuity of $A per year for n years with interest at r rate compounded t times per year is

$$S = \frac{A\left[\left(1 + \dfrac{r}{t}\right)^{tn} - 1\right]}{\left(1 + \dfrac{r}{t}\right)^{t} - 1},$$

and the corresponding expression for M_n is

$$M_n = \frac{\left(1 + \dfrac{r}{t}\right)^{tn} - 1}{\left(1 + \dfrac{r}{t}\right)^{t} - 1}.$$

Example 25.

To what sum will an annuity of $50 per year for 10 years amount, at 8% interest compounded quarterly?

$$S = \frac{A\left[\left(1 + \frac{r}{t}\right)^{tn} - 1\right]}{\left(1 + \frac{r}{t}\right)^{t} - 1} = \frac{50\left[\left(1 + \frac{.08}{4}\right)^{4 \times 10} - 1\right]}{\left(1 + \frac{.08}{4}\right)^{4} - 1}$$

$$= \frac{50(\overline{1.02}^{40} - 1)}{\overline{1.02}^{4} - 1} = \frac{50(2.2080 - 1)}{1.0824 - 1} \quad \text{(Table 1)}$$

$$= \frac{50 \times 1.2080}{.0824} = \$733.01.$$

Premise 5.

The yearly sinking-fund payment required to replace a capital expenditure of \$S when improved for n years at r rate of interest compounded t times per year is therefore

$$s = \frac{S\left[\left(1 + \frac{r}{t}\right)^{t} - 1\right]}{\left(1 + \frac{r}{t}\right)^{tn} - 1}.$$

Example 26.

An expenditure of \$1000 must be replaced in 8 years by a sinking-fund accumulation.

What yearly payments improved at 4% semiannually compounded interest are necessary to do this?

$$s = \frac{S\left[\left(1 + \frac{r}{t}\right)^{t} - 1\right]}{\left(1 + \frac{r}{t}\right)^{tn} - 1} = \frac{1000\left[\left(1 + \frac{.04}{2}\right)^{2} - 1\right]}{\left(1 + \frac{.04}{2}\right)^{2 \times 8} - 1}$$

$$= \frac{1000(\overline{1.02}^{2} - 1)}{\overline{1.02}^{16} - 1} = \frac{1000(1.0404 - 1)}{1.3728 - 1} \quad \text{(Table 1)}$$

$$= \frac{1000 \times .0404}{.3728} = \frac{40.4}{.3728} = \$108.37 \text{ per year.}$$

Effective Interest Rate— The foregoing discussion of interest compounded at fractional periods, while it does not cover all of the premises required for valuation work, should be sufficient to point out the substitutions necessary to convert any of the formulas for yearly interest into corresponding equations for interest compounded t times per year. It will be noted that whenever the value r is encountered in making such a transposition, it is necessary to consider r as $(R-1)$, because only by this means can the true fractional value r/t be properly substituted in the formula. In all cases the "effective rate" of interest,

or interest actually earned on \$1 in one year $\left[\left(1+\dfrac{r}{t}\right)^t - 1\right]$

must be substituted for r in making a conversion from annually compounded interest to interest compounded at other periods. Sometimes practical calculations of interest fail to take account of the difference between r and $(R-1)$ when fractional time intervals are used, but such methods will not stand mathematical analysis. To illustrate, take the simple problem of the sum to which an annuity of \$1 per year will amount in 2 years at 6% semiannual interest.

At the end of 1 year the annuity amounts to \$1.

At the end of 1½ years the annuity amounts to

$$1\left(1+\frac{.06}{2}\right) = \$1.03.$$

At the end of 2 years the annuity amounts to

$$1.03\left(1+\frac{.06}{2}\right) + 1 = \underline{\underline{\$2.0609.}}$$

Or, to use the equation given above:

$$M_n = \frac{\left(1 + \dfrac{r}{t}\right)^{tn} - 1}{\left(1 + \dfrac{r}{t}\right)^{t} - 1} = \frac{\left(1 + \dfrac{.06}{2}\right)^{2 \times 2} - 1}{\left(1 + \dfrac{.06}{2}\right)^{2} - 1} = \frac{\overline{1.03}^4 - 1}{1.03^2 - 1}$$

$$= \frac{1.125509 - 1}{1.0609 - 1} = \frac{.125509}{.0609} = \underline{\underline{\$2.0609}}.$$

Whereas, if r is taken at its face value of .06, as it is in short-cut methods, we have

$$M_n = \frac{\left(1 + \dfrac{r}{t}\right)^{tn} - 1}{r} \quad \text{(erroneous)}$$

$$= \frac{\left(1 + \dfrac{.06}{2}\right)^{2 \times 2} - 1}{.06} = \frac{\overline{1.03}^4 - 1}{.06} = \frac{1.125509 - 1}{.06}$$

$$= \frac{.125509}{.06} = \$2.0918, \text{ a figure which is different from the correct amount.}$$

The general formula used here to obtain the value of M_n holds true only when n is an integral number of years. If the sum of the annuity is desired at the end of any of the fractional interest periods between years, it will be necessary to compute the annuity sum by the formula to the end of the previous year and add to this value the interest accrued during the last partial year.

CHAPTER 12

MINE VALUATION —
UNIFORM ANNUAL INCOME

PRINCIPLE OF DEPLETING RESERVES — Most industries and enterprises have an indeterminate life, apparently perpetual, and therefore are not called upon to replace the original investment. This does not mean that such industries (railroads, utilities, manufacturing, wholesale and retail houses, etc.) will continue forever; it means merely that, except for competition, nothing is apparent which will cause a termination. Mining, however, differs from the ordinary industry in this respect: when the orebodies are mined out, there is nothing left. The original capital investment must, therefore, be returned to the investor by the time that the profitable life of the enterprise is ended. When the operating company does not make any provision for perpetuating its life by investing a portion of its earnings in other properties, the usual procedure is to remit periodically to the investor a dividend sufficiently larger than the risk return on his investment to enable him, if he reinvests this overplus at a safe rate of compound interest, to replace his original capital at the expiration of life of the mine. This overplus constitutes a return of invested capital.

HOSKOLD MINE VALUATION PREMISE — The equation derived below is a mine-valuation formula of the two-rate, or Hoskold type. It presupposes uniform earnings, uniform return (interest at r' rate) on capital and provides for redemption of capital at the expiration of the annuity (or operating) life by annual reinvestment of the balance of the yearly earnings (uniform overplus not allocated to interest payment at r′ rate) at a safe rate of interest (r).

The Hoskold premise, thus, assumes the original investment to be nonrecoverable until the end of the life period, at which time it is returned in full by the sinking fund.

In the formula, A represents the expected income, or yearly profit from the mine. This is an estimated figure of future annual earnings and is, of course, susceptible to more than one interpretation, the interpretations depending upon the engineer who has examined the mine and upon the data which he has collected during his examination. The actual mathematical solution of the formula is an exact problem, and the accuracy of the calculated valuation figure for the mine is, therefore, wholly dependent upon the accuracy of the estimated values for A, n, r, and r′ which are substituted in the formula. The foundation built beneath the formula during the mine examination determines the accuracy of the final figure. The principal estimates involved in the determination of A are reserve tonnage, rate of mining, estimated cost per unit, and expected profit per unit. The length of life of the property is a function of reserve tonnage and rate of mining and determines the value of n, the years of life of the annuity.

Premise 7. Present Value of Immediate (Nondeferred) Redemption Annuity — To determine the present value of $1 per year for n years, which will allow the purchaser of annuities one rate of interest on his purchase money, and the redemption of his capital at the expiration of the time by annual investment of the dividend overplus at another practicable rate, and to derive an equation which will satisfy the above conditions of two rates of interest:

Let V_p = present value,

$r′$ = speculative rate to purchaser on his capital investment,

r = practicable safe rate on redemption of capital,

A = annuity to be purchased,

n = years life,

M_n = amount of an annuity of \$1 per year for n years at r rate as before.

Then

$A - V_p r'$ = annual redemption, because $V_p r'$ is the expected interest on capital investment, and the difference between the total amount received and the expected speculative return must represent the overplus, or return of invested capital.

Note: The dividend overplus is the amount of earnings over and above that necessary to pay the expected return on the invested capital at the stipulated rate. This overplus is assumed to be invested periodically, as a sinking fund, at a safe rate of interest, to return the capital invested.

And

$(A - V_p r') M_n$ = total redemption amount = V_p = purchase price.

This is true because the capital investment must be returned at the expiration of the annuity life.

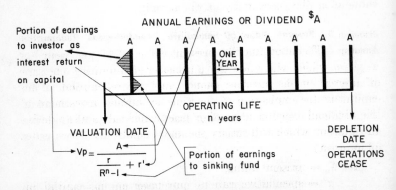

Fig. 30. Sketch of earnings and distribution by Hoskold premise — uniform income — no deferment.

$$V_p = (A - V_p r') M_n$$
$$= AM_n - M_n V_p r',$$
$$V_p + M_n V_p r' = AM_n,$$
$$V_p (1 + M_n r') = AM_n,$$
$$V_p = \frac{AM_n}{1 + M_n r'}$$

Dividing numerator and denominator by M_n gives

$$V_p = \frac{A}{\dfrac{1}{M_n} + r'}$$

wherein $\dfrac{1}{M_n} = \dfrac{1}{\dfrac{R^n - 1}{r}} = s =$ annual redemption fund payment which will amount to \$1 in n years at r rate compound interest.

$$V_p = \frac{A}{s + r'} \quad \text{or} \quad V_p = \frac{A}{\dfrac{r}{R^n - 1} + r'} \quad \text{(Hoskold formula)}$$

and, if $A = \$1$ per year

then $$V_p = \frac{1}{s + r'} \quad \text{or} \quad \frac{1}{\dfrac{r}{R^n - 1} + r'}.$$

Example 27.

What is the present value of an annuity of \$1 per year for 10 years with redemption of capital at 4% and interest on investment at 10%?

$$V_p = \frac{1}{\dfrac{r}{R^n - 1} + r'} = \frac{1}{\dfrac{.04}{1.04^{10} - 1} + .10}$$

$$= \frac{1}{\dfrac{.04}{1.4802 - 1} + .10} = \underline{\underline{\$5.456}}$$

or, directly from Table 7, under redemption at 4%, interest at 10% for 10 years,

$$V_p = \underline{\underline{\$5.4558}}.$$

Figure 32 is a graphical solution of this example.

Example 28.

What is the present value of an annuity of $500 per year for 10 years with redemption of capital at 4% and with interest allowed purchaser at 10%?

$$V_p = \frac{A}{\dfrac{r}{R^n - 1} + r'}$$

$$= \frac{500}{\dfrac{.04}{1.04^{10} - 1} + .10} = \underline{\underline{\$2728}},$$

or, from the foregoing example,

$$V_p = 500 \times 5.456 = \underline{\underline{\$2728}},$$

or, directly from Table 7 (redemption at 4%, interest at 10%, for 10 years),

$$V_p = 500 \times 5.4558 = \underline{\underline{\$2727.90}}.$$

Example 29.

A small mine, fully equipped and producing 30,000 tons of ore per year at a net profit of $1 per ton, is offered for sale. A fair estimate of ore reserves gives the property a life of 15 years. Assuming that the purchaser wants an interest return of 12% with redemption of capital at 5%, what price will he offer for the property?

The net income of this mine is equivalent to an annuity of $30,000 per year for 15 years; therefore

$$V_p = \frac{A}{\dfrac{r}{R^n - 1} + r'}$$

$$A = 30,000$$
$$r = .05$$
$$r' = .12$$
$$n = 15$$

$$= \frac{30,000}{\dfrac{.05}{1.05^{15} - 1} + .12}$$

Table 1 gives $\overline{1.05^{15}}$ *as 2.0789.*

$$= \frac{30,000}{\dfrac{.05}{2.0789 - 1} + .12}$$

$$= \frac{30,000}{\dfrac{.05}{1.0789} + .12} = \frac{30,000}{.04634 + .12}$$

$$= \frac{30,000}{.16634} = \$180,353,$$

or the purchase factor may be taken directly from Table 7, under redemption at 5% with interest at 12% for 15 years, and then

$$V_p = 30,000 \times 6.0117 = \$180,351.$$

Example 30.

It is estimated that a mine can produce 100,000 tons of ore per year at a net profit of 20¢ per ton. Tonnage reserve is calculated to be 2,000,000 tons. What is the present value of the mine in order to allow an 8% return on capital with redemption at 3%?

$$A = 100,000 \times .20 = \$20,000 \text{ per year}$$
$$n = 2,000,000 \div 100,000 = 20 \text{ years}$$
$$r' = .08$$
$$r = .03$$

$$V_p = \cfrac{A}{\cfrac{r}{R^n - 1} + r'}$$

$$= \cfrac{20,000}{\cfrac{.03}{1.03^{20} - 1} + .08}$$

$$= \cfrac{20,000}{\cfrac{.03}{1.8061 - 1} + .08} = \cfrac{20,000}{\cfrac{.03}{.8061} + .08}$$

$$= \frac{20,000}{.03722 + .08} = \frac{20,000}{.11722} = \$170,620.$$

The value of 1.03^{20} may be taken from Table 1, or the whole

redemption factor $\dfrac{.03}{1.03^{20} - 1}$ may be taken directly from Table

6 as .03722

or, from Table 7 under redemption at 3% with interest at 8% for 20 years, the value

$$V_p = 20,000 \times 8.5313 = \$170,626.$$

Present Value of Redemption Annuity with Interest Rates Identical —
Whenever the dividend overplus is put back into the business
by the investor or whenever a depleting-reserve enterprise pro-
longs its own life by plowing back surplus into land or plant,
it is justifiable to assume the same rate of interest on redemption of capital as on capital investment. This makes the rates
of interest r and r' identical, and the present-value equations
derived under Premise 7 can be stated in a simpler form, as
follows:

$$V_p = \cfrac{1}{s + r'} = \cfrac{1}{\cfrac{r}{R^n - 1} + r'},$$

and, since $r' = r$, this may be stated as

$$= \frac{1}{\dfrac{r}{R^n - 1} + r} = \frac{1}{\dfrac{r + r(R^n - 1)}{R^n - 1}}$$

$$= \frac{R^n - 1}{r + r(R^n - 1)}$$

$$= \frac{R^n - 1}{r(1 + R^n - 1)} = \frac{R^n - 1}{rR^n} ,$$

or, for \$A per year

$$= \frac{A(R^n - 1)}{rR^n} .$$

NOTE: *This final equation is identical with that derived under Premise 4 for the present value of an immediate annuity.*

For example, the present value of an annuity of \$1 per year for 10 years at 6% and 6% is

$$V_p = \frac{1}{s + r'} = \frac{1}{.07587 + .06} = \frac{1}{.13587} = \underline{\underline{\$7.360}}$$
$$\text{(Table 6)}$$

or

$$= \frac{1}{\dfrac{r}{R^n - 1} + r'} = \frac{1}{\dfrac{.06}{1.06^{10} - 1} + .06} = \frac{1}{\dfrac{.06}{.7908} + .06}$$

$$= \frac{1}{.13587} = \underline{\underline{\$7.36}} \text{ (Table 1)}$$

or

$$= \frac{R^n - 1}{rR^n} = \frac{\overline{1.06}^{10} - 1}{.06 \times \overline{1.06}^{10}} = \frac{1.7908 - 1}{.06 \times 1.7908}$$

$$= \frac{.7908}{.10745} = \underline{\underline{\$7.36}} \text{ (Table 1),}$$

or, directly from Table 7,

$$V_p = \underline{\underline{\$7.3601}} .$$

Premise 8. Present Value of Deferred Redemption Annuity — To determine the present value of $1 per year for n years, after m years deferment which will allow the purchaser of annuities one rate of interest on his purchase money during the life of the annuity, either the same or a different rate during the deferment period, and the redemption of his capital at the expiration of the life by annual investment of the dividend overplus at another practicable rate:

Let r = safe rate of interest on redemption,

r' = speculative rate of interest on capital investment during the life of the annuity,

r'' = rate of interest on capital during deferment period,

V_{bi} = value of annuity at the beginning of its interest-earning period, in order to distinguish this value from the present worth when dealing with deferred annuities.

Then V_p = present value = value at the beginning of the period during which the annuity payments are to be made, V_{bi}, discounted to present worth at r'' rate through the m years of deferment.

$$\text{Or} \quad V_p = \frac{\dfrac{A}{s+r'}}{(1+r'')^m} = \frac{\dfrac{A}{\dfrac{r}{(1+r)^n - 1} + r'}}{(1+r'')^m}$$

$$= \frac{\dfrac{A}{\dfrac{r}{R^n - 1} + r'}}{(1+r'')^m} .$$

[handwritten annotations in margin:]

$V_p = \dfrac{V_{b_1}}{(1+r'')^m}$

$V_{b_i} = \dfrac{A}{\dfrac{r}{R^m - 1} + r'}$

It will be noted at this point that the speculative return during the annuity life is simple interest at r' rate, whereas the deferment period discount is compounded at r'' rate.

Example 31.

What is the present value of an annuity of $1 per year for 10 years, after a deferment period of 5 years, with redemption of capital at 4%, and with interest allowed purchaser at 10% during life of annuity and at 10% during deferment period?

In this example the interest on investment is at the same numerical rate during both annuity life and deferment period.

$$V_p = \frac{\dfrac{1}{\dfrac{r}{R^n - 1} + r'}}{(1 + r'')^m} = \frac{\dfrac{1}{\dfrac{.04}{1.04^{10} - 1} + .10}}{1.10^5} = \frac{\dfrac{1}{\dfrac{.04}{1.4802 - 1} + .10}}{1.6105}$$

$$= \frac{\dfrac{1}{\dfrac{.04}{.4802} + .10}}{1.6105} = \frac{\dfrac{1}{.0833 + .10}}{1.6105} = \frac{\dfrac{1}{.1833}}{1.6105}$$

$$= \frac{5.456}{1.6105} = \underline{\underline{\$3.388}} \text{ or}$$

$$= \frac{1}{.1833 \times 1.6105} = \frac{1}{.2952} = \underline{\underline{\$3.388}}.$$

In the solution of this example the entire

numerator $\left(\dfrac{1}{\dfrac{r}{R^n - 1} + r'} \right)$ *may be taken as a*

factor directly from Table 7 (redemption at 4% and interest at 10% for 10 years) to simplify the solution of

$$\frac{1}{\dfrac{.04}{1.04^{10} - 1} + .10} = 5.4558.$$

Or from Table 6 the redemption factor may be taken directly as

$$\frac{.04}{1.04^{10} - 1} = .08329.$$

And from Table 1 the denominator factor

$$\overline{1.10^5} = 1.6105.$$

Example 32.

What is the present value, or purchase price, of an annuity of \$25 per year which will have a life of 20 years after a deferment period of 10 years, which will permit redemption of capital at 4%, and which will allow the purchaser interest at 8% during the life of the annuity and at 6% during the deferment period?

$$V_p = \frac{\dfrac{A}{s + r'}}{R''^m}$$

$A = \$25$
$r = .04$
$r' = .08$
$r'' = .06$
$n = 20$
$m = 10$

$$= \frac{\dfrac{A}{\dfrac{r}{R^n - 1} + r'}}{(1 + r'')^m}$$

$$= \frac{\dfrac{25}{\dfrac{.04}{1.04^{20} - 1} + .08}}{1.06^{10}}$$

From Table 1
$\overline{1.04}^{20} = 2.1911$
$\overline{1.06}^{10} = 1.7908$

$$= \frac{\dfrac{25}{\dfrac{.04}{1.1911} + .08}}{1.7908} = \frac{\dfrac{25}{.0336 + .08}}{1.7908}$$

$$= \frac{\dfrac{25}{.1136}}{1.7908} = \frac{220.07}{1.7908} = \underline{\underline{\$122.89.}}$$

Or the numerator factor which represents the value of the annuity at the beginning of its active life may be taken directly from Table 7, under redemption at 4% and interest at 8% for 20 years, to be

$$V_{bi} = 25 \times 8.8042 = \$220.10$$

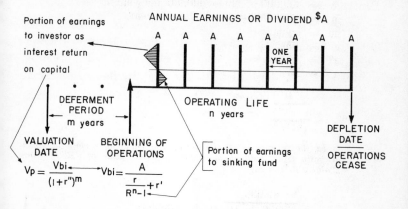

Fig. 31. Sketch of earnings and distribution by Hoskold premise — uniform income after deferment.

and the present-value factor taken directly from Table 2, under 6% for 10 years, would then give

$$V_p = V_{bi} \times \frac{1}{(R'')^m} = 220.10 \times .55839 = \underline{\underline{\$122.90}}.$$

Example 33.

A mining company wishes to sell an idle mine which under normal operating conditions can produce 300,000 tons of ore per year. The mine is fully equipped, but because of trade conditions it is considered inadvisable to start operating before 5 years. An examination of the property reveals a reserve of 3,000,000 tons of ore and estimates the average net profit at 20¢ per ton. No critical difficulties are anticipated in the operation. What is the present value of the property if the purchaser desires 10% on his investment during the life of the mine, 7% during the deferment period, and redemption of his capital at 5%.

$$A = 300,000 \times .20 = \$60,000 \text{ per year}$$
$$n = 3,000,000 \div 300,000 = 10 \text{ years}$$
$$m = 5 \text{ years}$$
$$r = .05$$
$$r' = .10$$
$$r'' = .07$$

$$V_p = \frac{\dfrac{A}{s + r'}}{(R'')^m}$$

In the solution of this equation the value of s may be taken directly from Table 6 as .07951 and the value of $(R'')^m$ from Table 1 as 1.4026.

$$= \frac{\dfrac{60,000}{.07950 + .10}}{1.4026} = \frac{60,000}{1.4026 \times .17950}$$

$$= \frac{60,000}{.25177} = \underline{\underline{\$238,313.}}$$

Or, to analyze the problem in a different manner, the value at the beginning of the active life (V_{bi}) may be computed, and this figure discounted to present worth through the deferment period, as follows:

$$V_{bi} = \frac{A}{s + r'} = \frac{60,000}{.07950 + .10} = \frac{60,000}{.17950} = \$334,262.$$

$$V_p = V_{bi} \times \frac{1}{(R'')^m} = 334,262 \times .71299 = \underline{\underline{\$238,325.}}$$

The value of $\dfrac{1}{(R'')^m}$ is here taken directly from Table 2.

Or the value at the beginning of operating life may be taken directly from Table 7 as

$$V_{bi} = 60,000 \times 5.5709 = \$334,254,$$

and $\quad V_p = V_{bi} \times \dfrac{1}{(R'')^m} = 334,254 \times .71299 = \underline{\underline{\$238,320.}}$

Or the entire problem may be solved by the use of a logarithm table only, or from Table 1 only, as follows:

$$V_p = \cfrac{A}{\cfrac{\dfrac{r}{R^n - 1} + r'}{(1 + r'')^m}}$$

$$= \cfrac{\cfrac{60,000}{\dfrac{.05}{1.05^{10} - 1} + .10}}{(1 + .07)^5} = \cfrac{\cfrac{60,000}{\dfrac{.05}{1.6289 - 1} + .10}}{1.4026}$$

$$= \cfrac{\cfrac{60,000}{\dfrac{.05}{.6289} + .10}}{1.4026} = \cfrac{\dfrac{60,000}{.07950 + .10}}{1.4026}$$

$$= \cfrac{\dfrac{60,000}{.17950}}{1.4026} = \frac{334,262}{1.4026} = \underline{\underline{\$238,316.}}$$

Graphs of Redemption Annuities — Fig. 32 is a graphical representation of a typical redemption annuity of $1 per year for 10 years with interest (r') on investment at 10% and with redemption allowed at the rate (r) of 4%. A deferment period is also shown, during which interest (r'') is allowed on the purchase at either 4% or 10%. The graph is thus divided into two parts by a vertical line at the center, the right-hand side representing the active-life period of the annuity and the left-hand side the period of deferment. The present value of the redemption annuity at any intermediate time during its 10-year life is shown at the lower right by the convex double dot-dash ($..—..$) line curve which is drawn through the successive yearly present values as taken from Table 7. An analysis of a 4-year annuity with a 4-year deferment period is shown by the

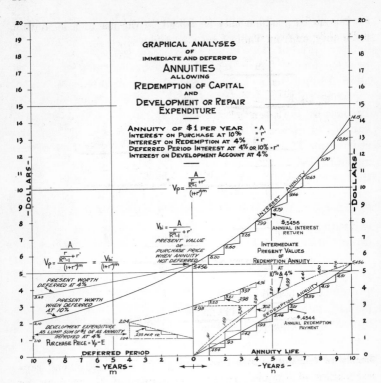

Fig. 32. Redemption annuity graphs.

concave single dot-dash (.—.) line in the lower central part of the graph.

By its nature a redemption annuity is composed of two parts: the interest on the investment, and the sinking-fund or redemption payment. Each of these parts is, in reality, an individual annuity, although the two are necessarily tied together by the stipulated conditions governing capital redemption. This relationship is readily apparent from an inspection of the graph, in which the lower, or redemption annuity, with its accrued interest amounts to the nondeferred present value of the entire annuity at the expiration of the allotted life period; whereas the interest annuity starts from this non-deferred present value figure and rises, in the same time period, to some higher figure depending upon the rates of interest allowed by the terms agreed upon in the purchase.

From Table 7 or from a solution of the formula given under Premise 7, the present value of an immediate, nondeferred, annuity of $1 per year for 10 years with interest at 10% and redemption at 4% is found to be $5.456; therefore, 10% of this amount, or $.5456, is the annual interest return expected by the purchaser. The remainder of the $1 yearly annuity payment, or $.4544, represents overplus which is to be reinvested at 4% per year in order to replace the invested capital at the expiration of the 10-year life. The graph shows that these conditions are fulfilled, for the redemption annuity in the lower right-hand corner, built up of vertical increments of $.4544 per year and of inclined increments representing interest improvements at 4%, amounts to the immediate, or nondeferred, present value figure of $5.456 at the end of 10 years. In the upper curve it is shown that the interest annuity starts from this value and, if left to accumulate at 10% per year, would amount in the 10-year period to $14.15; this, of course, is a theoretical consideration, since these yearly payments are always taken by the investor as the interest wage on his invested capital. If the annuity is deferred, the purchase is then the discounted value of the worth at the beginning of annuity payments, and may be read directly from the graph for any period of deferment up to 10 years. The equipment charge of a lump sum of $1, deducted on the graph from the present value of the annuity with a 10-year deferment period, could be similarly applied either at intermediate periods of deferment or to the present value if the annuity is to start immediately.

An annuity of $1 per year for 4 years, after a 4-year deferment, with interest on capital at 10%, with redemption at 4%, and with an equipment expenditure of $1 taken care of by

yearly installments improved at 4% during the entire deferment period, is shown by single dot-dash (.—.) lines in the
lower central part of Fig. 32. This annuity may be analyzed
in the same manner as the 10-year one just discussed.

YEARS' PURCHASE FACTOR— In the purchase of annuities the
present value, or purchase price,
per dollar of annuity income is sometimes spoken of as the
years' purchase or, in case the annuity pays a yearly amount
other than unity, it is termed the years' purchase factor.

These terms have come into use because the discounting
effect of interest must be considered in the purchase of future
income, and the purchase price is, therefore, not as much as
the sum of the several annuity payments which are bought.
The interest accrual on the purchase price compensates for
this apparent difference during the period over which the annuity payments are coming in.

Thus, the present value, or purchase price, of any given
annuity under specified conditions is equivalent to a certain
number of times the yearly annuity payment, or it represents
the number of payments which must be purchased, if the interest accrual is to purchase automatically the remainder of
the payments. It is, thus, the years' purchase price or the
years' purchase factor of the annuity.

A few instances will show its application.

(A) In Example 13, the present value of an annuity of $1
per year for 20 years at 6% compound interest is
found to be $11.47. The years' purchase of this an-
nuity is therefore 11.47, and the years' purchase factor
may be taken directly from Table 4 for all annuities
of this type for varying rates percent and time periods.
When the annuity is other than unity, this years'
purchase factor multiplied by the annual payments
gives the present value or purchase price.

(B) Likewise, a solution of Example 27 shows $5.456 to be the present value of an annuity of $1 per year for 10 years, with redemption of capital at 4% and interest on investment at 10%. It is thus necessary to purchase only 5.456 of the annual $1 payments in order to buy the annuity. Table 7 lists the years' purchase factors for a redemption annuity of this type for various rates percent and varying life periods. If the annuity to be purchased is for any amount other than $1 per year, its present value can be readily found by multiplying the yearly payment by the years' purchase factor in the table corresponding to the required rates and time.

CHAPTER 13

MINE VALUATION —
NONUNIFORM ANNUAL INCOME

VALUATION OF UNEQUAL INCOME
TO PRODUCE UNIFORM DIVIDENDS

Theory and Derivation of Formulas — The valuation of non-uniform income may be computed to satisfy the premises underlying any of the ordinary methods of valuation, when proper consideration is accorded to negative incomes or incomes which must be augmented because they are insufficient to satisfy the allocation demands placed upon them. In a valuation of this sort, each year's income, or annual payment, must be dealt with separately, because the several payments to be valued are not uniform in amount and, therefore, no simple formula can be resolved for evaluating the uneven series as a group. Each payment, however, must be allocated in a manner similar to all of the other payments in the series.

Premise 9. **Present Value of Nonuniform Income Series on Hoskold Redemption Basis** — To satisfy the Hoskold premise, the investor must receive annually a constant return on his capital, together with sinking fund payments sufficient to accrue to the original capital at the end of the life period.

The Hoskold premise may be applied to nonuniform income as follows:

Let V_p = present value,
P_m = yearly profit; such as P_1, P_2, P_3, etc., to P_n,
n = years life,

r' = speculative interest rate,

r = safe interest rate.

Then

$V_p r'$ = expected annual return on investment,

$P_m - V_p r'$ = annual payment to sinking fund,

and

$$V_p = (P_1 - V_p r') R^{n-1} + (P_2 - V_p r') R^{n-2} + \ldots\ldots\ldots$$
$$\cdots + (P_{n-2} - V_p r') R^2 + (P_{n-1} - V_p r') R + (P_n - V_p r')$$

$$= P_1 R^{n-1} - V_p r' R^{n-1} + P_2 R^{n-2} - V_p r' R^{n-2} + \ldots\ldots\ldots$$
$$\cdots + P_{n-2} R^2 - V_p r' R^2 + P_{n-1} R - V_p r' R + P_n - V_p r'$$

$$= (P_1 R^{n-1} + P_2 R^{n-2} + \ldots\ldots + P_{n-2} R^2 + P_{n-1} R + P_n)$$
$$- (V_p r' R^{n-1} + V_p r' R^{n-2} + \ldots\ldots + V_p r' R^2 + V_p r' R + V_p r')$$

$$= (\text{sum of } P_m R^{n-m} \text{ series}) - V_p r' (R^{n-1} + R^{n-2} +$$
$$\cdots + R^2 + R + 1)$$

$$= (\text{sum of } P_m R^{n-m} \text{ series}) - V_p r' \left(\frac{R^n - 1}{r} \right).$$

By transposition:

$$V_p + V_p r' \left(\frac{R^n - 1}{r} \right) = (\text{sum of } P_m R^{n-m} \text{ series}),$$

$$V_p \left[1 + r' \left(\frac{R^n - 1}{r} \right) \right] = (\text{sum of } P_m R^{n-m} \text{ series}),$$

$$V_p = \frac{(\text{sum of } P_m R^{n-m} \text{ series})}{1 + r' \left(\frac{R^n - 1}{r} \right)}.$$

Proof:

Assume P to be a series of uniform payments, each A in amount.

Then "Sum of $P_m R^{n-m}$ series" would be $\dfrac{A(R^n-1)}{r}$, as from Premise 3,

and V_p would $= \dfrac{A\left(\dfrac{R^n-1}{r}\right)}{1+r'\left(\dfrac{R^n-1}{r}\right)}$.

Dividing numerator and denominator by $\left(\dfrac{R^n-1}{r}\right)$ would give

$$V_p = \dfrac{A}{\dfrac{r}{R^n-1}+r'} \text{, the Hoskold formula as in Premise 7.}$$

Allocation of Negative and Insufficient Income   In the application of this formula, negative incomes and incomes insufficient to cover both interest and redemption payments are accounted for by withdrawal from the sinking fund to cover such deficiencies and by replacement thereof from the first available surplus.

This may be illustrated as follows, wherein a 5-year series of irregular earnings are present-valued at Hoskold rates of 10% and 4%:

End of Year	Yearly Income P_m	Factor R^{n-m}	Product $P_m R^{n-m}$
1	$300	1.1699	$ 350.97
2	50	1.1249	56.24
3	500	1.0816	540.80
4	70	1.0400	72.80
5	400	1.0000	400.00
		Sum of series	$1420.81

$$V_p = \dfrac{1420.81}{1+.10\,(5.4163)} = \dfrac{1420.81}{1.54163} = \$921.63.$$

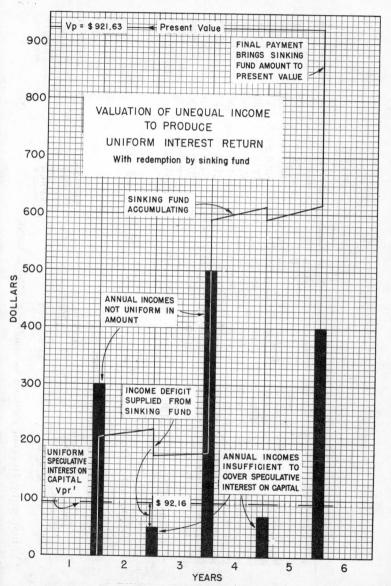

Fig. 33. Allocation of unequal income by Hoskold premise.

Years	R^{n-m} Factor @ 4%	Increasing Income P_m	Increasing Product $P_m R^{n-m}$	Decreasing Income P_m	Decreasing Product $P_m R^{n-m}$	Odd Income P_m	Odd Product $P_m R^{n-m}$	Uniform Income P_m	Uniform Product $P_m R^{n-m}$
1	1.4233	$1000	$1423.30	$10000	$14233.00	$6000	$8539.80	$5500	$7828.15
2	1.3686	2000	2737.20	9000	12317.40	3000	4105.80	5500	7527.30
3	1.3159	3000	3947.70	8000	10527.20	10000	13159.00	5500	7237.45
4	1.2653	4000	5061.20	7000	8857.10	5000	6326.50	5500	6959.15
5	1.2167	5000	6083.50	6000	7300.20	1000	1216.70	5500	6691.85
6	1.1699	6000	7019.40	5000	5849.50	7000	8189.30	5500	6434.45
7	1.1249	7000	7874.30	4000	4499.60	9000	10124.10	5500	6186.95
8	1.0816	8000	8652.80	3000	3244.80	2000	2163.20	5500	5948.80
9	1.0400	9000	9360.00	2000	2080.00	8000	8320.00	5500	5720.00
10	1.0000	10000	10000.00	1000	1000.00	4000	4000.00	5500	5500.00
	Sum of series		$62159.40		$69908.80		$66144.40		$66034.10

Denominator factor $1 + r' \left(\dfrac{R^n - 1}{r} \right) = 1 + .10(12.0061) = 2.20061$

Present Values of the above series:

$$V_p = \frac{62159.40}{2.20061} = \$28246$$

$$V_p = \frac{69908.80}{2.20061} = \$31768$$

$$V_p = \frac{66144.40}{2.20061} = \$30057$$

$$V_p = \frac{66034.10}{2.20061} = \$30007*$$

*Valuation by Hoskold formula $= 5500 \times 5.4558 = \$30007$.

Allocation of this income may be tabulated as below to show disposition to interest and sinking fund:

End of Year	Income	Interest on V_p	Balance to Sinking Fund	Total in Sinking Fund 1st of Year	Interest Accrual at 4%	Total in Sink. Fund End of Year
1	$300	$92.16	$207.84	0	0	$207.84
2	50	92.16	—42.16	$207.84	$8.31	173.99
3	500	92.16	407.84	173.99	6.96	588.79
4	70	92.16	—22.16	588.79	23.55	590.18
5	400	92.16	307.84	590.18	23.61	$921.63

Fig. 33 shows this allocation graphically.

Effect of Order of Receipt of Income The effect upon the present value of increasing, decreasing, odd, and uniform income payments over a given period of years and at the same interest rates is shown comparatively in the following instance, wherein the same group of income payments is rearranged according to each of the above classifications. The annuity life is taken at 10 years, and the incomes grade from $1,000 to $10,000. Interest rates are assumed at 10% for speculative capital and 4% on redemption. Calculations may be listed as on page 212.

The effect of having the bulk of the income received early or late during the period of years is readily seen from an inspection of the computed total present values. It is also apparent that the present value of certain groupings of odd incomes approximates very closely that of uniform income.

CHAPTER 14

INTEREST RATES

It is said that investment and speculation shade into each other. At one end we have the maximum of safety with a low interest rate, and at the other the maximum of risk and the promise of great return.

All of the factors expressing the desirability of the investment or speculation may be shown in the interest rate. These factors include safety of principal, stability of return, marketability, availability as collateral, tax exemption, freedom from care, promise of appreciation, and, of particular interest in mine valuation, amortization.

The gross interest rate is usually considered as made up of two parts: (a) net interest, or the amount paid for the use of capital without cost of administration and without any element of risk; and (b) the administration cost plus an insurance charge for the risk involved.

In order to determine what interest rates should be used in a particular valuation problem, we must analyze the interest rate with discrimination.

NET INTEREST — The net interest rate is generally used for the sinking fund accumulation in mine valuation. It is also called pure interest, or the normal or accumulative rate of interest. It is the rate necessary to pay for the accumulation of capital through the savings of those who have incomes more than sufficient to provide them with the necessities of life. Some with large incomes would undoubtedly save without the inducement of interest, but the amount of money which would be so saved is not sufficient to meet the demand for capital, and the interest rate or price paid for capital is determined by supply and demand.

Net interest presupposes the absolute safety of principal and perfect uniformity and stability of return. This ideal is not attainable in any investment, as evidenced by the change in value of the securities of foreign governments and municipalities caused by World War I. The investor must look ahead for the full life of his investment and decide whether the securities chosen will maintain their value. There are, however, securities offering a degree of relative safety which come near enough to the ideal for practical purposes. For investment in this country, United States bond issues and Treasury certificates best fill the requirements. Further, interest paid on savings bank deposits, the rediscount rate of the Federal Reserve banks, and the net earnings of life insurance companies on reserves are a guide to the interest rate on investments of maximum safety. Ignoring the extremes, the average long-time net interest rate is between two and four percent. The rate most commonly used in computing the sinking fund accumulation for mine valuation at the present time is four percent.

MANAGEMENT OR BANKER'S LOAN RATE — We have defined the net rate of interest to be that price that would be paid for the use of capital without the cost of administration and without any element of risk. Eliminating, for the present, the element of risk, in order to keep his funds continuously employed at the net rate of interest the investor must either care for the administration and management of his funds or must pay someone to do it for him. If he manages his funds himself, he must keep informed regarding the market for investment securities, must reinvest the interest and funds received from investments that have matured, and must occasionally change his investments in order to meet changes in the market. The payment for this care of investment capital, whether the work is done by the investor or by another instrumentality for him, is included in the interest rate.

If the owner of funds does not care to look after his own investments or if his savings are not large enough to warrant the time and expense or to obtain proper diversification of investments, he may turn them over to a banker who will pay him the net rate, or somewhat less, assume the cost of management, and reinvest his funds at a higher rate. The savings bank performs the service of collecting and loaning out savings and of maintaining a reserve to meet current demands for withdrawal by depositors. The bank endeavors to reduce the risk on its loans to a minimum, but even though it could be entirely successful, it must charge a sufficient amount in addition to the interest paid to depositors to pay for the services rendered.

That rate of interest which includes, with the net interest, the cost of administration or management of investment funds, will be designated as the management or banker's loan rate.

The interest rate paid on the more conservative investments, those in which the investor is a preferred creditor rather than the owner of a business—such as the interest paid on high-grade railroad, industrial, and public utility mortgage bonds—is the rate that should be taken as the management or banker's loan rate. Ignoring extremes, a rate of from four to six percent seems to best fill these requirements.

It may seem as if the banker would have to get a higher rate on his conservative investments than the individual, since he must maintain and allow for interest on his reserve, occasional losses on investments, and dividends on the bank's capital and surplus; but the more conservative investments made by the individual and those which qualify for savings loans by the banks are largely the same. The reserve required on savings deposits by banks which are members of the Federal Reserve system is only 3% of deposits, which is probably less than the idle funds waiting investment that the individual handling his own investments would have; the losses on the more conservative investments are small compared with the amount of money handled; and the interest paid in dividends on the bank's capital and surplus is not much greater than that paid on any other conservative investment.

The banker has the advantage of handling his investment funds on a larger scale than most individuals, which makes possible greater specialization and diversification. He also has an advantage in bargaining with the smaller owner of savings, and does not necessarily give him the full amount of net interest that could be obtained in a broader market covering larger amounts. This is partly offset by the greater expense to him of handling smaller accounts.

REMUNERATIVE, SPECULATIVE, OR — The investor purchasing a **CUSTOMARY RATE OF INTEREST** property or an interest in a property as evidenced by stock ownership, expects a certain profit above the banker's loan rate of interest, which can be obtained in the purchase of high-grade bonds. He expects to receive compensation for giving up the position of preferred creditor and for assuming ownership of the business. The amount of profit expected depends upon the type of industry and its geographical location.

Each industry possesses speculative features that affect its desirability as an outlet for investment capital. Such features are inherent in the industry itself and are not confined to individual units of that industry. The risks are reflected in the interest rates expected by those who invest their capital in each industry. The distance from the money market and the familiarity of investors with the industry also have a marked effect upon the interest rates demanded.

Agriculture is a good example of an industry that has suffered from such inherent disadvantages, which the government has tried to correct through the Federal Farm Loan system.

The railroad, iron and steel, automobile manufacturing, lumbering, textile, and oil industries and public utilities of various types all possess certain advantages and disadvantages from the standpoint of the owner of investment capital, and on investments in each of these industries a certain return is expected over and above the management rate of interest. This rate is determined by the demand for capital in the individual industry and by the supply of capital available for that purpose. The reluctance of the investor to assume the usual and customary risks of a business must be overcome by the promise of an increased return.

The mining industry is an outstanding example of those industries in which a high interest rate is expected. Mines are usually located far from the money centers of the country. Investors are not usually as well informed regarding mining as they are regarding the manufacturing, transportation, and public-service industries. The prices of metals are subject to greater fluctuations than are the prices of manufactured products, and this results in occasional periods of great profits alternating with longer periods of small profits or of losses. The enormous profits made by the original investors in some few mining enterprises and the lack of knowledge on the part of the public have made mining a fruitful field for unscrupulous promotors, so that the investing public has become timid regarding mining as an investment. These factors all contribute to decrease the supply of capital available to the mining industry and to increase the interest rate. Accordingly the rate of interest customarily expected by the investor in mining properties ranges upward from eight percent according to the branch of the industry, the location of the particular property, and the standing of the men backing it.

It is not anticipated that each individual mine or enterprise will yield the promised speculative rate that is necessary to attract capital. That part of this rate which is over and above the safe rate plus cost of management is bargained for as insurance that net interest plus reasonable cost of management will be received. Ignoring the element of profit, which will vary with relative abilities at bargaining between the investors and the seekers of capital, the average return from a large number of such investments should yield the management or banker's loan rate of return.

An alternative to expressing in the speculative interest rate the general risks of an investment, such as mining, is to compute the value at the average base rate which experience has shown will be realized from a number of such investments (management or banker's loan rate) and then to allow for the normal probabilities by a discount.

For example, if in valuing a property it is estimated that the actual realized income from a number of such investments should equal 6% (net interest plus cost of management, which in the case of mines is usually high), but that only 6 out of 10 such ventures will realize the full expectation, the valuation should be computed at 6% and the result discounted 40% or, in other words, multiplied by a factor of safety of 60%. This method may be used as a check on the interest rate generally accepted for the class of investment.

HAZARDS — MODES OF TREATMENT — Those risks of a mining or other business venture which are independent of time and which may be distinguished from the general speculative features of the industry as a whole or of a subdivision within the industry, will here be termed "hazards." A hazard, by definition, is a chance or risk dependent upon an uncertain event. It is, therefore, not associated inherently with interest, which is a direct function of time.

Two alternative methods may be used in evaluating specific hazards. They may be expressed either in the interest rate—by the calculating of a special "Equivalent Hazard Discount Rate of Interest"—or else by the application of an independent discount which will equal the estimated effect of the hazard or hazards. The former is sometimes more convenient from the investor's standpoint, as he is concerned primarily with the promised rate of return on his investment, but the latter has advantages from the standpoint of the engineer.

Equivalent Hazard Discount Rate of Interest Method — This method involves changing the equation used to discount the estimated annuity to present value by substituting an appropriately calculated rate of interest in the place of the speculative rate ordinarily used. This substitute rate, designated as the *equivalent hazard discount rate of interest,* is necessarily higher than the regular speculative rate since it has incorporated in it specific hazards over and above the risks normally found in ventures of the given class. In using this method, it is first necessary to estimate the effect of the hazards (or hazard) as a percentage of the valuation computed as if they were not present. Their effect is then applied to the valuation formula (by a conversion discussed in detail in a later chapter) as a reduction in present value, and the speculative interest rate is changed to absorb the reduction. The annuity is then present-valued by the revised equation.

Discount-for-Hazards Method — The use of this method requires no change in the present-value equation. Nor does it require any adjustment of the speculative rate of interest customarily used to evaluate risks of the given class. The valuation, ignoring the hazards, is computed in the usual manner by whatever formula is appropriate. Then each hazard is estimated separately, its chance of occurrence appraised, its effect calculated, and an offsetting deduction made from the present value.

Determining the proper discount for a hazard, however, is often a complex problem. For instance, because of subsidence there may be some doubt as to the permanence of a shaft in an operating mine. A study of conditions leads to an estimate that the chance of failure is 1 in 4. If the shaft fails, there will be the cost of a new shaft and equipment and perhaps a delay in production due to the moving of equipment. The new shaft may also either increase or decrease the cost of mining. The value of the property should be figured both with and without the new shaft and corresponding mining costs and, if this is the only hazard to be considered, a discount of 25% should be applied to the difference between the two valuations. If there are other hazards to be considered, this hazard must be reduced to its proper ratio to the full valuation. For example: The valuation of the property is $1,000,000 if the present shaft can be used, and $600,000 if a new shaft must be sunk. If the chance of failure of the shaft is assumed to be 1 in 4, the value of the property should be reduced to $900,000. This is a hazard of 10% on the value of the property as computed without consideration of hazards.

We can most conveniently combine this with other hazards by reducing them to the corresponding factors of safety, which are expressed as unity minus the hazard factor. If our hazard factors are 10%, 15%, 25%, and 5%, the corresponding factors of safety are 90%, 85%, 75%, and 95%. The combined factor of safety in this case is

$$.90 \times .85 \times .75 \times .95 = 54.5\%,$$

and the discount for hazards is 45.5%.

ADVANTAGES OF THE DISCOUNT-FOR-HAZARDS METHOD — The discount-for-hazards method of valuation has some decided advantages over the method of including all hazards in the interest rate. When incorporating hazards into the interest rate the engineer must base the increase in interest rate necessary to express a hazard which is independent of time on a calculation for a definite life period. If the period is changed, the interest rate, which is equivalent to the customary rate plus the hazard, also changes. The same speculative rate of interest does not represent the same degree of hazard when applied to investments of different lengths of life.

This relationship of interest rate and time (annuity life) is demonstrated graphically by Fig. 35 (p. 243), which shows the equivalent interest rates for various hazard discounts superimposed on an 8% speculative rate and a 4% rate on sinking fund.

Another advantage of the discount-for-hazards method of valuation is that it forces the engineer to give thorough consideration to each particular hazard and to appraise the chances of its occurrence. There is a tendency in the use of a hazard rate of interest to avoid thorough analysis of the specific hazards and to cover them generally with a high rate of interest which may be considerably more or less than is warranted by the conditions. Careless appraisal of this kind is to be avoided.

ATTITUDE OF MINING PROFESSION TOWARD HAZARDS AND DISCOUNTS — Hoskold used the interest rate to express all the hazards of an enterprise. That he realized the difficulty in determining the proper rate to express the risk is shown by the following quotation from his *Engineers' Valuing Assistant* (1877).

"Every purchaser of mining property should have ample allowance made upon his purchase, but the amount of such an allowance, as a *percentage*, must depend upon a point difficult to calculate—

"In the case of unopened mines it has been my practice in deducing the present value deferred, to allow 20 per cent. to a present purchaser, and redeem capital at 3 per cent. per annum; which I consider in a general way is a safe mode of dealing with any mine with average prospects; although in special cases, where a mine has a more certain character, I have allowed a percentage as low as 14, and in some of less certainty, as high as 25.

"A rule cannot be laid down expressing the attendant risk of mining adventure, as nearly all mines exist under circumstances differing widely from each other. It is a matter of experiment; each mine must, therefore, stand upon its own merits, and the amount of percentage to be allowed must also be varied according to the circumstances of each particular case."

Again in 1902[1] Hoskold says:

"In England, where the valuation of mines has long been practiced, it has been customary to allow the purchaser of mining property a high annual rate of interest. Upon collieries, for instance, the rate is from 14 to 20 per cent. per annum; and upon metalliferous mines still higher because the risk is greater. For foreign mines, the details of management, economy and profit are further removed from control, and consequently as the risk is proportionately increased, the purchaser should reckon upon the allowance of a far higher rate, depending upon the class and character of the mine, and probably from 25 to 35 per cent."

American engineers have in general adopted the Hoskold method of amortizing the capital investment but, if we can form an opinion from an examination of their published works and other contacts, they have not followed him in including all of the hazards in the interest rate. Both Hoover (*Principles of Mining* — 1909) and Finlay (*Cost of Mining* — 1909) follow the Hoskold method, but do not discuss the method of selecting the rate of interest in terms of risk.

Hoover says: "What rate of excess return the mine must yield is a matter of the risks in the venture and demands of

---

[1] Trans. AIME.

the investor. Mining business is one where 7% above provision for capital return is an absolute minimum demanded by the risks inherent in mines, even where the profit in sight gives warranty to the return of capital.''

Hoover uses rates of 7% and 8% on investment in his examples illustrating the use of the tables, and Finlay uses 7% in his example of the Miami Copper Company and used 5% in his appraisal of the copper and iron mines of Michigan for taxation purposes in 1911. These specific cases may be taken as evidence that Hoover and Finlay did not include the hazards of the individual properties in the interest rate but that, instead, they used the remunerative or speculative rate of interest, and either consciously or unconsciously used a discount for hazard, or factor of safety, in determining the other factors entering into the valuation. In the continuation of the Michigan Mine Appraisal by R. C. Allen, L. P. Barrett, and F. G. Pardee the discount-for-hazard method has been consciously applied, and 6% on investment has been taken as the customary rate.

C. K. Leith[1] recognizes discounts made in the factors entering into the valuation formula as an offsetting correction. ''In practice a very wide range of interest rates is used, depending on the special local conditions, or upon the practice of particular appraisers. In general, the range has been between 6 and 25 percent, with the trend toward a figure of 8 to 10 percent in recent years for standard mining enterprises in which the factors are well known. Where interest rates as low as 5 or 6 percent are used, there usually have been offsetting corrections or discounts in the other factors in the valuation, such as tonnage, production, or costs. In other words, part of the hazard is taken care of there rather than by the general interest rate.''

---

[1] C. K. Leith—''Mineral Valuations of the Future,'' A.I.M.E., 1938.

APPLICATION OF DISCOUNT FACTORS — This brings up the question of the relation between conservatism in estimates and the interest rates.

It will be apparent that the degree of optimism or of conservatism used in making the estimates that enter into the valuation has a bearing on the choice of interest rate. If a factor of safety has been applied to each separate estimate entering into a valuation, it may, however, be difficult to determine what the total, or combined, factor is.

For example, if the estimated selling price of $5.00 is reduced 10% in order to be conservative, and the estimated cost of $4.00 increased 10% for the same reason, the profit is reduced from $1.00 to 10¢, a discount of 90% in the profit factor, which will result in a 90% reduction in the valuation; whereas if the estimated selling price were $2.00 and the cost $1.00, the reduction on the same basis would be only 30¢, a discount of 30%, and a like reduction in valuation. If the annual output is reduced 10% below the estimate, it will result in a 10% reduction in valuation, but the total tonnage estimate on a property of long life might be reduced 50% without resulting in a 10% reduction in valuation. For instance, an increase in the life of an annuity from 50 years to 100 years will add only 7.1% to its present value at Hoskold rates of 8% on capital and 4% on redemption fund. The better practice is for the engineer to hold fast to the estimates which express his best judgment and to use either the interest rate or the discount-for-hazards method, or a combination of the two, to allow for the speculative features and hazards of the investment.

USE OF IDENTICAL SPECULATIVE — If all hazards are provided
AND SAFE RATES OF INTEREST   for by discounts and not included in the interest rate on the investment, there are strong arguments for using the same rate on the sinking fund as on the investment. In practice, a sinking fund is rarely set aside and invested at a safe rate of

interest; the hypothetical fund is reinvested, generally in the same business, or is returned to stockholders as return of capital. If it is retained and invested in other mining ventures, the administrative cost of these investments is included in the estimated costs of production of the enterprise.

This is the theory followed in the Michigan Mine Appraisal by F. G. Pardee, which is described later. The fact that some Michigan mines have been sold on the market for considerably less than the appraisal valuation may be explained as completely by an underestimation of the hazards involved as by an error in choice of interest rates.

The interest on the investment is of much greater importance in determining the value of the property than the interest on the sinking fund, since the former is figured on the full amount of the investment for the life of the property, and the latter on the sinking-fund accumulations, which approach the full amount of the investment only toward the end of the annuity period. Nevertheless, more attention is often given to the choice of interest rate on the sinking fund — whether it should be 3, 4, or 6 percent—than to whether the speculative or hazard interest rate on the investment should be 15, 20, or 25 percent.

INTEREST RATE DURING DEFERMENT PERIOD — The question of the rate of interest that should be applied during the deferment period has been the subject of considerable discussion. Should the engineer use the safe rate of interest, the speculative or hazard rate, or an intermediate rate? If specific hazards are included in the interest rate, and if they are not operative during the deferment period, they should not be included in deferment interest rate. Nor should the safe rate of interest be used, as it does not include administration costs. The management or banker's rate should not be used unless money is available to the individual industry at that rate. The rate that should be applied during the deferment period is the remunerative one defined in this discussion, as it is the rate at which money is available for investment in this industry excluding the specific hazards of the particular enterprise under consideration.

CHAPTER 15

MISCELLANEOUS INTEREST RATE CALCULATIONS

ANNUITY LIFE REQUIRED TO REDEEM CAPITAL — In purchasing a mining property or mining securities, or when considering a mine valuation from the standpoint of dividend and speculative rates of interest, it is sometimes essential to be able to determine n, the number of years of life of the enterprise required to repay the invested capital. It is obvious, from a study of the Hoskold-type valuation formulas already developed, that the years-life factor, n, is dependent upon the dividend overplus or, in other words, upon the difference between the rate of the actual dividend received and the expected rate of return on the invested capital. This overplus, or return of capital, constitutes a separate annuity, and the responsibility for its improvement at compound interest rests with the investor. It is assumed that as soon as it is received the investor will reinvest this overplus at a safe rate of interest until the annuity so formed has accumulated to the total of the capital invested. The investor is, therefore, vitally concerned with the question of whether or not the mining life (total apparent ore reserves divided by average tonnage mined per year) is sufficient for him to amortize his investment at the estimated average rate of dividend when a certain risk return is expected throughout the life of the property. In other words, will the estimated dividend overplus be sufficient to redeem the capital in the number of years it will take to mine out the reserve ore? That is, will the number of years of mining life be sufficient for the estimated overplus to replace the capital invested?

Each overplus constitutes an annuity payment and may be considered either in terms of actual dollars per year or in terms of a percentage of the invested capital. If dollars are the units used, the problem is to determine the number of years required for an annuity of this number of dollars per year to accumulate, at a safe rate of interest, to the number of dollars invested. If percentages are used, the question is to find the time required for an annuity of so many percent per year to amount to 100% when improved at a safe rate of interest. It will be simpler, in a general discussion of the problem, to consider the overplus as a percentage of the capital invested, because by so doing the definite amount of 100% is given as the goal to which the overplus annuity must accumulate; whereas the use of the dollar or money unit is adaptable only to individual problems, because the total number of dollars invested varies from one property to another.

Therefore, let the dividend overplus be considered as $X\%$ per year, the percent difference between the actual dividend rate received and the speculative rate (r') expected from the business.

This annuity of $X\%$ per year is then to be improved at a practicable safe rate of interest (r) until it totals 100% and so replaces the entire capital investment. From a previous derivation, an annuity of \$A per year amounts in n years at r rate to

$$S = \frac{A(R^n - 1)}{r}.$$

Substitution of the new values of $X\%$ for A and 100% for S gives

$$100\% = \frac{X\%(R^n - 1)}{r}, \quad 1.00r = X(R^n - 1),$$

$$\frac{r}{X} = R^n - 1, \quad \frac{r}{X} + 1 = R^n, \quad n = \frac{\log\left(\dfrac{r}{X} + 1\right)}{\log R}.$$

Thus, if the practicable rate of interest on the redemption annuity is 5%, and if the difference between the rate of the actual dividend received and the expected speculative rate is 5%,

$$n = \frac{\log\left(\dfrac{.05}{.05} + 1\right)}{\log 1.05} = \frac{\log 2}{\log 1.05}$$

$$= \frac{.301030}{.021189} = \underline{14.207} \text{ years required amortization life.}$$

The annuity life required to redeem capital may also be derived from the Hoskold two-rate valuation equation, as follows:

$$V_p = \frac{A}{\dfrac{r}{R^n - 1} + r'} = \frac{A(R^n - 1)}{r + r'(R^n - 1)}$$

$$V_p r + V_p r'(R^n - 1) = A(R^n - 1),$$

$$V_p r = A(R^n - 1) - V_p r'(R^n - 1)$$

$$= (A - V_p r')(R^n - 1),$$

$$R^n - 1 = \frac{V_p r}{A - V_p r'} = \frac{r}{\dfrac{A - V_p r'}{V_p}},$$

$$R^n = \frac{r}{\dfrac{A - V_p r'}{V_p}} + 1,$$

$$n = \frac{\log\left[\dfrac{r}{\dfrac{A - V_p r'}{V_p}} + 1\right]}{\log R},$$

and since $\dfrac{A - V_p r'}{V_p}$ represents the percent of the present value which is set aside each year in the redemption fund, this quantity may be termed $X\%$, giving

$$n = \frac{\log\left(\frac{r}{X} + 1\right)}{\log R}.$$

Table 9, in Part V of this text, is a list of life periods required to redeem capital at various combinations of dividend, speculative, and sinking-fund rates of interest.

Figs. 49, 50, 51, 52, and 53, interspersed with Table 9, are graphical representations of the life periods listed and are useful for quick, approximate interpolations in the matter of determining annuity life.

Example 34.

M invests \$100 in a depleting-reserve enterprise (mining, lumbering, etc.). He expects a 10% return on his money, plus the return of his invested capital. He receives dividends of \$15 per year. How long will the enterprise have to continue in order to redeem his capital, if he invests the overplus in bonds at 5%?

He is receiving annually a \$5, or 5%, overplus. The question is, therefore, how many years will it take an annuity of \$5 per year to amount to \$100 at 5% compound interest?

$$S = \frac{A(R^n - 1)}{r}$$

$$100 = \frac{5(\overline{1.05}^n - 1)}{.05} = 100(\overline{1.05}^n - 1)$$

$$= 100 \times \overline{1.05}^n - 100.$$

Therefore $200 = 100 \times \overline{1.05}^n$, $\overline{1.05}^n = \dfrac{200}{100} = 2$

$$n = \frac{\log 2}{\log 1.05} = \frac{.301030}{.021189} = \underline{14.207} \text{ years.}$$

Or, from Table 3, an annuity of $1 per year at 5% amounts to $19.5986 in 14 years, and to $21.5786 in 15 years. By interpolation this annuity would amount to $20 in 14.21 years and, therefore, an annuity of $5 (or 5%) per year would amount to $100 (or 100%) in 14.21 years.

Or, directly from Table 9, under redemption at 5%, interest at 10% and dividend at 15%, the required life is given as 14.2 years, a figure which is close enough for all practical purposes.

Example 35.

The Big-Bend Copper Company has 1,000,000 shares of stock outstanding, which are listed on the market at $2 each. At present the company is paying annual dividends of 30¢ per share. How long must such dividends continue in order to return the capital investment if the purchaser desires 10% interest with redemption at 4%?

The dividend rate on the present price is 30¢.

$$30¢ \div \$2.00 = 15\%.$$

The difference between the dividend and the expected interest rate is

$$15\% - 10\% = 5\% = X\%.$$

This overplus for amortization (5% per year) is to be annually reinvested at the safe rate (r) of 4%.

$$n = \frac{\log \left(\frac{.04}{.05} + 1 \right)}{\log 1.04}$$

$$= \frac{\log 1.80}{\log 1.04} = \frac{.255273}{.017033}$$

$$= \underline{\underline{14.99}}, \text{ years required to redeem capital under the conditions taken.}$$

Or, from Table 3, annuity of 5% per year, improved at 4% compound interest, will amount to 5 × 20.0236, or 100.12%, in exactly 15 years or, by interpolation, it will amount to an even 100% in 14.99 years.

Or, from Table 9, under redemption at 4%, dividend at 15%, and expected risk return at 10%, the required life is n = 15.0 years.

An examination of the Big-Bend property reveals 3,000,000 tons of reasonably assured ore which, at the normal mining rate of 300,000 tons per year and with the copper market at 14¢ per lb., can be expected to yield a profit of $1 per ton. This investigation shows that the assured life (10 years) of the mine is not long enough to satisfy the specified requirement as to speculative return and that the shares are not worth the price asked for them with the mine in its present condition.

This does not mean that the property is unworthy of further consideration, but simply that the stock valuation and the limitations placed on the property are not in accord with the expectations of the investor. It is evident, since the property can pay a yearly dividend of 15%, that it should net some return over and above capital redemption. Table 6 shows that the annual redemption payment which will amount to $1 in 10 years at 4% is $.08329 and, therefore, the annual percentage return which will amount to 100% under the same conditions is 8.33%. Subtraction of this return of capital from the annual dividend of 15% leaves the investor a 6.67% return on his investment. This, then, is the interest rate which the property can be expected to pay at the present price per share and with the given profit and life limitations. This same figure may be obtained by interpolation from Table 9 by inquiring for the interest yield when dividends are 15%, life 10 years, and redemption 4%. Thus, an investor who is satisfied with 6⅔% return over and above the return of his capital would purchase the mine at the price asked.

To satisfy the demands of the original investor, who desired 10% interest plus a return of capital, certain unforeseen improvements would have to take place with respect to the mine, as follows:

1. An extension of the orebodies beyond the anticipated reserves sufficient to prolong the mining life from the estimated 10 years to the required 15 years.

    This would mean $5 \times 300,000 = 1,500,000$ additional tons.

2. A rise in the market price of copper which would increase the profits and, therefore, the dividends, sufficiently to produce an overplus capable of retiring the capital investment within the given life of 10 years.

    To satisfy this supposition, the mine would have to be able to pay a dividend rate which would remit an overplus, above the required 10% risk return, sufficiently large to retire the investment in 10 years. From Table 6 it is found that annual payments of $.08329, improved at 4%, will amount in 10 years to $1, and, therefore, an overplus remittance of 8.33% per year would, likewise, amount to 100% in the same period and at the same rate. Thus, to fulfill this requirement, profits would have to increase sufficiently to enable the mine to pay annual dividends of 18.33% (10% speculative + 8.33% redemption). This would mean total annual earnings of $366,-600 instead of the estimated $300,000, or a rise in unit profit from $1 to $1.222 per ton. This dividend rate of 18.3% may be looked up directly in Table 9 under redemption at 4%, interest yield at 10%, and life of 10 years, by interpolating between the figures 10.3 years for a dividend rate of 18% and 9.4 years for a dividend rate of 19%.

3. Any combination of the two suppositions already given which would produce additional life and increased profits sufficient to net a 10% interest return and retire the capital investment.

For example, if 600,000 tons of additional ore were found and the market price were to improve so as to net profits of $1.11 per ton, the property would then have a life of 12 years and could pay annual dividends of $333,000, or 16.65%. In Table 9, under redemption at 4%, speculative rate of 10%, and life of 12 years, it will be noted that a property should return 16⅔% dividends in order to satisfy all the required conditions. If the above-mentioned anticipations were realized, this property would, therefore, be worth the price asked.

Example 36.

The Ajax Mining Company has outstanding 100,000 shares of stock, which are listed on the market at $10 each. The company is mining a lead-zinc orebody at the rate of 100,000 tons per year. A fair estimate of reserve ore gives an assurance of 1,500,000 tons. Profits may be conservatively estimated at $1.50 per ton, and the present dividend rate is $1.50 per share per year. If an investor desires a 10% return on his money with redemption of capital at 4%, will he consider this stock an advisable purchase?

Estimated life, $n = 15$ years

Dividend rate $= 15\%$.

From Table 9 the required life with the dividend rate established at 15%, expected hazard return at 10%, and redemption at 4%, is found to be 15.0 years; the shares therefore seem to be priced to suit the investor. The present value of the mine on the basis of these calculations is, therefore, $1,000,000. This figure could also be taken from Table 7 as

$$V_p = 150,000 \times 6.6693$$
$$= \$1,000,400.$$

If, however, the investor desires only 8% hazard return with redemption at 4%, what can he afford to pay per share for the stock?

In Table 9, with redemption set at 4%, interest at 8%, and life at 15 years, it is found that a 13% dividend rate will fulfill the conditions.

Therefore, earnings per share ÷ required rate per share = value per share

$$\$1.50 \div .13 = \$11.54 \text{ per share.}$$

Or, from Table 7, the total value of the property under these conditions is

$$V_p = 150,000 \times 7.6958$$
$$= \$1,154,400$$

and the value per share = $\$11.54$.

Table 9 is, therefore, of primary value for the consideration of mining securities from an investment standpoint, because it gives a ready comparison between years of life, annual dividends, speculative rates, and redemption rates. It does not supplant any of the tables which precede it, but it does present the desired information in a better form for certain uses.

SIMULTANEOUS SINKING FUND — The instance may arise in
AND DIMINISHING ANNUITY   mining or other industry in
                                 which it would be desirable
to allocate the savings effected by new equipment to simultaneous payment for said equipment and provision for future replacement of this equipment by sinking fund accrual.

To illustrate, a manufacturer borrows $100,000 to re-equip his plant. It is estimated there will be a direct saving of $19,000 per year in operating costs. Assuming that the next such re-equipment, 10 to 15 years hence, will cost $120,000, he wishes to use the entire $19,000 each year, first, to repay the present borrowed capital and second, to set up a sinking fund to meet the next future replacement. He wants both accounts to terminate at the same time. How shall the money be split and how long must the present equipment last? Assume that interest on each account is at 4%.

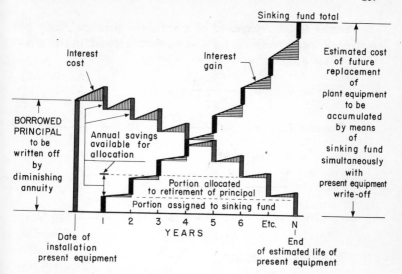

Fig. 34. Simultaneous sinking fund and diminishing annuity.

Although identical interest rates would be unusual, such an assumption will reduce the problem to its simplest form, as follows:

Let P = borrowed cost of new equipment presently installed,

M = yearly saving in operating cost effected by present new equipment,

S = estimated future cost of next replacement of equipment,

r = interest rate — identical for loan and sinking fund,

A = annual payment toward retirement of borrowed capital,

s = annual sinking-fund payment toward next future replacement of equipment,

n = years to extinguish loan and accrue sinking fund.

Premise 6, for repayment of a borrowed principal, may be combined with Premise 5, for sinking-fund accrual, in the solution of this problem, as follows:

Premise 6, $R^n = \dfrac{A}{A - Pr}$.

Premise 5, $S = \dfrac{s(R^n - 1)}{r}$, $R^n = \dfrac{Sr + s}{s}$.

Then, with r identical,

$$\frac{A}{A - Pr} = \frac{Sr + s}{s} ,$$

and, with a definite sum M available to provide A and s,

$$M = A + s.$$

Substituting will give

$$\frac{A}{A - Pr} = \frac{Sr + M - A}{M - A} ,$$

which may be reduced to

$$A = \frac{P(M + Sr)}{P + S} .$$

This value for A may then be substituted back in the original equation to find n. Results may then be checked by using s and the other original equation to solve either for the total sinking-fund accrual or to find the years required for such accrual.

The numerical data above will give the following:

$$A = \frac{100,000(19,000 + 120,000 \times .04)}{100,000 + 120,000}$$

$= \$10,818.20$, annual payment to debt retirement.

$$R^n = \frac{10,818.2}{10,818.2 - 100,000 \times .04} ,$$

$$\overline{1.04}^n = 1.5867.$$

Value of n may be interpolated from Table 1 or solved by logarithms.

$$n = \frac{\log 1.5867}{\log 1.04} = \frac{.200495}{.017033} = 11.77 \text{ years.}$$

Check:

$$s = M\text{-}A = \$8181.80,$$

$$S = \frac{8181.8(\overline{1.04}^{11.77} - 1)}{.04}$$

$$= \frac{8181.8(1.58664 - 1)}{.04}$$

$$= 8181.8 \times 14.666 = \$119,994,$$

or,

$$R^n = \frac{120,000 \times .04 + 8181.80}{8181.80}$$

$$= 1.5867 \text{ and n would again be } 11.77 \text{ years for sinking fund accrual.}$$

An alternative solution, when interest rates are identical, is to apply the entire amount M in each equation, substituting it for A in one and for s in the other, and then total the years life obtained.

With interest rates different for borrowed capital and sinking fund, the problem may be worked readily by a trial and error method as follows:

Let P, M, S, s, and A be the same as before,

$r_1 = $ interest rate on borrowed capital,

$r_2 = $ interest rate on sinking fund.

Then $R_1{}^n = \dfrac{A}{A - Pr}$ and $R_2{}^n = \dfrac{Sr_2 + s}{s}$

$$n = \frac{\log \dfrac{A}{A - Pr_1}}{\log R_1} \qquad n = \frac{\log \dfrac{Sr_2 + s}{s}}{\log R_2}$$

Substituting M-A for s and equating will give

$$\frac{\log \dfrac{A}{A-Pr_1}}{\log \dfrac{Sr_2 + M\text{-}A}{M-A}} = \frac{\log R_1}{\log R_2} \ .$$

With the ratio $\log R_1 \div R_2$ known, trial values for A may then be substituted to arrive at a final value. The remainder of the calculation and check is as before.

EQUIVALENT HAZARD DISCOUNT RATE OF INTEREST — Whenever certain of the factors entering into a mine valuation are doubtful, it may be desirable to determine the equivalent interest rate which will suitably express this additional hazard. The conditions can best be fulfilled by estimating the probabilities for the factors in doubt, assuming the interest rates which would be applicable were no doubt present, and then computing the equivalent interest rate which will include the estimated probabilities. For instance, suppose that the items entering into a valuation are doubtful, in total or combined effect, to the extent of 25% (in other words, there are three chances out of four that the valuation is correct) and that the accepted rates of interest on the normal speculative features of similar mines are 8% on capital (r') and 4% on redemption (r). What equivalent rate (r'_h) will express the estimated extraordinary hazard?

Note that the symbol r'_h is used to represent the equivalent-hazard-discount rate of interest to distinguish it from the speculative rate r', used to express only the customary risks of the industry.

This may be computed by referring back to the Hoskold two-rate formula $V_p = \dfrac{1}{s + r'}$, but first it will be necessary to know the life of the annuity or property .

Assume the life (n) to be 10 years. From Table 7 the present value of an annuity of \$1 per year for 10 years at 8% and

4% is found to be \$6.1240, and from Table 6 the redemption fund payment is \$.08329 per year. Applying the hazard discount of 25% to the present value reduces it from \$6.1240 to \$4.5930.

The Hoskold formula may now be solved for r' as follows:

$$V_p = \frac{1}{s + r'},$$

$$s + r' = \frac{1}{V_p},$$

$$r' = \frac{1}{V_p} - s.$$

Substituting r'_h for r' and inserting the numerical values above gives

$$r'_h = \frac{1}{4.5930} - .08329 = .21772 - .08329$$

$$= .13443.$$

Therefore, the equivalent interest rate (r'_h) necessary if the hazards are included is 13.44%.

If, however, the life (n) is assumed to be 20 years instead of 10 years, with all other conditions the same as before, the equivalent rate necessary if the hazard discount is included will be somewhat less than for the shorter period, as follows:

According to Table 7, V_p for 20 years at 8% and 4% is \$8.8042.

A hazard discount of 25% reduces this value to \$6.6032.

According to Table 6, the annual redemption payment is \$.03358.

$$r'_h = \frac{1}{V_p} - s = \frac{1}{6.6032} - .03358$$

$$= .15144 - .03358 = 11.79\%, \text{ equivalent rate.}$$

A 50% hazard discount (only one chance in two that the valuation is correct) will give considerably higher equivalent rates, as follows:

For the ten-year period with 8% and 4% as normal rates, a 50% discount reduces the present value to

$$6.1240 \times .50 = 3.0620.$$

$$\text{Therefore, } r'_h = \frac{1}{3.0620} - .08329$$

$$= .32658 - .08329$$

$$= 24.33\%, \text{ equivalent rate.}$$

For the 20-year period, with the same normal rates, the reduced present value is

$$8.8042 \times .50 = 4.4021$$

$$\text{and} \qquad r'_h = \frac{1}{4.4021} - .03358$$

$$= .22716 - .03358$$

$$= 19.36\%, \text{ equivalent rate.}$$

If the life period (n) is carried to infinity, the redemption payment (s) becomes zero and $r' = \dfrac{1}{V_p}$.

Therefore, with a 25% hazard discount and the normal risk rate of 8%, the equivalent rate is

$.08 \div .75 = 10\frac{2}{3}\%$, or the limit which is approached as the life increases.

With a 50% hazard discount and a normal risk rate of 8%, the limit is $.08 \div .50 = 16\%$.

Equivalent rates of interest (r'_h) are shown graphically in Fig. 35 to include hazard discounts up to 60% when used in conjunction with Hoskold rates of 8% on capital and 4% on redemption. These are plotted for life periods to 50 years in

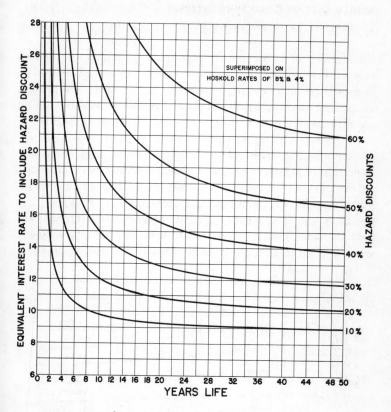

Fig. 35. Equivalent hazard discount interest rate.

order to illustrate the relation between time and the interest rate. The number of variables involved precludes a complete set of such graphs in this text.

A visual inspection of the chart shows that the equivalent-hazard-discount-rate of interest is extremely high for short life periods and that it approaches a value of $\dfrac{r'}{1 - \text{hazard discount}}$ as the life is extended toward infinity.

SINGLE RATE OF COMPOUND INTEREST — The Hoskold mine-
EQUIVALENT TO HOSKOLD RATES   valuation formula
                                            (Premise 7) with its
combination of two rates of interest — speculative or hazard
rate on invested capital and safe rate on return of capital —
is sometimes subject to comparison, in its effect on present
value, with the single-rate equation (Premise 4) used in valuing
annuities where return of capital is not an essential feature.

Fig. 36 is a group of curves plotted to show the single rate
of compound interest which is equivalent in present-valuing
to certain of the more commonly used combinations of Hoskold
rates. Curves are given for Hoskold rates of 4% to 10% on invested capital with sinking-fund accumulations at 4%.

As an example, what single rate of compound interest will
give the same present value as Hoskold rates of 8% and 4%
when applied to an annuity of 20 years life? Proceed up along

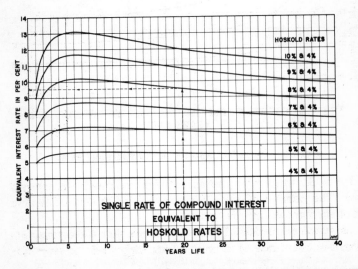

Fig. 36. Single rate of compound interest equivalent to
Hoskold rates.

the 20-year line from the bottom of the chart to the intersection of this line with the 8% and 4% curve, thence horizontally to the left edge, where the equivalent single rate may be read off as 9.53%.

Similar curves may be calculated for Hoskold rates other than those shown, by interpolating between interest columns in Table 4 for the present values listed in Table 7.

HOSKOLD REMUNERATIVE DISCOUNT FACTOR — The Hoskold two-rate equation may be expanded to show the "remunerative discount factor" which it expresses over and above the safe, or sinking-fund, rate of interest as follows:

$$V_p = \frac{A}{\dfrac{r}{R^n - 1} + r'} = \frac{A}{\dfrac{r'(R^n - 1) + r}{R^n - 1}} = \frac{A(R^n - 1)}{r'R^n - r' + r}$$

$$= \frac{Ar\left(\dfrac{R^n - 1}{r}\right)}{r'R^n - r' + r}$$

$$= \frac{ArR^n\left(\dfrac{R^n - 1}{r}\right)}{(r'R^n - r' + r)R^n}$$

$$= \frac{rR^n}{r'R^n - r' + r} \times \frac{A(R^n - 1)}{rR^n}$$

= remunerative discount factor × present value of an annuity of A per year for n years at r rate compound interest.

Thus, $\dfrac{rR^n}{r'R^n - r' + r}$ is a multiplying factor which expresses the normal added risk of the enterprise being valued over and above the net or sinking fund rate of discount.

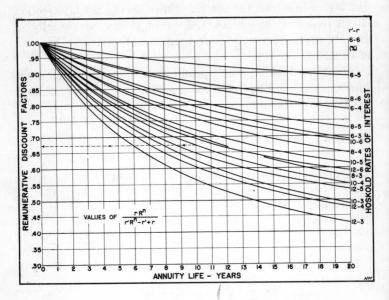

Fig. 37. Remunerative discount factors for Hoskold
rates of interest.

Fig. 37 is a graphical representation of remunerative discount factors for Hoskold rates of 6, 8, 10, and 12% on invested
capital and 3, 4, 5, and 6% on sinking-fund accumulations.

For instance, what remunerative discount is included in
Hoskold rates of 10% and 4% when applied to an investment
of 10 years life? This may be solved directly from Fig. 37 by
starting at 10 years on the bottom ordinate, thence vertically
upward to the 10 and 4 curve, thence horizontally to the left
edge, where the factor is found to be .67.

This same value may be obtained arithmetically by substituting the respective values in the formula given above for the
remunerative discount factor or by dividing the factor of Table
7 (5.4558) by the factor of Table 4 (8.1109).

PERPETUITIES — Any annuity coming from a source that has no apparent termination may be classed as a perpetual annuity or a perpetuity. Some of the common perpetuities are incomes from trust funds, preferred stocks, land rentals, etc., where no life limitations are evident. The term "perpetual" is not ordinarily interpreted in its literal sense to mean "lasting forever" or "infinite" but is usually considered to refer to an indefinite life of at least 100 years' assurance, because the present worth of an annuity has practically approached its limit at the end of such a period.

Premise 10. Present Value of an Annual Perpetuity — Invested at r rate of interest, a principal sum sufficient to produce an income of $1 annually may be considered the present value or purchase price of a perpetuity of $1 per year, since the two incomes are identical.

As an example, the present value of an annual perpetuity of $1 at 4% interest is $\dfrac{\$1}{.04} = \$25$.

This is true because $25 invested at 4% will produce $1 annually forever, an income equal to the perpetuity purchased.

Thus $V_p = \dfrac{1}{r}$ or $= \dfrac{A}{r}$ if the annuity is not unity, because $V_p r = 1$, or A.

This equation may be evolved also from a consideration of the present worth of an annuity when the period for which it is to continue and the rate percent are known, as follows:

The sum to which an annuity of $A per year for n years at r rate will amount is

$$S = \frac{A(R^n - 1)}{r} \qquad \text{(Premise 3)}$$

and the present value of such an annuity is

$$V_p = \frac{A(R^n - 1)}{R^n r} \qquad \text{(Premise 4)}$$

$$= \frac{A}{r} \times \frac{R^n - 1}{R^n}.$$

Or this may be written as

$$= \frac{A}{r} \times \left(1 - \frac{1}{R^n}\right)$$

and, as n increases, the expression

$$\left(1 - \frac{1}{R^n}\right) \text{ approaches unity.}$$

Therefore, if the annuity is of perpetual life

$$V_p = \frac{A}{r}, \text{ as given above.}$$

Example 37.

What is the present value of a perpetuity of \$1 per year at 5% interest?

$$V_p = \frac{1}{r}$$

$$= \frac{1}{.05} = \$20.$$

Example 38.

What is the present value of a perpetuity of \$50 per year at 5% interest?

$$V_p = \frac{A}{r}$$

$$= \frac{50}{.05} = \$1000$$

or, from example given above,

$$V_p = 50 \times 20 = \$1000.$$

Premise 11. Present Value of Other Than Annual Perpetuities — In like manner, the present value of a perpetuity of $1 payable every nth year is equal to the annuity payment divided by the interest accumulated on $1 during the n-year period between payments.

The sum of the interest is found as follows:

A principal of $1 increases in n years at r rate compound interest to $(1 + r)^n$ or R^n dollars. Deduction of the original principal leaves the interest, which is $(R^n - 1)$ dollars. Then, the present value of a perpetuity of $1 payable every nth year with the first payment due n years hence is $V_p = \dfrac{1}{R^n - 1}$, because in the n-year interval between payments, V_p dollars at r rate will earn the annuity payment of $1.

If the perpetuity is for $A, $V_p = \dfrac{A}{R^n - 1}$.

Example 39.

What is the present value of a perpetuity of $1 payable every fifth year, at 6% compound interest?

$$V_p = \frac{1}{R^n - 1}$$

$$= \frac{1}{1.06^5 - 1} .$$

The value of $\overline{1.06}^5$ may be taken directly from Table 1, under 6% for 5 years, as follows:

$$= \frac{1}{1.3382 - 1}$$

$$= \frac{1}{.3382} = \underline{\underline{\$2.9568.}}$$

Example 40.

What is the present value of a perpetuity of $250, payable every fifth year, at 6% compound interest?

$$V_p = \frac{A}{R^n - 1}$$

$$= \frac{250}{1.06^5 - 1}$$

$$= \frac{250}{.3382} = \underline{\underline{\$739.21}},$$

or, from example given above,

$$V_p = 250 \times 2.9568 = \underline{\underline{\$739.20}}.$$

Present Value of a Deferred Perpetuity — The present value may be found by multiplying the value of the perpetuity at the beginning of its interest-earning period by the present value of $1 due m years hence. Let $V_{bi} =$ such value at the beginning of interest period to distinguish it from present value. The value at the beginning of the interest-bearing period is computed as though the perpetuity were to start immediately, and this computed value, discounted through the deferment period of m years at the given rate percent, gives the present value of the deferred annuity. Therefore,

$$V_{bi} = \frac{1}{r}$$

and

$$V_p = \frac{V_{bi}}{R^m}.$$

V_p improved at r rate of compound interest for m years will equal the V_{bi} of the perpetuity. This V_{bi} is a sum which, at r rate, will earn the perpetuity of $1 in the period between payments.

Example 41.

What is the present value of a perpetuity of $1 per year at 6% interest, the first payment due 10 years hence?

$$V_{bi} = \frac{1}{r}$$

$$= \frac{1}{.06} = \underline{\underline{\$16.67}}.$$

$$V_p = \frac{V_{bi}}{R^m}$$

With the first payment due 10 years from valuation date, this yearly perpetuity is the same as an immediate annuity after 9 years' deferment.

$$= \frac{16.67}{1.06^9} = \frac{16.67}{1.69} = \underline{\underline{\$9.86}},$$

or, to combine the formulas,

$$V_p = \frac{\dfrac{1}{r}}{R^m}$$

$$= \frac{\dfrac{1}{.06}}{1.06^9} = \frac{1}{1.06^9 \times .06}$$

$$= \frac{1}{1.69 \times .06} = \frac{1}{.1014} = \underline{\underline{\$9.86}}.$$

Example 42.

What is the present value of a perpetuity of $25 per year at 5% interest, the first payment due 8 years hence?

$$V_{bi} = \frac{A}{r} = \frac{25}{.05} = \underline{\underline{\$500}}.$$

$$V_p = \frac{V_{bi}}{R^m}$$

As above, actual deferment is one year less than apparent unless V_{bi} is calculated as an annuity due.

$$= \frac{500}{\overline{1.05}^7} = \frac{500}{1.4071} = \$355.34,$$

or, to use a combined formula,

$$V_p = \frac{\dfrac{A}{r}}{R^m} = \frac{A}{R^m r}$$

$$= \frac{25}{\overline{1.05}^7 \times .05}$$

$$= \frac{25}{1.4071 \times .05} = \underline{\$355.34.}$$

Example 43.

What is the present value of a perpetuity of \$50, payable every third year, at 6% compound interest, if the first payment is not due until 8 years hence? If the perpetuity were to start immediately the first payment would be due 3 years hence, so this problem is equivalent to an annuity payable every third year after a 5-year deferment period, and

$$V_p = \frac{\dfrac{A}{(R^n - 1)}}{R^m} = \frac{\dfrac{50}{\overline{1.06}^3 - 1}}{\overline{1.06}^5}$$

The values of $\overline{1.06}^3$ and $\overline{1.06}^5$ may be taken directly from Table 1, as follows:

$$= \frac{\dfrac{50}{1.1910 - 1}}{1.3382} = \frac{\dfrac{50}{.191}}{1.3382}$$

$$= \frac{261.78}{1.3382} = \underline{\$195.62,}$$

or $\qquad V_{bi} = \dfrac{A}{R^n - 1} = \dfrac{50}{1.06^3 - 1} = \$261.78$

and $\qquad V_p = \dfrac{V_{bi}}{R^m} = \dfrac{261.78}{1.3382} = \underline{\$195.62}.$

In this case \$261.78 is the value at the beginning of the interest-bearing period (V_{bi}) and represents a sum which will earn the perpetuity, because the interest on this sum for 3 years amounts to

$$
\begin{aligned}
I &= P(R^n - 1) \\
&= 261.78(1.1910 - 1) \\
&= 261.78 \times .191 = \$50.
\end{aligned}
$$

The purchase price (V_p) of \$195.62 represents the discounted value of the V_{bi}, because in 5 years at 6% compound interest, V_p will improve to V_{bi}, as follows:

$$
\begin{aligned}
S &= PR^n, \\
V_{bi} &= V_p R^n = 195.62 \times 1.3382 = \underline{\underline{\$261.78}}.
\end{aligned}
$$

Separate Treatment of Initial Perpetuity Payments — In computing the present value of a perpetuity, one or more of the initial payments may be removed from the perpetual series for separate consideration, and the remainder of the series will still constitute a perpetuity.

Thus, assume that a perpetuity of \$1 payable at the end of each year is to be present-valued at 5%.

The ordinary computation, as given under Premise 10, would be

$$
V_p = \frac{A}{r} = \frac{1}{.05} = \$20.
$$

Now, suppose that the first 20 payments of this perpetuity are removed from the series and treated as a separate annuity. Their present value from Table 4 would be \$12.4622. The remainder of the series would still be a perpetuity but there would be a deferment period of 20 years prior to its first payment. The present value of this remaining series, from Table 2, would then be $20 × .37689 = $7.5378. The sum of the two separate calculations gives $12.4622 + $7.5378 = $20.0000, or the same present value as by the ordinary method of computing.

Separation of perpetuity payments is useful, particularly in handling a deferred series where the period of deferment is less than the period between payments, a condition which may be illustrated as follows:

Example 44.

Given a perpetuity of $2000 payable each sixth year with the first payment due 3 years hence. Find its present value at 7% compound interest.

Consider the first payment as a principal sum due 3 years hence. The remainder of the series then constitutes a perpetuity payable each sixth year after a deferment period of 3 years.

Interest between payments =

$$R^n - 1 = \overline{1.07}^{\,6} - 1 = .5007,$$

V_{bi} of remaining perpetuity =

$$\frac{A}{R^n - 1} = \frac{2000}{.5007} = \$3994.41,$$

and present value of the remaining perpetuity plus the separate payment is

$$(3994.41 + 2000)\ .81630 = \$4893.20.$$

If, instead of separating the first payment from the remaining perpetuity, the entire series is considered as a perpetuity payable each sixth year, its present value may be computed as of 3 years ago plus interest accrual to date to give:

$$V_p = \frac{2000}{.5007} \times \overline{1.07}^3 = 3994.41 \times 1.2250 = \underline{\underline{\$4893.15}}.$$

Graphs of Perpetuities — Graphs of perpetuities, though simple to draw, fail to produce impressive curves, because of the repetitive nature of the perpetuity itself. Further, the perpetuity curve, unlike other characteristic annuity curves, does not approach infinite limits but, rather, continues to infinity in one direction only as an infinite number of repetitions of the earning-paying cycle of the perpetuity. Fig. 38 shows the present value of several ordinary perpetuities plotted to an ordinate of dollar units and to an abscissa of yearly time units. The graphs give the present values, or purchase prices, at the beginning of the interest-earning period of perpetuities of $1 per year at 3, 4, 5, 6, and 10% interest; $1 each second, third, fourth, and fifth year at 4% interest; $1 each fourth year at 10% interest; and the present value of a perpetuity of $1 each year at 4% interest when deferred up to 10 years at the same rate. The interest-earning period is carried only to 10 years, sufficient to show at least two complete cycles of the perpetuity. To analyze this repetitive earning-paying cycle, take a perpetuity which pays $1 each year and assume that 5% is the interest rate agreed upon in the transfer of this income. The present value, or purchase price, of this perpetuity, if it is to start immediately, is $1 \div r$ or $20. As will be seen from the graph, this is true because $20 will earn $1 each year when improved at 5% interest. The perpetuity curve, therefore, consists of an infinite series of repetitions, each of one-year duration, in each of which the $20 purchase price improves to $21 and then pays the $1 income which reduces it to the starting point of $20 and so completes the cycle. The cycle consists of earning the income and then paying it to the purchaser, and therefore has been termed, in this discussion the earning-paying cycle of the perpetuity. When a perpetuity is payable each second year, this cycle, as shown by the graph, is completed in

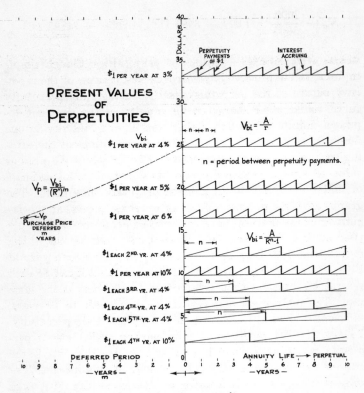

Fig. 38. A perpetuity.

a two-year period; when payable each third year, the cycle requires three years, and so on. In each case, the purchase price must earn the payment in the allotted period of time. When a perpetuity is to start immediately, the present value (V_p), purchase price, and value at the beginning of the interest-bearing period (V_{bi}) are all identical numerical quantities; but when a perpetuity is deferred, the value at the beginning of the interest-earning period (V_{bi}) must be distinguished from the present value (V_p).

CHAPTER 16

CASE VALUATIONS — MINERAL PROPERTY

GENERAL FEATURES

DEVELOPMENT AND EQUIPMENT CHARGES

Effect on Present Value — Ordinarily the terms "present value" and "purchase price" may be used interchangeably. Under certain conditions, however, they are not synonymous. A conspicuous instance is the case of a mine which requires additional equipment or development prior to production; the cost of such development and equipment must be deducted from the present value of the series of annual earnings in arriving at the purchase price. The net purchase price is then the present worth of the future earnings of the improved property minus the present discounted expenditures necessary to effect such improvements.

Thus, if E equals the required immediate expenditure for development and equipment, then

$$\text{Purchase price} = V_p - E.$$

Development and Equipment Deductions — Development and equipment moneys may be spent in one of three ways:

1. As a lump sum at a definite time.
2. As annual or periodic lump sums of equal or specified amounts at stated times.
3. As a continual nonuniform expense over an indefinite period of time.

In the first of these three methods, if the lump sum for development and equipment is to be spent immediately after purchase of the property, it is necessary merely to subtract the entire sum from the present value to obtain the net price. If, however, the mine is to be purchased at once but the reconditioning is not to be done until a certain future time, the mine lying idle during the interim, the present worth of the future lump sum for development and equipment should be subtracted from the valuation figure to give the net price.

For example, suppose a clause is added to Example 33, given above, which states that an expense of $50,000 must be incurred immediately upon acquisition of the property in order to preserve the equipment and mine workings for the 5-year period during which the mine will be idle. The purchase price under these conditions would be

$$V_p - E = 238,300 - 50,000 = \underline{\$188,300,}$$

because the amount paid plus the necessary expenditure of $50,000 would bring the total cost to the purchaser up to the valuation figure that was estimated.

However, suppose the condition of the mine is such that it may be allowed to lie idle for the 5-year period and then, by a lump expenditure of $50,000, is put into condition for immediate operation. In this case it is justifiable to deduct from the valuation only the present value of $50,000 due 5 years hence at, for instance, 5% compound interest, because such a sum would improve to the required $50,000 in 5 years at 5%.

Therefore, the purchase price $= V_p - \dfrac{S}{1.05^5}$ because $E = \dfrac{S}{1.05^5}$

$$= 238,300 - \frac{50,000}{1.2763} = 238,300 - 39,175 = \underline{\$199,125.}$$

According to the second method, the plant improvements are paid for by annual or periodic lump sums. These sums may or may not be of equal amounts, and the periods between payments may not necessarily be uniform. The evaluator must, however, know the amount of each expenditure and the time at which it is to be made, in order to be able to compute the present discounted total of the series, which is then subtracted from the valuation figure to give the net price.

To illustrate with specific cases, refer again to Example 33 and add a clause to the effect that it is estimated the mine can be kept in operating condition and the necessary development work done during the 5-year period of idleness by an annual expenditure at the beginning of each year of $10,000. Allowing 5% interest on the equipment fund, the immediate sum which would be equivalent to the total periodic payments may be determined as follows:

$$E = 10,000 + \frac{10,000}{1.05} + \frac{10,000}{1.05^2} + \frac{10,000}{1.05^3} + \frac{10,000}{1.05^4}.$$

Table 2 gives the values as

$$= 10,000 + 9,523.80 + 9,070.30 + 8,638.40 + 8,277.00$$
$$= \$45,459.50.$$

Or, substituting the figures used above in the formula for an annuity due as given under premise 4, gives

$$E = \frac{10,000\,(\overline{1.05^5} - 1)}{.05 \times \overline{1.05^4}}$$

$$= \$45,459.50.$$

Purchase price = 238,300 − 45,460 = $192,840.

In case the annual equipment expenditure of $10,000 were to be made at the end of each year instead of at the beginning, the series would be:

$$E = \frac{S}{R} + \frac{S}{R^2} + \frac{S}{R^3} + \frac{S}{R^{n-1}} + \frac{S}{R^n}.$$

$$= \frac{S(R^n - 1)}{R^n r},$$ the form developed previously for the present value of an immediate annuity.

Therefore $E = \dfrac{10,000(\overline{1.05}^5 - 1)}{\overline{1.05}^5 \times .05}$

$\qquad = \dfrac{10,000(1.2763 - 1)}{1.2763 \times .05} = \dfrac{2763}{.06382} = 43,294$

or, directly from Table 4 under 5% for 5 years,

$\qquad E = 10,000 \times 4.3295 = \$43,295$

and the purchase price $= V_p - E$

$\qquad\qquad\qquad\qquad = 238,300 - 43,295 = \underline{\underline{\$195,005.}}$

To illustrate with still another case, suppose that the mine of Example 33 can be kept in best condition by expending $10,000 at the end of the second idle year, $10,000 at the end of the fourth year, and $30,000 at the end of the fifth year. Assuming 5% on equipment money, the summation of present values is:

$$E = \frac{10,000}{\overline{1.05}^2} + \frac{10,000}{\overline{1.05}^4} + \frac{30,000}{\overline{1.05}^5}$$

$\qquad = 9,070.30 + 8,227.00 + 23,505.90 = \$40,803.20$, the discounted equivalent of the sums which must be spent in the future.

The purchase price under these conditions would be
$\qquad 238,300 - 40,803 = \underline{\underline{\$197,497.}}$

The third method of development expenditure, in which the program is of indefinite time and nonuniform amounts, is usually applied to an operating property. There is no mathematical solution of the problem, because the variables are not known beforehand, and therefore the usual procedure is to charge the account to operating expense as each item is incurred. An estimate of such expense could be made and deducted from the valuation figure to arrive at the purchase price.

LESSOR-LESSEE INTERESTS

Royalty — Royalty, as used in connection with mining, may be defined as the payment to the owner of mineral rights for the privilege of mining and producing the mineral. Originally, royalty referred to crown ownership and the granting of concessions on the basis of a payment to the royal owner for the minerals produced by the concessionnaire.

Royalty applies only to operations where two parties, the owner and the operator, by joint agreement, are working the property. The owner of the mineral rights, or fee, is the lessor; the operator is the lessee. By terms of the usual agreement, or lease, the owner grants to the operator the right to enter upon the property for the purpose of mining under specified conditions as to time, royalty, minimum payment, etc. The operator, or lessee, does not own the mineral in place but has the right to extract and to acquire title to the mineral so extracted. No royalty is involved when the fee owner is also the operator of the property.

Royalty is generally viewed as a division of gross profit between fee owner and operator[1]. To the fee owner, the royalty represents gross profit; part a return of his investment, part a return on his investment. To the operator, royalty is a cost, over and above which he must make his own profit.

Interest Rate — Royalty is a prior lien on operating profits and, as such, should not carry a risk rate as high as the speculative interest rate on the operator's profit. Thus, at a lower discount rate, the present value of the lessor's interest, if other considerations were equal, would be higher than for the lessee

---

[1] Blakey, R. G., "Taxation in Minnesota," Univ. of Minn. Press, 1932; p. 252.

Leith, C. K., "Mineral Valuations of the Future," A.I.M.E., 1938; p. 79.

Minnesota Tax Commission, 9th Biennial Report, 1924; Chap. V, p. 19.

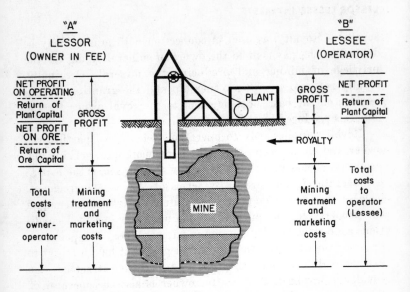

Fig. 39. Sketch of lessor-lessee interest.

and might, theoretically, approach the present value of a combined owner-operator interest. In any case, there may be a difference in present value between the sum of the separate present values of the royalty and operating interests and the present value of the single operation by the fee owner.

Lessor-Lessee Operation — Valuation of either the lessor or lessee interest separate from the other would be unusual in mine valuation work. Valuation premises, generally, are based on viewing the operation as a whole regardless of ownership.

Fig. 39 illustrates the parallel factors of the lessor-lessee situation. In this diagram, the same mine orebody and plant is assumed under two types of operation. In case A, the owner and operator are one and the same person or company. In case B, the fee-owner has leased the property on a royalty basis to an operator. Output, operating costs, and selling price of the product are assumed to be identical in both instances. To simplify further, interest rates and present value are not considered and items are not to scale.

Case A. — Over and above mining, treatment, and marketing costs, the owner-operator receives a gross profit from which must be deducted his annual, or periodic, return of capital invested in ore (depletion) and his periodic return of plant investment (depreciation) before arriving at his net profit, or interest return on investment.

Net profit, on the diagram, is split, for comparison with Case B, into separate portions resulting from ore and operations.

Case B. — Royalty is a cost to lessee. Lessor takes the royalty payment and separates it into return of capital and net profit, as before, but not necessarily in identical amounts, as he may consider the speculative risk different under the two situations.

Over and above lessee's total costs, which include royalty, there remains a gross profit which lessee, as operator, separates into return of plant investment and net profit on operations.

Depletion — It would appear from the above that depletion affects only the fee, or lessor interest. The usual situation, however, is not as simple as the bare example. Lessee, in sinking shafts and developing the orebody, ties up some portion of his capital investment, irrevocably, with the orebody. Plant investment, also, is usually limited in usefulness to some considerable extent to the particular orebody. The operator thus acquires what has been termed an economic interest in the mine and is generally considered to be entitled to depletion, rather than depreciation, on this portion of his investment. The U. S. Income Tax Law of 1936 provides that depletion be equitably apportioned between lessor and lessee.

The examiner should investigate the background of tax and other legal rulings to determine their application to the circumstances of a particular lessor-lessee situation as a basis for determining the advisable depletion allowance for either of the separate interests.

TREATMENT AND MARKETING OF ORES — A mine has value only when its product can be sold at a profit. Evaluation of a mineral deposit must, therefore, include consideration of problems of marketing. This may be simple or complex, depending upon the minerals or metals involved and upon trade requirements as to grade and usable form.

Grades of Ore — Iron ore, chromite, and manganese, for instance, are marketable as direct shipping ores when their grades, as mined, are above the minimum specifications accepted by the trade. Steel-making and chemical industries use them as raw materials. Evaluation of such mineral deposits need consider only mine, transport, and sale. No further treatment is involved, so far as the mine is concerned.

Certain lower grades of hematite, containing free silica, may be beneficiated to merchantable grades by washing. Coal is cleaned and often graded to size to prepare it for market. The character of the material is not changed by such beneficiation processes. Their consideration adds to the evaluation problem because of the added plant and cost involved.

Some types of treatment are more specialized and border on manufacturing, as with asbestos, which is cleaned, expanded and graded carefully, although no real change of form is involved.

Most ores require transformation treatment between mine and market. Copper, lead, and zinc ores are typical of mine products that must be milled, smelted, and refined to produce usable metal. The ores may be oxide, sulphide, carbonate, or silicate; the usual product is metal, although some lead-zinc concentrates are processed directly to oxide for pigment.

The examiner of a mining property for valuation purposes must necessarily be familiar with the type of treatment required to put the ore into merchantable form and with the trade customs involved in processing and marketing the particular product or products. In general, this means knowledge of mineral dressing and familiarity with trade practices in the milling, smelting, and refining industries. The independent mine producing an ore subject to treatment may do its own milling or may sell its ore to custom mills and smelters either on the terms outlined in their mill and smelter schedules or by special contract negotiation.

Smelter Schedules — Custom milling and smelting of nonferrous ores, usually with precious metal values, are highly competitive businesses. Each plant, whether mill, smelter, or refinery, is designed to treat to best advantage a particular type or group of ores tributary to its location. Flow sheets and equipment vary among custom plants. Some are primarily copper plants, some lead, some zinc; some lead smelters are equipped for zinc recovery, others not. Thus, the ore requirements vary from plant to plant; even among those similarly equipped there will be varying requirements from time to time because of the characteristics of the load in process. A particular ore may, thus, not be acceptable at one treatment plant whereas it may be much sought after by another. Zinc, in a lead ore, may be penalized at one smelter because of the difficulty of treatment while at another it may be recovered but probably without payment. A gold quartz ore may be sought after by a smelter needing siliceous flux.

Recovery of gold and silver from zinc concentrates requires retreatment of residues obtained from either of two processes: electrolytic deposition of zinc, or retort distillation. Cost of retreatment is reflected in smelter schedules; some zinc plants do not pay for gold and silver content, whereas others, located near lead smelters, pay at varying rates. Even minute amounts of certain impurities, such as cobalt or germanium, in zinc concentrates preclude processing by the electrolytic process. Iron is an undesirable impurity for either recovery process and may be penalized separately or by inclusion in the general smelter charge.

The evaluator must determine the most advantageous treatment and sale of the product of the mine he is investigating. Mine location, mill and smelter locations, treatment and transportation charges are the important items.

Net smelter return, for any given ore, is calculated on the basis of the current schedule for the smelter to which the ore is sold. This schedule may be of the open type, applicable broadly to general classes of ores, or may be a special schedule negotiated for the particular ore. Terms of payment (smelter schedules) vary from one smelter to another and, also, are revised from time to time.

Data on location of custom plants, types of ores treated, and typical smelter schedules may be found in Peele's Mining Engineers' Handbook[1] and other mining and metallurgical literature[2]. Von Bernewitz[3] gives average yearly prices from 1924

---

[1] "Mining Engineers' Handbook," R. Peele and J. A. Church; 3rd ed., 1941; John Wiley & Sons, Inc.; Sec. 32 by A. L. Walker.

[2] Such as:
"The Trend of Flotation," A. J. Weinig and C. B. Carpenter; Colorado School of Mines Quarterly, Vol. 32, No. 4, Oct. 1937.
"Textbook of Ore Dressing," Richards and Locke, 3rd ed., 1940, Chap. XVII; McGraw-Hill Book Co.
U. S. Bureau of Mines, Washington, D. C.;
    I.C. 6842, "Gold and Silver Custom Plants," 1935.
    I.C. 6926, "Open Schedules for Gold and Silver Ores at Western Custom Smelters," 1936.

[3] "Handbook for Prospectors and Operators of Small Mines," Von Bernewitz; 4th ed., 1943, McGraw-Hill Book Co.

for a number of metals and nonmetallic minerals and also a scale of approximate freight rates on ores.

The U. S. Bureau of Mines has issued Reports of Investigations on individual mineral properties too numerous to list, as well as circulars on the mining, treatment, and marketing of specific minerals and products. This source of information may be helpful to the examiner, particularly for domestic properties. In foreign work, similar public sources may be available.

Metal Prices — Domestic ores generally are sold on the basis of quotations at recognized market centers. The published Engineering and Mining Journal prices for copper and lead at New York and for zinc at E. St. Louis, for instance, are the usual basis of settlement for ores of these metals. Silver and gold of domestic origin are sold on the basis of U. S. Mint prices; of foreign origin, on market quotations. Lake Erie base prices are usually used for contracts for iron ores from the Lake Superior region. Similar markets throughout the world are used for other metals and minerals.

In case the net value of the reserve ore is difficult, for any reason, to estimate within reasonable limits, the examiner should submit a composite sample (from several hundred pounds to a carload) of the material to one or more milling and smelting companies for their tests as to recovery and their proposals as to payment schedule. He should also investigate the possibility of negotiating a special contract for his particular ore that would be more favorable than the open or published schedule.

SELECTED PROBLEMS

Following are three examples of mine valuations worked out in considerable detail to illustrate proper methods of handling the several estimates and accounts needed to satisfy the particular case. Each has been chosen to point up certain features. Case one — an undeveloped iron mine — brings in plant, development, and working capital in addition to the usual estimates of reserves, production, and life; case two, — an independent, operating lead-zinc mine — stresses treatment and marketing; case three — a property producing nonuniform income.

Obviously, it is not possible to give illustrations to cover all of the variations, physical, chemical, and commercial, that an examiner might encounter in mineral valuation. Such variations of circumstances from one mineral property to another enter into all of the features of a mine valuation except rigid mathematical calculation. Some of these variables are: grade and type of ore; degree of development; plant and treatment; ownership and integration of operation.

The logical approach to a complex problem of this type is an understanding of principles and an exercise of reasonable judgment to cope with the variations. The outline and specific arrangement of calculations used in the ensuing illustrative cases are not intended as fixed procedures for arriving at values, but rather as methods of treatment subject to alternative procedures when such can be done without deviation from principles.

VALUATION OF AN UNDEVELOPED — The present value of an undeveloped iron ore mine is
IRON ORE PROPERTY here calculated in detail to illustrate the various computations which need to be made in arriving at an estimate of value. The figures used in this illustrative case are not those from an actual mine. They have been chosen to bring into the example a variety of conditions and at the same time adhere closely to representative figures for actual operations such as are found on the Mesabi Range in the Lake Superior iron ore region.

This example is of interest, also, because it shows that much of the profit from a mining business comes from the capital invested in plant, development, and allocated as working capital, rather than directly from the ore.

General Data The outlines of the orebodies have been determined by churn drilling and are such that both open-pit and underground methods will have to be used to mine out the ore completely. Further, the ore is so situated that the mine can be operated to best advantage by first working out the main body by open-pit methods and then attacking the outlying portions by underground means.

Under normal operation the schedules of production are estimated at 500,000 tons per season for the open-pit and 200,000 tons per year for the underground.

A deferment period of 3 years will be required to equip the open-pit mine, strip the overburden sufficiently to begin mining, sink a shaft for drainage, and install the underground pumping plant.

Hoskold rates of 8% on invested capital and 4% on sinking-fund accumulations are estimated to represent the risk involved.

Valuation Items

1. Reserve Tonnage and Years Life.

An estimate of tonnage and grade, based on the churn-drilling records and made according to customary practice by means of plans, cross sections, and sample assays, shows the reserves to be divided as follows:

Reserve ore available for open-pit mining	6,500,000 tons
,, ,, ,, ,, underground ,,	600,000 ,,
Total reserve ore	7,100,000 ,,
Nonmerchantable material	255,000 ,,

Note: Round figures have been used in this example to simplify the arithmetical calculations whenever such practice will not affect the principles involved or deviate from practical quantities.

Active production life, in accord with the schedules recommended, will be as follows:

Open-pit life $= 6,500,000 \div 500,000 = 13$ years
Underground life $=\quad 600,000 \div 200,000 = \underline{\quad 3\quad}$ ''
                    Total operating period $= 16$ years

Open-pit production, being limited to the period of boat transportation, is assumed for six months only per year, whereas underground production may continue the year 'round, with the winter output stock-piled to await shipment.

Production per month is, therefore
        Open pit $= 500,000 \div\ \ 6 = 83,333$ tons
        Underground $= 200,000 \div 12 = 16,667$ ''

2. Selling Price and Annual Receipts.

Iron ore is sold on analysis according to the Lake Erie base price in effect at the time of the transaction. Since this base price may fluctuate from one year to another, the value of the ore in a reserve property may be estimated on an average base covering several years just preceding the valuation date, provided that such period seems fairly representative of ore-marketing conditions which may be expected to maintain themselves into the near future. In this instance a 5-year average is taken. The sales value of the ore, using the analyses of the drill-hole samples taken throughout the orebodies, is then computed as follows:

Lake Erie Base Price — 5-year average — for standard-grade ores with 51.50% natural iron content:

                Mesabi non-Bessemer $4.40 per ton
                    ''   Bessemer   4.55 ''   ''

Average analyses, adjusted to agree with operating experience:

Type of Ore	Dried at 212° F.			Moisture	Natural Iron	L.E. Value per ton
	Iron	Phos.	Silica			
Bessemer	59.32	.032	7.58	11.00	52.79	$4.807
Non-Bessemer	58.14	.069	9.20	13.50	50.29	4.297
Paint rock	52.65	.095	8.45	18.00	43.17	3.148

Calculation of the above selling prices is as follows:

Natural iron $=$ Dried iron $\times$ (1 — moisture)

Bessemer Ore—

Value per unit of iron = $4.55 ÷ 51.50 = $.0884

Iron content above standard grade = 52.79—51.50 = 1.29%

Value of iron above standard = 1.29 × $.0884 = $.1140

Premium for low phosphorus content

(Progressive scale below .045%) = .1430

Base price for standard ore $4.55

L. E. Value of ore = 4.55 + .114 + .143 = $4.807 per ton.

Non-Bessemer Ore —

Value per unit of iron = $4.40 ÷ 51.50 = $.0854

Iron content below standard grade = 51.50—50.29 = 1.21%

Deduction for low iron content = 1.21 × $.0854 = $.1033

L.E. Value of ore = $4.40 — $.103 = $4.297 per ton.

Paint Rock—

Unit value same as for non-Bessemer ore = $.0854

Iron content below standard grade = 51.50 — 43.17 = 8.33%

Deductions and penalties for low iron :—

$51.50 — 50.00 = 1.50$ units

$+$ no penalty = 1.50 effective units

$50.00 — 49.00 = 1.00$ units

$+ 50\%$,, = 1.50 ,, ,,

$49.00 — 43.17 = 5.83$ units

$+ 100\%$,, = 11.66 ,, ,,

Total below standard grade = 14.66 effective units

Deduction from base price = 14.66 × $.0854 = $1.252

L.E. Value of paint rock = $4.40 — $1.252 = $3.148 per ton.

Average value of ore:

Type of Ore	Tons	L.E. Value per ton	Total Value
Bessemer	1,650,000	$4.807	$ 7,931,550
Non-Bessemer	5,100,000	4.297	21,914,700
Paint Rock	350,000	3.148	1,101,800
			$30,948,050

Average L.E. Value per ton =

$$\$30,948,050 \div 7,100,000 = \$4.359.$$

Annual gross receipts —

Open-pit operations $= 500,000 \times \$4.359 = \$2,179,500$

Underground   " $= 200,000 \times$ $4.359 = \$$ $871,800$

Note: It is questionable whether the paint rock should be included as "ore" since it has such a low natural iron content. If the average grade of the ore, from a sales standpoint, is such that it falls below specified limits when diluted (or graded) with the low-iron paint rock, then, of course, the paint rock must be treated as nonmerchantable and either discarded as waste or stock-piled separately for future use. Assuming, however, that the matter of grade is not a deciding factor, the inclusion of the paint rock as ore will lower the costs per ton and will increase the annual receipts. The question then resolves down to the cost of removing this material relative to its value. It is included here with the ore although, as will be noted later when costs per ton are tabulated, its sales price is $.333 less than the average cost of the open-pit ore. Against this apparent loss, however, must be balanced the cost of mining ($.281 per ton), which will be an expense whether the material is sold or not, and its share of the development and overhead costs, all of which will tend to reduce the apparent loss.

3. Direct Mining Cost.

The costs of mining by both open-pit and underground methods have been estimated from the records of similar operating properties in the same locality after giving due consideration to all variations which may be anticipated in the operation of this particular property. The estimated unit costs do not include allowances for plant and development expense, as these are to be estimated separately. They do, however, cover the cost of mining 255,000 tons of other nonmerchantable material (sometimes called lean ore) which cannot be sold but which is to be stock-piled for future possible use.

Open-pit Ore —

Method of Mining	Tons	Cost per ton	Total Cost
Power shovel —			
ore	5,300,000	$.25	$1,325.000
nonmerchantable	190,000	.30	57,000
Milling and scram—			
ore	1,200,000	.35	420,000
nonmerchantable	65,000	.40	26,000
			$1,828,000

Open-pit cost per ton of ore = $1,828,000 ÷ 6,500,000 = $.281.

Underground Ore —
Estimated average cost per ton = $1.300.

Mining Cost per year —
Open-pit operation = 500,000 × $ .281 = $140,500.
Underground '' = 200,000 × $1.300 = $260,000.

4. Miscellaneous or Overhead.

This cost includes administration, legal, fire insurance, medical and hospital, compensation, contingent fund, crushing and screening, cost adjustment, stock-pile loading, and taxes on stock pile and equipment. It has been estimated from the average of similar properties in the vicinity, as follows:

Open-pit mining $.121 per ton
Underground '' .201 '' ''

Miscellaneous cost per year:
Open-pit operation = 500,000 × $.121 = $60,500
Underground '' = 200,000 × .201 = $40,200

5. Transportation.

The cost of rail and lake freight (plus insurance) may be established by published tariffs or by private contract and is dependent upon the locality from which the ore is shipped.

$$\begin{aligned} \text{Rail and lake freight} &= \$1.740 \text{ per ton} \\ \text{Insurance} &= \underline{.001} \text{ ,, ,,}} \\ \text{Total} &= \$1.741 \text{ ,, ,,} \end{aligned}$$

Transportation cost per year:

Open-pit operation $= 500,000 \times \$1.741 = \$870,500$
Underground ,, $= 200,000 \times \$1.741 = \$348,200$

6. Selling Commission.

The customary selling commission for iron ores is $.10 per ton.

Selling cost per year:

Open-pit ore $= 500,000 \times \$.10 = \$50,000$
Underground ore $= 200,000 \times .10 = \$20,000$

7. Taxes.

Tax costs differ from one locality to another and are dependent upon local rates on property, franchise rates on business, and federal rates on income. Further, both the rates of income and occupation (franchise) taxes and the method of calculating these are changed frequently through the enactment of new regulations. An estimate of the various tax costs, based on rates prevailing at the date of valuation, is as follows:

Inactive tax rate on reserve ore = $.0095 per ton.

Inactive (or idle) taxes per year =
$$7,100,000 \times \$.0095 = \$67.450.$$

Assuming that inactive taxes are paid semiannually, their present value as of the beginning of the deferment period at 8% interest will be 1/2(67,450) × 5.2421 = $176,790. (Table 4).

When a reserve property starts producing, it changes from an inactive to an active status and is assigned a new tax rate.

Estimated ratio of active to present inactive rate = 1.80

Estimated active taxes per year = 67,450 × 1.80 = $121,410

Estimated active taxes per ton of production

$$= \frac{\$121,410}{500,000} = \$.2428.$$

It is assumed that, after the open-pit ore is worked out and the property becomes an underground mine with a lowered rate of production, the tax rate per ton may be expected to be reduced by approximately 30 percent for the remaining life.

The occupation (or franchise) tax and the Federal income tax on corporations are similar in that they are both computed from the sales value of the ore less certain statutory deductions. They are both, in a sense, taxes on profits and, as such, may be considered excises for the privilege of doing business. The corporation income tax, to the extent of the normal tax on individual incomes, is a true income tax. It is not proper to consider this portion of the tax as a cost, whereas the excess of the corporation income tax over and above the normal amount for an individual may properly be taken as a cost of doing business.

Occupation tax — open pit = $ .084 per ton
= $42,000 per year

— underground = $ .043 per ton
= $8,600 per year

Federal income tax
(excess only)   — open pit = $ .075 per ton
                                   = $37,500 per year

                       — underground = $ .023 per ton
                                     = $4,600 per year

8. Working Capital.

The amount of working capital required to keep the business going is more or less directly proportional to the rate of production. It must cover the immediate outlay for mining, miscellaneous, and transportation costs, the purchase of supplies that must be kept on hand, and the payment of taxes. It is estimated here as follows:

Open pit —

Capital required is estimated at three-fourths of 2 months' mining, miscellaneous, and transportation costs, and 6 months' taxes, plus 1 month's supplies.

Mining cost	$ .281
Miscellaneous	.121
Transportation	1.741
	$2.143 per ton

$$2.143 \times 83,333 \times 2 = \$357,167$$

Active taxes for 6 months
$$83,333 \times 6 \times .243 = \$121,400$$
$$\$478,567$$

Three-fourths of 478,567   = $358,925
Plus 1 month's supplies @   21,000

Open-pit Working Capital = $379,925

Interest charge per year @ 8%   = $30,394

$$\text{Interest charge per ton} = \frac{\$30,394}{500,000} = \$.061$$

Underground —

Capital required is the cost of 6 months' mining, miscellaneous, and taxes, plus 2 months' transportation, plus 1 month's supplies.

Mining cost	$1.300
Miscellaneous	.201
Tax (active)	.170
	$1.671

Transportation $1.741

$$[6 \times 1.671 + 2 \times 1.741]\ 16,667 = \$255,138$$

Plus 1 month's supplies @   20,000

Underground Working Capital = $245,138

Interest charge per year @ 8%   = $19,611

$$\text{Interest charge per ton} = \frac{\$19,611}{200,000} = \$.098$$

9. Plant and Development.

These items, estimated from experience at similar properties in the area, cover the cost of the open-pit plant (machinery, shops, buildings, track, etc.), stripping the open-pit orebody, shaft-sinking and development for drainage and underground mining, trimming pit walls, and underground pumping, hoisting, and mining equipment.

The open-pit plant is to be installed during the first year of deferment and the underground shaft and pumping plant during the last, or third, year, just prior to the beginning of active pit-production.

It is estimated that 65% of the open-pit stripping will be done during the 3-year deferment period — 15% during the first year, 25% during each of the other two years — with the remaining 35% of the work distributed uniformly over the first 5 operating years. From the sixth to the tenth operating years, inclusive, it will be necessary to trim back the rock walls of the open pit so that the bottom ore will be accessible. The additional underground development and plant required to start mining the outlying orebodies will be put in during the thirteenth operating year.

Estimated plant and development costs:

Stripping —

3,730,000 cu.yd. surface @ $.30 per cu.yd. = $1,119,000

422,000 cu.yd. rock @ $.75 per cu.yd. = 316,500

Total stripping cost $1,435,500

Rock-wall trimming —

Direct estimate @ $.10 per ton = $650,000

Plant (open-pit and underground) = $.125 per ton.

Total estimated amount = 7,100,000 × $1.25 = $887,500

Direct estimate of allocation

Open-pit plant   = $737,500
Underground   ''   = $150,000

Shaft and underground development —

Direct estimate = $150,000

It is further estimated that 75% of the cost of shaft and underground plant and development should be charged against the open-pit ore, with the remaining 25% directly attendant upon the underground ore. The final allocation of plant and shaft development expense is then:

Open-pit = $737,500 + 3/4($300,000) = $ 962,500
Underground = 1/4($300,000)   =   75,000

Total $1,037,500

Tabulation of these scheduled expenditures, as follows, will be helpful toward calculating their combined effect upon the valuation:

	Year	Open-pit Plant	Stripping	Rockwall Trimming	Shaft & U.G. Dev.	U.G. Plant	Yearly Total	
Deferment Period	A	$737,500	$215,325				$952,825	**Accrue to**
	B		358,875				358,875	
	C		358,875		$112,500	$112,500	583,875	

Beginning of Open-pit Production

	Year	Open-pit Plant	Stripping	Rockwall Trimming	Shaft & U.G. Dev.	U.G. Plant	Yearly Total	
Productive Life Open pit	1		$100,485				Annuity	**Present value to**
	2		100,485				due of	
	3		100,485				$100,485	
	4		100,485				per yr.	
	5		100,485				for 5 yr.	
	6			$130,000			Annuity	
	7			130,000			due of	
	8			130,000			$130,000	
	9			130,000			per yr.	
	10			130,000			for 5 yr.	
	11							
	12							
	13				$37,500	$37,500	$75,000	

Beginning of Underground Production

	Year
U.G.	14
	15
	16

The discounted value of the (irregular series of) plant and development outlays is to be deducted as a lump sum from the valuation. In this example the beginning of open-pit operations will be chosen as the time for making this deduction although some other convenient date, such as the valuation date itself would be as good a choice.

The combined value of these irregular expenditures as of this chosen date may be determined by accruing the preproduction, or deferment period outlays and discounting those to be made during the operating period to the beginning of operations, as noted on the tabulated chart above.

It is assumed that all moneys are to be available at the beginning of the year in which they are to be spent. Interest is taken at 8%, compounded annually.

Accrual of deferment-period expenditures —

Open-pit.

$$\$952,825 \times \overline{1.08}^3 = 952,825 \times 1.2597 = \$1,200,274 \text{ (Tab. 1)}$$
$$358,875 \times \overline{1.08}^2 = 358,875 \times 1.1664 = 418,592 \text{ (Tab. 1)}$$
$$583,875 \times 1.08 = 630,585$$

Discount of production-period expenditures —

Open-pit.

$$\$100,485 \times 4.3121 = 433,301 \text{ (Tab. 4)}$$
$$130,000 \times 4.3121 \times .68058 = 381,515 \text{ (Tab. 4}$$
$$ \text{and 2)}$$

Underground.

$$\$75,000 \times .39711 = \underline{29,783} \text{ (Tab. 2)}$$

$$\begin{array}{r} \text{Total } V_{bi} \text{ of plant and} \\ \text{development moneys} \end{array} \qquad \$3,094,050$$

Computation of Present Value and Purchase Price   A tabulation of gross receipts and costs may now be set up, as follows, to show net profit:

	Open-pit		Underground	
	Per Ton	Per Year	Per Ton	Per Year
Gross Receipts	$4.359	$2,179,500	$4.359	$871,800
Costs				
Direct Mining	.281	140,500	1.300	260,000
Misc. & Overhead	.121	60,500	.201	40,200
Transportation	1.741	870,500	1.741	348,200
Selling Commission	.100	50,000	.100	20,000
Taxes — active	.243	121,400	.170	34,000
— occupation	.084	42,000	.043	8,600
— income	.075	37,500	.023	4,600
Interest on				
Working Capital	.601	30,400	.098	19,600
	$2.706	$1,352,800	$3.676	$735.200
Net Profit	$1.653	$ 826,700	$ .683	$136,600

The discounted value of these future earnings, as of the beginning of the production period, may now be calculated in either of two ways as follows:

1. On basis of profit per ton —
    Open-pit
    $\$1.653 \times .54889 \times 6,500,000 = \$5,897,549$ (Table 8)
    Underground
    $\$.683 \times .83261 \times 600,000 \times .36770 = 125,460$ (Tab. 8 & 2)

    Total V_{bi} $\$6,023,009$

2. On basis of profit per year —
   Open-pit
      $826,700 \times 7.1355 =$ $5,898,918 (Table 7)
   Underground
      $136,600 \times 2.4978 \times .36770 =$ 125,459 (Tab. 7 & 2)

                Total V_{bi} $6,024,377

If carried to sufficient decimal accuracy, the above results would be identical.

            Average V_{bi} = $6,023,693.

This figure of $6,023,693 is the amount that operations, if the projected schedule is attained, will return to the investor together with interest.

Purchase price may now be determined by (a) deducting the equivalent, as of this date, of the plant and development outlays, (b) discounting the balance through the deferment period, and (c) deducting the present worth of idle taxes, as follows:

V_{bi} of earnings, as above	$6,023,693
Less V_{bi} of Plant and Development	3,094,050
Purchase value as of $_{bi}$	$2,929,643
Discount for 3-year deferment period at 8%	$\times$ .79383
	$2,325,638
Less present value of idle taxes	176,790
Net purchase price	$2,148,848
Purchase price =	$2,150,000

Note: In the second edition of this book, plant and development expenditures were amortized by translating them into costs per ton of production to cover outlays plus interest. This procedure follows customary mine accounting and may be preferred for certain types of valuation, such as routine operating valuations where purchase is not a consideration, and comparative valuations for assessment purposes.

Lump-sum deduction is used here, as it conforms more closely to fundamental concepts of mine valuation and is correct actuarial practice.

Net reduction in valuation is not necessarily identical by the two procedures because of the difference in effective discount between a single rate (or identical speculative and sinking-fund rates) and a combination of the same speculative rate with a (lower) sinking-fund rate. This difference in effective discount is discussed on page 244 and shown in Fig. 36.

VALUATION OF AN OPERATING — A small lead-zinc mine, which
LEAD-ZINC PROPERTY might be found in the Rocky Mountain area, is chosen for this example primarily to illustrate the problem of marketing a complex ore and to stress the importance of giving thorough study to all alternative production and treatment practices in evaluating the worth of such a property. Data are not from any actual property and are rounded in many instances to simplify calculations.

General Data The example mine, assumed to be offered for sale, has been operated continuously by the original management for the past 12 years on a generally profitable basis. Records are available of past operations.

The property consists of 8 patented claims, some 5 miles from the nearest town, and is served by an all-weather highway. Title is clear. Contiguous areas show signs of having been test-pitted but none has been opened for operation. All employees except the watchman live in the nearby town. Electric power is available from the local utility company and is used throughout except for heating and shop furnaces, which are equipped for oil.

Mining is entirely underground and is done by square-set stoping. Operations are now on the 300- and 400-ft. levels with the 500-ft. level partly developed. The ore is hand sorted underground to maintain shipping grade.

Shaft is 3-compartment, vertical, timbered, equipped with cage and 4-ton skip. The steel headframe has a truck-loading pocket of 30 tons capacity and rock-dump trestle.

Remainder of plant consists of transformer station, water supply, hoist-compressor house, shop building and garage, timber-framing yard, fuel and explosive storage, and office. Equipment is modern and in well-kept condition.

Current production on one-shift operation is 4000 short tons per month. The ore is trucked 6 miles to a railroad siding. Two trucks are used with a third as a spare. The crude ore is shipped directly to a lead smelter.

Orebodies are of the fissure-vein type, containing galena, sphalerite, and pyrite with minor values in precious metals.

With metal prices above recent or anticipated averages, selected ore currently going to the smelter runs about 12% Pb and 8% Zn; more careful selection was needed during periods of lower metal prices to produce higher grade ore, but at some sacrifice in monthly tonnage. The above brief description will serve to outline the type of property chosen for this example.

Analysis of Valuation Problem Key decisions to be made in a valuation of this type are:

1. Determination (estimate) of reserves and grade on basis of:
   a. Selective mining to produce high-grade mine product. Cost of mining and volume are secondary to grade in this consideration down to the point of marginal return.
   b. Less selective or straight mining with cost of mining balanced against maintenance of reasonable grade of mine product.
2. Estimate of expected future price levels as they will affect:

    a. Cost of operation: wages, supplies, equipment, etc.

    b. Return for sale of product: metal prices, mill and smelter charges, etc.

3. Determination of most advantageous overall plan of operation:

    a. Shipment of mine product as direct smelting ore. Depends on continuity of grade, costs, and return. Coupled with (1a) above.

    b. Production of milling-grade ore to be:

        (1) Shipped to custom mill

        (2) Milled at property

        Involves balancing of cost of mill construction and operating against charge for custom treatment and transportation.

4. Determination of optimum operating rate, striking a balance among:

    a. Capital outlay required for new or expanded plant and equipment.

    b. Cost of mining and milling.

    c. Net smelter return, including freight charges.

5. Life — depends on combination of above.

6. Rate of return on investment.

Ore Reserves and Grade   In appraising the future of the property, it is evident from an inspection of known reserves that the current grade of ore cannot be maintained even by selective mining for more than a few years. Furthermore, a drop in metal prices would seriously affect the margin in direct smelting ore.

After careful study, it is determined that the best plan of operation is to mine less selectively, with open stoping wherever permissible, to produce a lower grade ore which can be milled to lead and zinc concentrates.

Ore reserves, estimated on this basis from maps, drilling records, check sampling, and a thorough geologic study, are:

		Net Assured
Fully blocked out and considered assured	300,000 tons	300,000
Partly blocked out and estimated to be 80% assured	450,000	360,000
Inferred; partly drilled; estimated 40% assured	750,000	300,000
Further possible extensions not estimated	......	......
Total		960,000 tons

Vein widths and proportions among the several minerals are fairly consistent throughout extensions which have been developed or drilled. Wall rocks show little variation also. It is estimated that a fairly uniform grade of ore can be produced throughout the visible life of the property.

Average grade of reserve ore on dry analysis is estimated at: Pb, 10%; Zn, 7%; Cu, .4%; Ag, $2\frac{1}{2}$ oz; Au, .09 oz; Fe, 20%; S, 28%; and SiO_2, 34.6%.

Mine ore will average $3\frac{1}{3}$% moisture.

Production Rate and Life Without enlargement of the present shaft, mine output can be increased to 6,000 tons per month. Added plant and equipment would be required, such as drills, cars, more power on hoist, and shop equipment. This would cost $50,000, installed.

At this increased rate of production the life of the reserves, as outlined, would be approximately 13 years.

Milling In order to determine milling qualities of the ore and recoveries that might be obtained, a representative carload was forwarded to a custom plant equipped for both gravity and flotation processes. Charges were guaranteed in lieu of a shipping contract.

Test results were reported as follows:

Material	Mine Ore "Heads" Analysis Dry Basis	Lead Concentrates Analysis (Dry)	Percent Recovery	Zinc Concentrates Analysis (Dry)	Percent Recovery
Pb (galena)	10%	65.62%	86.5%	6.23%	6.5%
Zn (sphalerite)	7%	4.51%	8.5	50.90%	76.5
Cu (chalcopyrite)	.4%	1.62%	53.3	.82%	21.6
Ag	2.5 oz.	12.13 oz.	63.9	3.80 oz.	16.0
Au	.09 oz.	.327 oz.	48.0	.106 oz.	12.5
Fe	20%	4.67%	3.1	5.02%	2.6
S	28%	17.71%	8.3	31.68%	11.9
SiO_2	34.6%	5.85%	2.2	5.35%	1.6
Products Wt., dry	100%	13.19%		10.52%	

Custom milling at the nearest suitable mill, en route to the smelter, it was estimated, would cost approximately $4.00 per ton, plus trucking and freight to the mill on the full mine output. If milled at the property, transportation charges to the smelter on the reduced tonnage of concentrates plus moisture would be only slightly higher than for similar shipment from custom mill to smelter.

Mill construction is estimated to cost $250,000, including water supply and tailings disposal facilities; operation $2.00 per ton. Amortization, using Premise 6 at 10 years and 10 per cent, figures roughly to $.60 per ton.

Without detailing the comparative estimates and calculations, it will be assumed that the decision is in favor of valuing the mine on the basis of a mill at the property rather than shipment to a custom plant.

From the above it may be computed readily that 6,000 tons of mine ore per month would be 5,800 tons, dry, of mill feed which would result in 765 tons of lead concentrates and 610 tons of zinc concentrates, dry basis, of the grades indicated.

At this point, the engineer may consider that the experimental results, as to grades of concentrates and recoveries, will not be readily attainable in the proposed mill operation. This will call for revision of data to realistic levels. Such review is more apt to be needed when preliminary tests are made in the laboratory than when a mill run is carried out.

Metal Prices It is assumed, for purposes of this illustration, that the following have been estimated as the average market prices expected for the metals during the life period:—

Pb, 7½¢ per lb.; Zn, 8¢ per lb.; Cu, 14¢ per lb.;
Au, $35. per oz.; Ag, 75¢ per oz.

Smelter Returns Net smelter return may now be estimated as outlined below. It will be noted that the terms of settlement used in this example are not identical with the schedule of any particular smelter. Aside from the fact that these terms vary among smelters and from time to time, this has been done primarily to impress upon the evaluator the necessity for contacting all custom plants tributary to the mine geographically so as to be able to determine the most advantageous terms to be expected should the plan of operation of his evaluation be put into effect.

Lead Concentrate

Analysis	Typical Settlement Terms	Payments
Au .327 oz.	100% at $31.82	$10.40
Ag 12.13 oz.	95% at Mint price for domestic	8.65
Pb 65.62%	90% (wet assay less 1½ units) at N.Y. market price less 1½¢ per lb. $(65.62\text{-}1.5) \times 20 \times 90 \times (7\frac{1}{2}\text{¢-}1\frac{1}{2}\text{¢})$	69.25
Cu 1.62%	(Wet assay less 1 unit) at N.Y. price less, say, 6¢ per lb. $(1.62\text{-}1.00) \times 20 \times (14\text{¢-}6\text{¢})$	.99
Fe 4.6%	at, say, 6¢ per unit	.28
	Total payments	$89.57

		Charges
Zn 4.51%	5% free; excess at 30-50¢ per unit	.00
SiO₂ 5.85%	10¢ per unit; or up to a maximum charge	.58
S 17.71%	2% (or 3%) free; excess at 25¢ per unit; maximum charge, say, 2.50	2.50
	Base charge; variable; escalator clauses on Pb content or value	6.50
	Rail freight, wet weight, including tax	6.00

Analysis	Charges
Zn 4.51%	.00
SiO_2 5.85%	.58
S 17.71%	2.50

	Total charges	$15.58	15.58
	Net Smelter Return (per ton of conc.)	$73.99

Zinc Concentrate

Analysis	Typical Settlement Terms	Payments
Au .106 oz.	80% at $31.82	$ 2.71
Ag 3.80 oz.	80% at Mint price for domestic	2.28
Zn 50.90%	80% at E. St. Louis market price less ¼¢, $50.90 \times .80 \times 20 \times (8¢\text{-}25¢)$	63.12
Pb 6.23%	Deduct, say, 3 units. Pay for 80% of excess at N.Y. market price, less, say, 2¢ $3.23 \times 20 \times .80 \times 5\frac{1}{2}¢$	2.84
Cu .82%	No payment	.00
	Total payments	$70.95

	Charges

		Charges	
Fe 5.02%	Usually 6% free ; excess at 50¢	——	
SiO$_2$ 5.35%	May charge up to 10¢ per unit	——	
S 31.68%	May charge up to 25¢ per unit, or	——	
	Base Charge, with or without escalator based on zinc price, may cover all items	30.00	
	R. R. freight, wet weight, including tax	8.50	
	Total charges	38.50	38.50
	Net Smelter Return (per ton of conc.)		$32.45

Total monthly income may be computed as :

$765 \times \$73.99 = \$56,600$ from Pb conc.

$610 \times 32.45 = \underline{19,800}$ from Zn conc.

Total $76,400

Return per ton of ore is, therefore, $12.75.

Costs Costs for mining the proposed output of 6,000 tons per month and milling it at the property are estimated as :—

	Per ton of ore
Mining, including normal development	$ 7.00
Milling	2.00
Miscellaneous and overhead[1]	1.00
Trucking (conc. only)	.30
Taxes — ad valorem and franchise	.50
Income	.40
Interest on working capital	.30
Total	$11.50

Mining cost includes normal development required to maintain operations. No preproduction development program is con-

---

[1] Includes administration, legal, medical, compensation, insurance, and miscellaneous maintenance.

templated in this instance, as the mine is opened and operating.

Working capital consists of moneys required to finance current mining, milling, transportation, and miscellaneous costs until cash returns from metals sold are received. In this instance, it is estimated, working capital will be needed sufficient to finance 3 months' operations. Interest on this capital is chargeable as a cost. The capital itself is a revolving fund and is therefore not consumed.

Depreciation, normally a cost in mine accounting, is not included in the above costs for the reason that it is inherent in the valuation formula, which returns the entire original capital to the investor at the end of the life period. This would also cover any new plant contemplated as of the valuation date, the cost of which is deducted from the present value in arriving at the purchase price.

Depletion is likewise inherent in the valuation formula and need not be considered separately except for purposes of estimating income taxes.

All taxes, except income tax at the rate for an individual, are chargeable as costs. This would include ad valorem, franchise, occupation, state corporation income taxes, and the excess of federal income taxes on corporations over individuals.

Present Value and Purchase Price   Mill construction and equipment cost is estimated at $250,000 which, with $50,000 for other plant and mine equipment, will bring total immediate outlay to $300,000.

Purchaser desires a 10% return on his investment with capital redemption at 3%.

Present value and purchase price may be calculated as follows:

Return per ton of ore	$12.75
Cost per ton of ore	11.50
Profit per ton	$ 1.25
Profit per year $1.25 × 72,000 =	$90,000

Present value factor for 13 years at 10% and 3%	× 6.0965
Present value of operations	$548,685
Less immediate outlay for plant and equipment	300,000
Net purchase price	$248,685
or,	$250,000

If mill construction and other alterations will require some considerable period of time, it would be necessary to consider such deferment in calculating present worth.

A PROPERTY PRODUCING NONUNIFORM INCOME — A separate mineral ownership within an operating mine will return predictable nonuniform income to its owner when the estimated advance of mining cuts obliquely through the parcel so as to mine out varying areas or volumes per year. Fig. 40 is a plan map of a situation of this type wherein an irregular acreage, owned by another party, splits a mine into two parts for some distance down the dip from the outcrop. In this example, the orebody is assumed to be an extensive, dipping bed with thickness and values well outlined by drilling and by adjacent workings. A deposit of this type might be found in the copper district of Michigan, the iron fields of Alabama, or the gold reefs of the Rand, wherein the orebodies are of great lateral and vertical extent and, over certain areas, are often extremely regular in dip, thickness, and ore content. Similar conditions may also be found in horizontal beds, as with coal, potash, gypsum, or other mineral.

To reduce calculations, the ore bed is assumed to be of uniform dip and thickness, and the rate of mining advance, the recovery, and the mining cost for each 1000 feet of depth along the dip are all assumed to be uniform. To assume a uniform rate of mining advance implies merely that the parcels of land

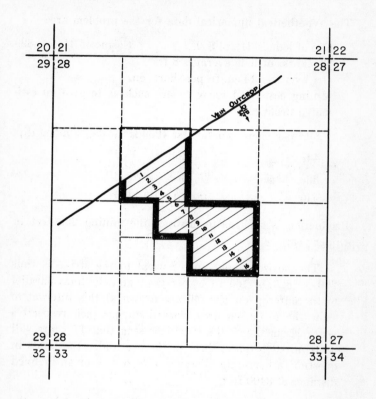

Fig. 40. Irregular land parcel within a mine.

are an ownership separation only, and that the mining operations are continued on one or both sides of the area in question.
With the conditions fixed as above, it is obvious that the tonnage extracted each year from the lands in question will be
proportional to the horizontal area mined out in the same
period. The purpose of the problem is to determine the present
value of the mineral so that the operating company may purchase or lease the ground.

The hypothetical numerical data for the problem are:

Dip of lode is 34° to S. E.   Cosine of 34° = .829
Thickness of lode averages 8 ft.
Ore averages 14 cu. ft. per short ton.
Mining costs and recovery are such as to give an estimated profit of

50¢ per short ton for 1st 1000 ft. of depth along dip.
44¢ ,, ,, ,, ,, 2nd ,, ,, ,, ,, ,, ,,
36¢ ,, ,, ,, ,, 3rd ,, ,, ,, ,, ,, ,,
24¢ ,, ,, ,, ,, 4th ,, ,, ,, ,, ,, ,,

Production is such as to advance the mining 200 feet in depth per year.

The horizontal advance normal to the strike is thus 200 × .829, or 165.8 feet per year, and the lines parallel to the outcrop on Fig. 40 are drawn at this interval to show the projected area worked during each respective year. From the sketch it will be seen that 17 years will be required to mine through the ore under the lands in question, a horizontal distance of 2820 feet or an inclined distance of 3400 feet.

Preliminary calculations to obtain factors by which the horizontal area mined each year may be converted into dollars of profit are as follows:

Each square foot of horizontal area mined is underlaid by $\frac{1}{.829}$, or 1.206 sq. ft. of lode area, which represents 1.206 × 8, or 9.648 cu. ft. of ore, or .689 short tons.

Since the mining advance is at the rate of 200 feet per year, or 1000 feet in 5 years, the profits per square foot of horizontal area will be

.689 × 50 = 34.44¢ per sq. ft. of land area for 1st 5 yrs.

.689 × 44 = 30.32¢ ,, ,, ,, ,, ,, ,,   ,,   ,, 2nd ,, ,,

.689 × 36 = 24.80¢ ,, ,, ,, ,, ,, ,,   ,, 3rd ,, ,,

.689 × 24 = 16.54¢ ,, ,, ,, ,, ,, ,,   ,, 4th ,, ,,

The respective horizontal areas mined each year may be scaled with a planimeter or measured and computed arithmetically from a large-scale plat of the property. They are listed in the following table along with the corresponding profit factors to give the estimated income for each respective year of mining:

Yr.	Horizontal Area Mined	Profit Per Sq. Ft.	Profit Per Yr.	Yr.	Horizontal Area Mined	Profit Per Sq. Ft.	Profit Per Yr.
1	26060 sq. ft.	$.3444	$8975	10	21200		6428
2	25320		8720	11	25630	.2480	6356
3	20830		7174	12	26060		6463
4	14980		5159	13	25650		6361
5	13030		4488	14	20930		5191
6	13030	.3032	3951	15	15020		3725
7	16010		4854	16	9040	.1654	1495
8	19770		5994	17	3000		496
9	19840		6015				

Assuming that the investor desires a 10% (r′) return on his capital with redemption fund accruals at 4% (r), the present value of this series of uneven annual incomes may be calculated by the Hoskold type formula as follows:

Year	Income P_m	Factor R^{n-m}	Product $P_m R^{n-m}$
1	$8975	1.8730	$16,810
2	8720	1.8009	15,704
3	7174	1.7317	12,423
4	5159	1.6651	8,590
5	4488	1.6010	7,185
6	3951	1.5395	6,083
7	4854	1.4802	7,185
8	5994	1.4233	8,531
9	6015	1.3686	8,232
10	6428	1.3159	8,459
11	6356	1.2653	8,042
12	6463	1.2167	7,864
13	6361	1.1699	7,442
14	5191	1.1249	5,839
15	3725	1.0816	4,029
16	1495	1.0400	1,555
17	496	1.0000	496

Sum of series $134,469

$$V_p = \frac{\text{Sum of } P_m R^{n-m} \text{ series}}{1 + r'\left(\dfrac{R^n - 1}{r}\right)}$$

$$= \frac{134,469}{1 + .10\left(\dfrac{1.04^{17} - 1}{.04}\right)}$$

$$= \frac{134,469}{1 + .10(23.6975)}$$

$$= \frac{134,469}{3.36975}$$

Present Value $= \quad$ $39,905

Or, roughly, $40,000

PART III

VALUATION OF OIL PROPERTY

Oil Drill-Rig.

PROPERTY RIGHTS IN OIL

INTRODUCTION [1]

Valuation of oil property follows the same general pattern as valuation of mineral property. Both are subject to depletion, and capital investment must be returned before exhaustion of the resource. The fundamental economic factors of production, profit, and life form the basis of the valuation in both instances and the estimated future earnings resulting therefrom are discounted to present worth at suitable interest rates. Assets other than the resource product, such as plant, equipment, working capital, etc., whether for oil or mineral, are valued similarly.

Many of the physical features affecting the valuation of oil property, however, are so different from those corresponding in mineral valuation, either in their effect upon the economic factors or in the methods used for their determination, that some separate treatment of oil property valuation is considered necessary. The scientific and engineering background required of the evaluator differs also on these issues.

The examination of oil property involves the geology of anticlinal and other oil structures, the principles of reservoir behavior and of proper application of reservoir energy, and the marketability of the crude oil, whereas examination of mines deals with ore and vein structures and their probable continuity, assay values, and recovery through efficient mining and milling. In both cases an understanding is required of the economics of the respective industry and the principles of discounting future earnings to present value by a suitable premise.

---

[1] This part has been written by Dr. W. L. Whitehead, Assoc. Prof. of Geology, Mass. Inst. of Tech., assisted by the author.

CHAPTER 17

PROPERTY RIGHTS IN OIL

DOMESTIC VS. FOREIGN ATTITUDES— In most foreign countries, minerals, including oil and gas, below the surface of the ground are owned by the sovereign state or the crown. The right to exploit minerals is usually granted to private interests by the government either according to statutes or by special concessions. The statutory provisions are often complex; rights to minerals sometimes exist in old land grants and investigation of the legal aspects of oil and gas holdings is always advisable in valuation of lands abroad. In the United States oil and gas belong to the owner of the land underneath which these substances lie.

HISTORY AND EVOLUTION— Oil and gas are migratory. They move through the porous and permeable rocks below the surface in relation to pressure gradients. Judges in the United States in early lawsuits recognized this fugitive nature of oil and gas and, comparing them with wild animals moving across the boundaries of land, gave them the status of such property in common law. The owner of the land thus has the right to take possession of oil and gas while these fluids are under his property by drilling wells and extracting oil and gas from them.

LAW OF CAPTURE— The *law of capture* has resulted in the active and aggressive development of oil fields. Drainage of oil or gas takes place toward any well and, if the well is close to the boundary of a property, part of the oil will be drained from the adjoining property. To protect his oil and prevent drainage, the owner of the latter property must drill a well near the boundary opposite to or offsetting the first well. When property rights are shared, the drilling of such an offset well is usually obligatory.

OFFSET DRILLING — Until recent years *offset drilling* of wells, in some fields closely spaced, was accompanied by flush production of oil and gas. Flush wells produce while pressure in the reservoir is near the initial amount and much gas is still dissolved in the oil; the wells commonly flow naturally and if valves are opened wide, produce at high rates. This flush output, if maintained, will lower the reservoir pressure near wells so produced and soon cause active drainage from adjoining areas. The purpose of this practice was not only to obtain large quantities of oil in a short time but to recover a maximum amount of oil under conditions of highly competitive offset drilling. The method is considered wasteful of gas, which was often blown into the air or burned in flares at the well. When flush production ended after a period of months and lifting of oil by pumping followed for the many years of life of the well, the oil was dead, contained little dissolved gas to aid in lifting to the surface and in helping gravity flow the oil underground to the well. The original energy of the compressed, dissolved gas available for underground flow is utilized inefficiently in flush production and for only a short time. Close spacing of offset wells and concomitant flush production thus results in low ultimate recovery of oil from a property and in waste of the original reservoir energy.

CONSERVATION — In the United States the interest of the several states in *conservation* of their natural resources in oil and gas has been long established. Blowing of gas into the air or burning it, unless necessary to the production of oil, has been banned in some states from early days. Statutes regulating production practices to some extent were common in oil-producing states when, about 1930, the discovery simultaneously of large fields in Oklahoma and Texas caused serious overproduction. The swift development of the great East Texas field under conditions of keen offset drilling was a dominant factor in the situation. Enforcement of conservation laws was attempted and new laws were passed in both Oklahoma and Texas.

By 1935 laws regulating the rate of production from wells, the permissible gas-oil ratio (cubic feet per barrel) and the spacing of wells (acres per well) were on the books of most oil producing states. Regulation was delegated to a conservation commission or other designated body empowered to enforce the laws. Difficulty in enforcement had been met because of the sale to pipelines of "hot oil" produced illegally above the allowable quantity and was not finally overcome until federal regulations were enacted requiring certificates of production according to state law for shipment of oil in interstate commerce. The supervision of enforcement of the Connally Hot Oil Act is now the duty of the oil and gas division of the Department of the Interior.

At the present time, except in Illinois, the owner of oil and gas is allowed to produce these substances only at an allotted rate determined by the proration fixed by the state in which the oil or gas is produced. He is permitted by state license to drill oil wells spaced usually at one well to 20 or 40 acres, according to conditions in the field, and gas wells normally spaced one to the square mile. The gas-oil ratio is also regulated. Flush production and uncontrolled offset drilling are, except in a single important oil-producing state, no longer rights of the producer of oil and gas.

FORMS OF OWNERSHIP — Oil and gas in the *public domain* belong to the United States government.

Development and production of oil and gas on these lands, except in the areas of national parks and national monuments, are provided for under laws passed by the Congress.

Ownership in *fee* by private interests in the United States comprises full ownership of all surface and underground rights. Oil and gas are seldom produced under full ownership represented by the general *warranty deed*. Such ownership was not adapted to the exploitation of substances to be ultimately exhausted. The oil operator does not wish to be burdened with the land after all the recoverable fluids are produced.

Legally the land owner has the right to separate the underground minerals from the land and to convey or grant the mineral rights. The *mineral deed* conveys oil and gas in place and today is commonly used for royalties. The *oil-and-gas lease* is the customary conveyance covering the minerals themselves. It is essentially a grant of oil and gas with the exclusive rights to obtain them.

Leases — All the unrestricted lands held in private ownership in the principal oil-producing states are operated for oil and gas under the oil and gas mining lease. This instrument is usually a simple printed document. Although a short term lease may be verbal, to be acceptable in a valuation, an actual documentary lease should exist. The owner or *lessor* by this document grants certain rights in the minerals of his property to the *lessee*.

The mineral rights conveyed by the lease consist either of the right to explore for and take possession of the minerals or of the exclusive right to them, whereby subsequent possession results simply from the exercise of this right. Included is the right of entry on the surface of the property for the purpose of exploration, development, and production of the specified minerals with provision for reimbursement to the owner for damage to crops.

Certain forms of leases have had widespread use. Their provisions have become well established in accordance with custom and court decisions.[1] The contract must be supported by a consideration specified in the lease and called the *bonus*. Description of the property is in the lease and *title* is generally evidenced by a certified abstract of title. The *term* of a lease is usually 2 to 5 years, and "as long thereafter as oil or gas, or either of them, is produced from said land by the lessee." Other provisions uniformly customary are the one-eighth royalty, date upon which drilling must commence, and rentals. The last are payments to cover the privilege of deferring the commencement of a well after the date specified.

Inherent in the lease is the obligation to drill a well or to pay the rentals in lieu thereof. In the event that oil or gas is found on adjoining property, the drilling of offset wells is required if producing wells have been drilled adjacent to the property line on the bordering lands. The lessee is obliged to comply with state regulations in drilling and producing oil and gas and is expected to develop and exploit the leasehold in a workmanlike manner. Drilling obligations under these circumstances may become an important element in valuation of undeveloped properties. They imply compulsory capital investments.

Special provisions in leases are not uncommon and may differ widely concerning natural gas, casing-head gas produced with oil, and gas distillate or condensate produced as vapor with natural gas and liquefied by pressure changes in the gas at the well-head.

Consolidation of small properties in a *community lease* sometimes causes complex situations of ownership. Special provisions of these or other kinds require careful attention during valuation of property affected by them.

---

[1] Oil and Gas Leases and Royalties; S. H. Glassmire, 2nd Ed., 1938, Thomas Law Book Co., St. Louis, Missouri.

Special forms of leases are used for public lands, school lands, river beds, and Indian lands. Uniformity of form even for ordinary leases is not general because of conflicting laws and customs. It is not practical to adopt a standard form for general use in all oil-producing states.[1]

Assignment of a lease as a whole or in part is an implied right of the lessee in the absence of a contrary express provision in the lease. This right is sometimes specifically withheld or is made subject to the approval of the lessor. Where assignment is difficult for this or other reasons, the value of a lease is affected adversely.

Royalty — The oil and gas reserved to the owner of the land, when produced, is the *royalty*. Royalty is part of the proceeds or profits from the land and has been construed broadly to include the bonus and rentals. The royalty proper is oil royalty, natural gas royalty, and casing-head gas royalty.

Oil royalty in the oil-producing regions of the United States is usually *one-eighth* of the gross proceeds. It is payable in kind on demand, but is customarily paid in money directly to the owner by the pipeline company purchasing the oil from the lease. Exceptionally, as in Ohio and California, the prevailing royalty is *one-sixth* of the oil. On Indian lands, state or school lands, one-sixth or even higher royalty may be paid.

In early leases *gas royalty* was fixed at a flat rate, usually $200 or $300 per annum, regardless of the quantity of gas produced. In more recent years gas royalties are generally specified in leases to be "one-eighth of the gross proceeds at the prevailing market rate." Gas is metered at the wells.

Casing-head gas is produced with the oil from an oil well. It is saturated with the vapor from the light fractions of crude oil and may be treated to produce gasoline. The status of royalty on such gas and the gasoline obtained from it has had

---

[1] Glassmire, op. cit. p. 350.

a complex history in legal decisions in the various oil-producing states. Lease forms now specify the royalty to be paid on casing-head gas and should conform to the usage in the state where the lease is located. Natural gas containing distillate or condensate, mixtures of hydrocarbons heavier than gasoline condensible upon reducing the pressure of gas coming from the well, is also sometimes subject in leases to special provisions regarding royalty.

Royalty always represents to the lessor a profit from the land, for he receives his share of the oil and gas without cost. For this reason it is not subject to some risks inherent in the cost of exploration for and production of oil and gas. Nevertheless after a sale of royalty or a fraction of royalty in a lease the royalty may not represent a profit to the buyer, for minerals are wasting assets and the price of purchase of rights must be amortized during the productive life of the royalty. Royalties being paid in kind are open to the same hazards as the working interest of the lease in the event of changes in the rate of output or character of the fluids produced. The royalty holder, therefore, equally with the operator, is interested to know the geological and technological factors affecting the future productivity of his property.

CHAPTER 18

FIELD EXAMINATION
AND VALUATION FACTORS

EXPLORATION — Oil and gas are contained in underground reservoirs that consist of porous and permeable rock covered by an impermeable cap rock. The rocks are generally layered formations of marine sedimentary beds, although exceptionally terrestrial or even volcanic strata are present. The common oilfield reservoir is composed of porous sand or sandstone covered and sealed by a bed of shale. Limestones, porous and permeable on account of weathering at an unconformity or because of the original open character of reef-rock or oolitic sand, constitute the reservoirs of some of the great oilfields of West Texas, Mexico and the Middle East.

The fluids contained in an undisturbed reservoir are in static *equilibrium*. Gas, oil, and water lie in gross relations in the reservoir according to their densities, gas at the top, oil below, and water under the oil. The oil contains dissolved gas in the quantity determined by the amount of gas available and by the equilibrium of the crude oil with gas at the pressure and temperature of the reservoir. When wells penetrate the undisturbed reservoir, changes, principally in pressure, affect the system, fluid flow takes place, and, as pressure drops, gas begins at some definite pressure to come out of solution in the oil. The history of change in such a hydrodynamic phase system may be complex. It is a principal concern of the petroleum physicist and engineer and is a matter of primary importance in the valuation of oil leaseholds.

Geological Types of Oilfields — The task of the geologist in exploration for oil and gas is chiefly the study of the solid components of the reservoir and determination of favorable stratigraphic and structural environments for drilling. He has found that the fugitive and migratory hydrocarbons move slowly during long geologic eras through the permeable rocks and collect in the reservoir at localities where the structure forms a trap for the fluids. The trap commonly is at a place where accumulating oil and gas are arrested under the cap rock after upward migration along pervious beds or masses of rock.

Structural Traps *Structural traps* are formed by deformation of the originally flat-dipping beds. They generally are on anticlines, elongated arches in the strata, or on more symmetrical domelike folds. The oil and gas are trapped along the crest of the arch or at the top of the dome. Oilfield structures of this type may vary in horizontal dimensions from a mile or less in diameter to great fields a dozen miles long and three to four miles wide. Areas are from a few hundred acres to twenty thousand or more acres. The vertical interval on the base of the cap rock from the crest of the arch to the bottom of the adjoining depression or syncline is called the closure of the structure. It is the measure of the capacity of the trap to contain oil, but because the structure may not be completely filled by trapped oil or gas, the closure is not an indication of the actual quantity of these fluids in an oilfield. Other structural traps lie where faults have caused porous and permeable beds to be cut off and thrown in contact with impervious rock.

Stratigraphic Traps *Stratigraphic traps* present a remarkable variety of interesting structures. They may be a long, winding, estuarian channel filled with sand and buried in shale or a crescential bar surrounded by and covered with fine lagoonal sediments. They may be sand deposits once along the shoreline of an ancient sea and now tilted so that their upturned edge constitutes a trap. Similarly tilted bodies of sand may form traps where the upper edge has been dissected by erosion at an unconformity and shale deposited across the outcrop on the old surface. Weathering and solution of limestone adjacent to an unconformity has been the cause of certain stratigraphic traps. One part of the great Oklahoma City field, which is a complex structure below an unconformity, is a buried, weathered limestone hill. Both coral and algal limestone reefs when buried in impermeable sediments may trap oil and gas. Some of the largest known oilfields are stratigraphic traps. The Bradford field on the Pennsylvania-New York boundary is at the marine sandy toe of a delta in the Devonian sea. The East Texas field, an eroded sand body overlapping a shoreline to the east, is 136,000 acres in proved extent.

Determination of Structure — The first stage in exploration for oil and gas is geological survey of the surface of the ground. In the United States the areas of the oil-producing states have been repeatedly and carefully surveyed by federal or state organizations and by the petroleum companies. Nevertheless, occasion often arises, even today, for resurvey of these regions in further detail for some special structural or stratigraphic purpose. In areas of newer exploration and in many foreign lands detailed geological work is always in active progress by both governmental and private interests. Reports on geological surveys should be available always for valuation of petroleum properties.

Geophysical Methods Geophysical work in normal exploration follows geological mapping. The gravimeter determines minute changes in the gravitational field of the earth and may detect structural features significant to exploration. Investigation of the earth's magnetic field by delicate magnetometers also has been of service to structural studies. Recently, adaptation of this instrument to use from the air has greatly accelerated the rate at which magnetometric surveys may be conducted. Both of these techniques are useful in reconnaissance because of their relatively low cost. The standard procedure for detailed structural survey by geophysical methods is by means of the seismograph. The depth to a bed chosen for its contrast in density with strata above and below is determined by reflected seismic waves. In layered sedimentary rocks of uniform character, seismic surveys may sometimes outline structures promising for oilfield exploration with surprising exactness. Procedures other than these accepted methods of geophysical exploration should be questioned critically before considering them for use in exploration for oil and gas. In determining the prospective value of unexplored lands, doubtful consideration should be given to other than standard geophysical techniques carried out by competent observers and interpreted by expert geophysicists.

Drilling The final stage in testing promising structures for oil and gas is by the drill. All test wells drilled outside of producing fields on the basis of geological, geophysical, or other information are called *wildcat wells*. Statistical data are available by states annually on the ratio of successful wildcat wells to dry holes drilled in the United States. The ratio is at times useful in evaluating prospective territory in a general way. Similar ratios also are published [1] comparing success on the basis of method used for locating exploratory holes, geological, geophysical, or other.

Upon completion of an oil well opening a new field in the United States, it is usual practice to drill out the field within a relatively short time. In smaller fields, development may be completed within a year; even in the East Texas fields, 116,000 acres, or 85 percent of the final area, was proved four years

---

[1] F. H. Lahee, Exploratory Drilling in 1946, Amer. Assoc. Pet. Geol. Bulletin 31, No. 6, pp. 917-930.

after discovery. As the productive oil wells are drilled, the geologist and petroleum engineer obtain, by cores from the wells and by samples, the requisite information to outline the distribution of gas, oil, and water in the reservoir and to establish temperature, pressure, and the equilibrium relations of the fluids.

The information from *dry holes* forms an important part of the data for subsurface geology. This branch of investigation in oil-bearing regions is concerned with the compilation of well logs and the interpretation of underground stratigraphy and structure. In certain areas it has become a principal method of exploration. Correlation of formations in wells is done by means of micropaleontology, sedimentary analysis, heavy mineral content or other comparison of cuttings and cores, and by means of special sampling or well-survey techniques. Electric logging of wells to indicate porosity and permeability of the strata penetrated has become a general and accepted method of correlating formations in wells. In more unusual circumstances, use is made of radioactivity logs or of neutron logs. Success in the search for new fields, particularly those in stratigraphic traps, is due in a marked and growing degree to the contribution from the subsurface geologist.

RESERVOIR CHARACTERISTICS

The Reservoir Rock — Natural oil reservoirs consist of porous and permeable rock, the pore spaces of which contain oil and gas under pressure. Physical characteristics of the rock, determined from cores obtained in wells penetrating the reservoir, vary widely. Some reservoirs are made of fine sand, others of coarse-grained, loose-packed sand, and limestone reservoirs may be composed of cavernous rock with large solution channels.

Porosity   The *porosity* of the reservoir rock is its capacity to hold fluids. In limestones porosity is often highly variable and an average value for the reservoir may be difficult or impossible of determination. Sand bodies are more uniform in porosity, but where they are deposited in lenticular layers or are interstratified with thin beds of shale, the oil-producing sand bed, the pay, may be only a few feet or even a few inches in thickness. Good sands have about 20 to 30 per cent porosity. Porosity as generally measured is the percentage of total rock volume represented by connected pore space.

Permeability   *Permeability* is a measure of the ease with which fluids may traverse the porous rock under a driving pressure. For oil reservoir rocks it is usually expressed in darcies[1] or, more conveniently, in millidarcies. An average permeability of about 500 millidarcies is common in measurements on good reservoir rocks, although productive sand formations in oil fields may range in permeability from 50 to over 1000 millidarcies. This permeability to a single phase in homogeneous flow is generally called the *specific permeability*. It is a constant physical characteristic of the reservoir rock upon which the measurement was made.

No direct relation exists between porosity and permeability. Sands with large grains and little interstitial fine material tend to have high permeability. Tight or cemented sands with small, poorly connected pore spaces will have low permeability.

Oil, Gas, and Water — In a reservoir containing oil and gas, these fluids are confined at the top by the cap rock, the impermeable barrier forming the trap. Salt water generally fills the porous

---

[1] Muskat, M., ''Flow of Homogeneous Fluids,'' p. 76, McGraw-Hill Book Co., Inc., New York, 1937.

Water at 20°C (with 1 centipoise viscosity) will flow through a rock with 1 darcy permeability at the rate of 1 cc. per second per cc.[2] area per atmosphere differential pressure per cm. length or at the rate of 1 gal. per minute per sq. ft. per 1 ft. head of water per 1 ft. length.

reservoir rock underneath the oil and gas. If a well drilled from a location on the surface near the border of the oil field encounters this free water, it is called *edge water*. *Bottom water* is that found in a well drilled through the oil-filled reservoir rock to the underlying free-water zone. The plane of contact of edge or bottom water with the superincumbent oil or gas is usually about horizontal.

Water also is present in a substantial amount throughout the oil- and gas-bearing zones in sand reservoirs. This *interstitial water*, commonly called *connate water*, occupies the smaller pores and tubelike spaces between sand grains, where it is held by capillary forces. Because of the greater solid-liquid interfacial tension between sand grains and water than between sand and oil, these forces have considerable magnitude and most reservoir sands are water-wet. Determination of interstitial water presents a difficult problem, for cores when extracted from wells are usually contaminated with water introduced from the drilling mud. To facilitate estimation of the amount of contamination from this source, trace chemicals are often added to the mud. Measurement of the water in cores in the restored state, purported to be that of the rock in the undisturbed reservoir, has recently been described[1] as an accurate method of determining connate water. The water content of normal sand reservoirs varies with the physical characteristics of rock and fluids, but generally ranges from 10 to 40 percent. Sands with less than average amounts of fine silt, consequently more permeable, contain the lower percentages of water. Silty oil-bearing sands may rarely contain as much as 65 percent water. The amount of interstitial water is a factor of primary concern in valuation of an oil property, since it directly affects the reserves.

The amount of free gas in the oil zone of a static undisturbed reservoir is probably negligible. As production from

[1] The Link V.12, No. 6, pp. 8-11, June 1947
     The Carter Oil Company, Tulsa, Oklahoma.

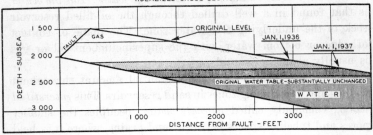

MILE SIX POOL
FALL OF GAS OIL CONTACT
(IDEALIZED CROSS SECTION)

Fig. 41. Fall of gas-oil contact.

*From ''Petroleum Reservoir Efficiency and Well Spacing,'' (1943)
courtesy of Standard Oil Co.*

wells reduces pressure, free gas appears with the oil whenever
pressure falls below that required to hold gas in solution in the
oil. The areas of such gas-oil mixture are closely related to the
pattern of pressure and of flow to the wells. The time of their
appearance after the beginning of production is dependent on
the equilibrium conditions of the hydrocarbon fluids in the
reservoir, on the rate of water advance, on well-spacing, and
on rate and methods of production. It may, as in the East
Texas field, be many years after discovery, or may be almost
immediately after the drilling of the first wells.

Above the oil zone in many fields, free gas occupies the
upper part of the reservoir. This *gas cap* represents the excess
of gas not soluble in the oil under the original conditions in the
reservoir. The oil-gas contact at the base of the gas cap in a
homogeneous reservoir is normally a horizontal plane, but
may become somewhat irregular where marked variations in
porosity and permeability are present. A feature of great practical import after production begins in this type of reservoir is
growth of the gas cap. As pressure drops and gas is expelled
from solution in the crude oil of the oil zone, the gas in many

fields migrates upward to be added to the gas cap. Such accretions cause the oil-gas contact to move downward and laterally so as to affect oil production in areas adjacent to the gas cap. Oil-bearing leases may in this way become gas-producing with concomitant loss in productive value.

Under these conditions, during production the pores of the reservoir rock contain three phases, oil with its equilibrium content of dissolved gas, free gas, and water. The relative amounts of these fluids at any place in a reservoir are affected by the rate of pressure change, by the solubility of gas in the crude oil, and by the vertical permeability of the reservoir rock permitting migration upward to the gas cap. Calculation of the free gas content in a producing reservoir is a complex, but not insuperable problem. The gas-free oil remaining in reservoirs during the late stages of production is usually determined from samples or cores. Interstitial water in such cores may be measured and the free gas found by difference after calculating the volume of the oil-gas solution restored to reservoir temperature and pressure.

This oil-gas solution is commonly called *reservoir fluid*. The total volume of reservoir fluid at a specified pressure, temperature, and composition which contains a unit volume of original oil as measured under standard surface conditions (14.73 lbs. per sq. in. absolute and 60° F.) has been designated *formation volume*.[1] Direct sampling of reservoir fluid is accomplished by bottom-hole sampling in wells closed in so as to establish in them the reservoir pressure. Solubility of gas in the crude oil of a field is measured experimentally in the laboratory in bombs at the appropriate pressures and temperatures as determined by bottom-hole measurements in the wells.

In the oil zone of a static reservoir the fluids have been in equilibrium for a long period before production begins. No free

---

[1] "Volumetric and Phase Behavior of Hydrocarbons," B. H. Sage and W. N. Lacey. Stanford University Press; 1939, p. 231.

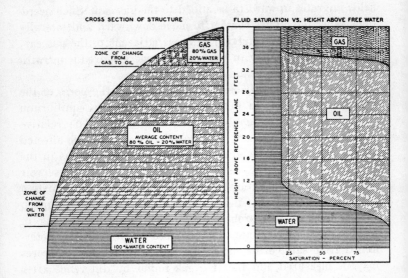

Fig. 42. Typical distribution of oil, gas, and water in the reservoir.

*From ''Petroleum Reservoir Efficiency and Well Spacing,'' (1943)
courtesy of Standard Oil Co.*

gas is to be found in such an oil zone and the larger pores of
the rock are filled by two phases only, interstitial water and
reservoir fluid. If the amount of gas available is less than the
volume soluble in the crude oil at the pressure and temperature
of the primitive reservoir, the reservoir has no gas cap in its
original state. A considerable drop in pressure may be required
in some oil fields to bring the oil-gas solution to the *bubble-point.*
Reservoir fluid is generally assumed to remain in equilibrium
at the approximately constant reservoir temperature during
this drop in pressure; therefore, as long as pressures remain
higher than the bubble-point, the two phases water and reservoir fluid occupy alone the pores of the rock. The percent of
the volume of pores filled by reservoir fluid is termed the

saturation. Saturation in a static reservoir with gas-free oil zone is represented in Fig. 42.

It is evident that the formation volume or volume factor[1] is greater than unity when expressed in terms of crude oil under surface conditions of temperature and pressure. The loss of volume of reservoir fluid when converted to crude oil in the stock tanks at the surface is called the *shrinkage.*

FLUID FLOW — Flow of the reservoir fluid to a well is according to the relation[2]

$$k = \frac{\mu QL}{A(P_1 - P_2)},$$

where

k is the permeability in darcies,

μ the viscosity of the reservoir fluid in centipoises,

L the length in centimeters,

A the area in square centimeters,

$P_1 - P_2$ the pressure difference in atmospheres,

Q the amount of flow in cubic centimeters.

For a sand of a given permeability and with fluids at a constant pressure difference, it is evident that the rate of flow is governed directly by the viscosity of the reservoir fluid. The viscosity of the fluid is increased by reduction in the content of dissolved gas when gas escapes from the reservoir fluid (Fig. 43). Maintenance of gas in solution in the reservoir fluid, therefore, is a requisite for optimum conditions of flow in the reservoir to the wells in an oil field. In order to attain this condition and conserve gas, a low gas-oil ratio is sought in operating wells.

---

[1] Petroleum Production Vol. I, Park J. Jones.
    Reinhold Publishing Company, New York, 1946, p. 105.
[2] M. Muskat, ''The Flow of Homogeneous Fluids through Porous Media,''
    pp. 76-101, McGraw-Hill Book Co., New York, 1937.

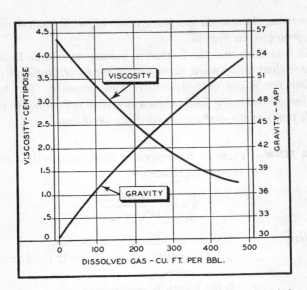

Fig. 43. Change in viscosity and gravity of crude oil due to dissolved gas.

From "Petroleum Reservoir Efficiency and Well Spacing," (1943) courtesy of Standard Oil Co.

The permeability of the reservoir rock is measured in the laboratory by single-phase flow of a homogeneous fluid, a gas or a liquid, through dry cores. In the reservoir, this *specific permeability* is affected by the presence of interstitial water. Such flow is described as two-phase flow and, although water is not produced with the oil in the well when interstitial water is below 50 percent, the permeability to reservoir fluid is lowered by the presence of the water. This reduced permeability varies with the saturation of oil in the pore spaces and is called the *effective* or relative *permeability*.[1] It is expressed as a percent-

---

[1] M. C. Leverett, "Flow of Oil-water Mixtures through Unconsolidated Sands, Petroleum Technology," vol. 132, pp. 149-171, Am. Inst. Min. & Met. Eng., 1939.

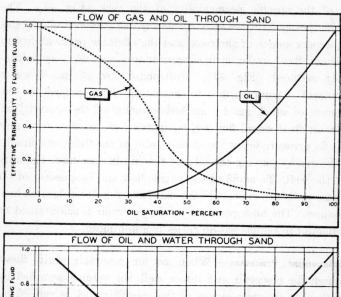

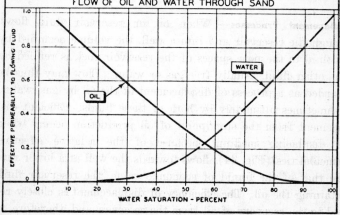

Fig. 44.: Typical saturation — permeability relationships.

From ''Petroleum Reservoir Efficiency and Well Spacing,'' (1943)
courtesy of Standard Oil Co.

age of the specific permeability of the rock (Fig. 44). The specific permeability is affected also by the presence of free gas in the pore spaces of the rock, and the effective permeability to reservoir fluid under such circumstances may be very appreciably reduced (Fig. 44). Multiphase flow of gas-oil-water mixtures[1] is complex, but is characterized, in general, in the presence of much gas by marked lowering of the quantity of reservoir fluid or oil flowing, by increase of gas flow with any drop in pressure below the bubble-point of the fluid, and finally by the gas by-passing the oil and flowing in dominant amounts into the well. To avoid excessive gas flow and by-passing of oil by gas, wells are operated with carefully regulated bottom-hole pressures. The back pressure on the reservoir is maintained at an amount to reduce gas-oil ratios to a minimum.

Displacement Processes — When oil or reservoir fluid flows through the reservoir and into a well, the volume occupied by this fluid in the pore spaces of the reservoir rock is refilled by some other fluid, usually free gas or water. Flow may thus be regarded as a process of displacement of the oil by gas, water, or sometimes ultimately by both of these fluids. Efficient displacement from the standpoint of oil production occurs when the displacing medium, because of the relative effective permeabilities (Fig. 44), flows towards the well at a lower rate than that of the liquid of economic value, the reservoir fluid containing the oil. The efficiency of displacement is closely related to the recovery of oil from the reservoir and, therefore, is of material concern in valuation of oil property.

The lesser efficiency of gas as a displacing medium in comparison with water results from the very low viscosity of gas

---

[1] M. C. Leverett and W. B. Lewis, ''Study Flow of Gas-Oil-Water Mixtures through Unconsolidated Sands,'' Petroleum Technology, vol. 142, pp. 107-116, AIME, 1941.

and from the fact that, when free gas is present, it enters preferentially the larger pore spaces, in which fluids flow most readily. The position within the pore spaces and, to some extent, the amounts of gas, oil and water, are related to their respective interfacial tensions and that of the fluids to the solid components of the sand. Water always wets silica grains in the presence of gas and oil. Thus, when enough gas has been released from solution in the reservoir fluid to form continuous channels in the porous, liquid-wet rock, the gas flows easily and moves toward the well before it has time to exert effective displacement of the more viscous oily liquid. When the displacing medium is water, the water tends to wet the sand and to enter and occupy the smaller and capillary pore spaces. The reservoir fluid is displaced into the larger and more permeable pores and flows readily through them towards the well. Under these conditions the water acts efficiently to effect displacement.

Recent laboratory work[1] with cores indicates that, under experimental conditions, displacement by gas may sometimes be more effective than by water. Cores of sandstone of low permeability, in some cases, show greater maximum oil displacement by gas, but either gas or water gives efficient displacement from limestone cores.

Aside from their relationship to the efficient mechanics of displacement[2] in fluid flow, oil viscosity and sand permeability greatly influence the time required for completion of the displacement of oil from sand. Low permeability and high viscosity usually indicate extended time to be needed for a given

---

[1] H. J. Welge, "Displacement of Oil from Porous Media by Water and Gas," A.I.M.E., T.P. 2433, 1948.

[2] The following sections on recovery and drive mechanisms are largely based on the discussion in "Petroleum Reservoir Efficiency and Well Spacing" by the Committees on Reservoir Development and Operation of the Standard Oil Company (New Jersey) Affiliated Companies and of the Humble Oil and Refining Company. The authors gratefully acknowledge their indebtedness to this report.

displacement, relative to the time required with high permeability and low viscosity. This general relationship is important in valuation where the time factor, among others, may have considerable economic weight in determining the limits to which fluid flow and the displacement process will finally be carried.

Recovery — All of the oil contained in a sand cannot be recovered by fluid flow and displacement of the reservoir fluid. The maximum possible yield has been the subject of much study, and it has been found that both the relation of saturation to permeability and the play of the forces of interfacial tension in capillary openings determine a certain minimum residual oil saturation in a sand. This saturation varies with the characteristics of the reservoir fluids and of the sand. For conditions normally encountered, it usually ranges from 10 percent to 20 percent of the pore space. The initial interstitial water content of oil sand, hence the original oil saturation, varies widely, and no one figure for percentage recovery of oil in place, or recovery efficiency, can be applied universally. For comparison of relative recovery efficiencies, a figure of around 80 percent of oil in place may be regarded as a maximum possible oil recovery under average conditions.

DRIVE MECHANISMS — Recovery of oil from the reservoir is a process of selective displacement of the reservoir fluid by either gas or water. Three major mechanisms are recognized :

1. With no free gas present and no water influx, simple release of pressure causes gas to evolve from solution and results in expulsion of some of the oil and most of the gas from the reservoir rock. A large amount of dead oil, that is, oil with no gas remaining in solution, is left in the pore spaces. This recovery process is known as *dissolved gas drive* and is the least efficient mechanism.

2. With a free gas cap present but no water influx, displacement by the free gas expanding downward drives oil out of the porous reservoir body. This process is known as *gas cap drive*. It is efficient and can yield a high oil recovery.

3. Displacement of the reservoir fluid by water rising from below is known as *water drive*. This process is usually the most efficient natural mechanism for oil recovery.

Action of gravitational forces may have an important bearing on the relative efficiencies of the three drives. Gravitational segregation of oil and of gas which has been released from solution, and similar segregation of oil and water, favor the maintenance of a reasonably sharp interface between the fluids. Another result of such segregation sometimes permits drainage of considerable quantities of oil to low points in a structure from which it may be recovered by pumping.

In practice, no one of these three drives is apt to continue throughout the complete life of a field. Both reservoir characteristics and operating control greatly influence the degree to which a particular drive is effective and hence influence the ultimate recovery expectancy.

TYPES OF OIL POOLS — The kind of drive in oil recovery, the quantity of gas dissolved in the oil and the amount or rate of flow of the water underlying the oil zone combine to give different types of reservoir behavior during oil production. An oil pool may show consistent characteristics of behavior over a long time and remain during its productive life an example of a single type. Usually the behavior of water underlying the oil is fairly uniform throughout the life of a field. If a gas cap is present, its behavior also is normally subject to prediction. Some oil pools, nevertheless, show marked changes of behavior and fields of such type are of especial interest in valuation of oil property.

The types of reservoir behavior in general may be classified as follows:

I   *Pools of constant reservoir volume without water drive*
    a. Reservoir fluid saturated with gas at initial pressures in the oil field.
    b. Reservoir fluid undersaturated with gas at initial pressures.

II   *Pools of variable reservoir volume with water drive*
    a. Reservoir fluid saturated with gas at initial pressures.
    b. Reservoir fluid undersaturated with gas at initial pressures.

Constant Volume — Constant volume of the reservoir containing oil and gas during the production of oil is a characteristic of oil fields with no water drive. The reduction of volume in the oil zone caused by extraction of oil and gas is taken up by the displacement of gas either derived from the dissolved gases in the reservoir fluid or from expansion of a gas cap. Pressure drop accompanying production in fields in this group is rapid unless gas-oil ratios of producing wells are efficiently controlled.

a. In a field with no water drive, or with a fairly constant elevation of the oil-water interface, and with the oil saturated with gas, a gas cap usually is present in the upper part of the reservoir. If no gas cap is initially present, it will begin to form immediately with the decrease in pressure caused by the first production of oil from the wells.

The drive in an oil pool of this type is by free gas expanding downward from the gas cap as the field pressure decreases and by the concomitant expansion of gas released from solution in the reservoir fluid. The principal feature of change during recovery of oil is the advance to lower elevations and the movement laterally in plan of the oil-gas interface. Fields of this type have uniform and predictable progress in gas-cap expansion closely related to oil production.

Recovery of oil from pools in this group varies markedly with the methods of operation and control of wells. Recovery of oil with poor control may fall below 50 percent; with good control it approaches the maximum expectable recovery, 80 percent (Fig. 45).

b. In an oil field with no water drive and with the oil under-saturated in dissolved gas, no gas cap and no free gas are to be expected under the initial conditions of stable equilibrium. When wells disturb these conditions, as oil production begins, pressure soon falls near the wells to the bubble-point of the reservoir fluid and dissolved gas is freed from solution. The displacing agent of the oil is this gas and such oil pools typically have dissolved gas drive.

Recovery during the period of such drive, even under most careful regulation of wells, is low (Fig. 45) and may be little more than 20 percent. Many oil pools have been operated throughout productive life with dissolved gas drive.

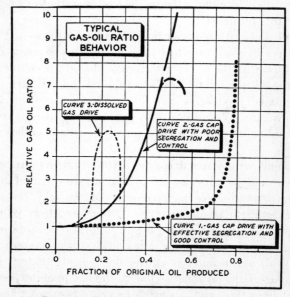

Fig. 45. Typical gas-oil ratio behavior.

From "Petroleum Reservoir Efficiency and Well Spacing," (1943) courtesy of Standard Oil Co.

Some fields, with initial gas content of the reservoir fluid near the saturation point, show development of a gas cap after an early stage of dissolved gas drive. Under such conditions recovery improves during later stages of operation, but the gas cap often is poorly developed and gives less efficient drive than in a saturated oil pool with well-defined gas cap.

Variable Volume— Variable reduced volume of the oil-gas reservoir during production is caused by the incursion of water in oil fields with water drive. The rate of displacement by water is limited by the permeability of the reservoir rock to water and, if fluid withdrawal is regulated to correspond to the optimum advance of the water drive for maximum efficient displacement, pressure drop during production may be maintained at a low rate of decline. Highly efficient operation of fields in this group is possible.

a. Oil pools with reservoir fluid saturated with gas and with water drive have an excellent medium for displacement operating not only at the upper interface of the oil-gas contact but also at the oil-water interface below the oil zone. Under properly regulated production, pressure decline in such oil fields is at a low rate. Withdrawal of oil annually of about three to five percent of the ultimate yield usually results in satisfactory recovery.

b. Fields with water drive and with oil undersaturated in gas, when fluid withdrawals are held at a rate to maintain the reservoir pressure, give high recovery of the oil. The great East Texas Field is of this type. After seventeen years of operation, free gas has not yet begun to form by ex-solution in the reservoir. Cores from wells taken along the western edge of this field, where water is advancing, indicate that recovery in that part of the oil zone is close to the maximum expectable recovery from this sand, about 85 percent. Somewhat less recovery may be made of the oil produced in the eastern part of the field after reservoir pressure drops to the bubble-point of the reservoir fluid and dissolved gas drive becomes a factor in displacement of the oil.

In oil pools with water drive and in those with gas cap drive, net oil recovery for the entire field may be efficient and show the high figures mentioned above, but recovery of the oil initially in place on a lease in the area of advancing water or gas may be lower. Part of the oil under these leases is swept by the displacing medium onto adjoining leases, upward in elevation on the sand by the water drive and downward by the gas drive. In the critical areas along the oil-water or oil-gas interface, the rate of advance of the driving medium determines the productive expectancy and the recovery of oil on the lease. Valuation of leases in an oil field with water drive or with a gas cap requires careful estimation of the effect of this factor on the economic life of the property.

CHAPTER 19

CASE VALUATION — PRODUCING PROPERTY

EXAMPLE LEASE — WATER DRIVE FIELD — Valuation of an example oil property is worked out here in some detail to demonstrate the principles involved and to call attention to the basic information needed for such a calculation. Data for this example are patterned to some extent after the East Texas oil field and have been selected to stress methods rather than extended computations. For this reason, round figures have been assumed for many of the items, actual determination or forecasting of which might require considerable statistical analysis.

As a prototype for the example, the East Texas field has the advantage of having been in prime production for some years under strict proration. Data on this field are well known and may be found in trade journals[1] and technical society publications[2].

Type Field Geologic structure of the example oil-bearing formation is a simple monoclinal stratigraphic trap with water drive. For the Example Field, as for East Texas, measurements of reservoir pressure, temperature, water encroachment, physical characteristics of the reservoir rock, and equilibrium

---

[1] Such as "World Petroleum," March 1936.
[2] Such as "Bull. of Amer. Assoc. Petroleum Geologists," Vol. XVII, 1933, Part 2.

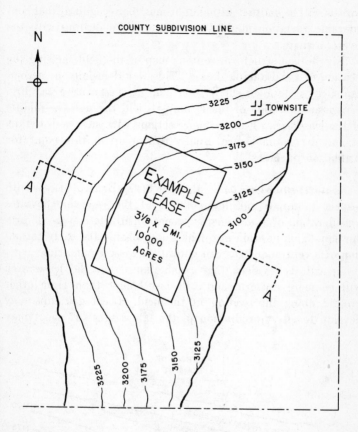

Fig. 46. Structural contour map of example oil field and lease.

data on the reservoir fluid are assumed to have been determined repeatedly and published, thus enabling relatively accurate prediction of reservoir behavior.

Object of the problem outlined below is to calculate the money value of a group of land parcels which are to be consolidated into a single operating unit. Details of the individual parcels will be omitted, although it must be recognized that considerable variation might be encountered in dealing with the several owners.

Fig. 46 is a structural contour map of the field showing the location of the Example Lease. This would usually be accompanied by a detailed subdivision map of the entire area. Fig. 47 is a cross section of the Example Field through the middle of the lease area. Full geologic sections with such well details as may be available are usually drawn up at this point for evaluation purposes.

Lease Conditions and Data   Position of the Example Lease with respect to upper and lower limits of the reservoir obviates consideration of water encroachment until a late stage of production. This position also makes improbable the early formation of a continuous gas cap within the lease boundaries.

It will be evident that production from the lease area will be more uniform and will last longer than from other ground along this section in the field. Local gas caps may develop to affect production in the late stages. If so, it may

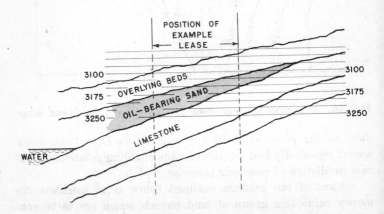

Fig. 47. Position of example lease with respect to structure.

become necessary to close off these pockets in wells by cementing.

Productive life of the lease will be estimated to the end of normal operations. In all probability, end-phase operation by individual owners and "stripper" production will continue for some time beyond this period but will be ignored in this calculation, as effect on present value is negligible.

The Example Lease is assumed to be in its fifth year of production with 100 wells now flowing. The field was placed under proration at the beginning of the current year with wells in the lease area curtailed to 55 barrels each per day. This limit, it is considered, will also apply to all new wells needed to develop the full acreage of the lease property.

Valuation date for the property being assembled into the lease block is set for the end of this year. It is assumed that production will be limited by proration throughout the remaining normal life of the field and, therefore, that one well per 20 acres will be permitted for development of the lease area. This assumption constitutes a marked departure from practice in the East Texas field.

Total production from the lease ground prior to the valuation date, it is estimated, will be 50,000,000 barrels. The assumed program for development of the lease property calls for 200 new wells during each of the first two years after valuation date.

It is assumed that daily output will then remain constant until the latter part of the normal life, when some decline may be expected.

Assumed data are as follows:

Example Lease, area	10,000 acres
Example Lease, shape	3⅛ x 5 miles
Date of initial production	5 years ago
Production to date	50,000,000 bbls.
Wells now producing	100

Total wells when fully developed   500
Development period   2 years
Prorated daily output per well   55 bbls.
Prorated daily output for lease   27,500 bbls.
Prorated annual output for lease   10,037,500 bbls.
                          or, say,   10,000,000 bbls.

Reservoir pressure, bottom hole
Initial   1640 lb./in^2
Two years ago   1390
One year ago   1330
Present   1300

Pressure decline per 1,000,000 bbls. of production is estimated at 2.75 lbs.; or approximately 28 lbs. per year at the anticipated production limit of 10,000,000 bbls.

Thickness of oil-bearing sand, average   35 ft.
A.P.I.* Gravity of crude   38°-42°
                         Average   40°

Porosity, Effective — 25%

Cores from representative wells are usually tested for porosity and permeability. Grain size of sand and nature of cementing material are important factors. There is apt to be considerable variation in porosity from one part of a field to another. An average value is estimated from well-core data.

Connate Water[1] — 15%

Estimated from core specimens taken at various elevations in the oil-bearing layer. Water content usually greater near the bottom of the sand.

---

* American Petroleum Institute.
[1] "Connate Water in Oil and Gas Sands," R. J. Schilthuis, Trans. A.I.M.E. Vol. 127, 1938, pp. 199-214.

Shrinkage — 20%

Gas solubility tests of Example Field reservoir fluid indicate approximately 360 cu. ft. of gas released per bbl. of fluid in dropping from 760 lb./in.^{2}, the gas release pressure, to atmospheric pressure at 90°F. Liberation of gas accounts for most of the shrinkage, although a minor portion, possibly 3 to 4%, is caused by cooling of the fluid from the reservoir temperature of 145°F.

Residual Oil — 25%

This factor is an estimate of the oil which will adhere to the sand grains or otherwise be entrapped so as not to be recoverable. Permeability of the sand and viscosity of the reservoir fluid are among the principal factors affecting ultimate recovery and retention of residual oil in the sand. The combined effect is often difficult to determine accurately.

Method of Estimating Evaluation of the Example Lease will be based on the volumetric method. The classical decline-curve methods[1] are not applicable to the Example Lease because of curtailment of output by proration. During such uniform production from a property, the volumetric method of estimation of reserves is commonly used. Decline curves, in states where production is controlled by proration, will normally apply only to "stripper" operations.

Methods of estimation based on material balance[2] are technically complex and are beyond the scope of this discus-

---

[1] Petroleum Production Engineering, "Oil Field Exploitation," L. C. Uren, McGraw-Hill Book Co., 2nd Ed., 1939.

[2] "A Method of Estimating Oil and Gas Reserves," D. L. Katz, Petroleum Dev. & Tech., 1936, Trans. A.I.M.E., Vol. 118, pp. 18-32.

"Active Oil and Reservoir Energy," R. J. Schilthuis, ibid, pp. 33-52.

sion; so also is the use of electrical models, as developed recently by Carter Oil Co., based on theoretical considerations in respect to fluid flow.[1]

By the volumetric method, calculations and estimates will be as follows:

1. Lease reserve, output, and life.
2. Flow vs. pumping.
3. Costs: development, operating, and royalty.
4. Working capital.
5. Selling price of oil.
6. Profit.
7. Present value.

Recoverable Reserve   The generally accepted formula[2] for volumetric treatment is:

$$R = 7758 \times T \times P \times (1-c) \ (1-s) \ (1-r),$$

where   R = ultimate recovery of oil in barrels per acre,

     7758 = barrels (U. S. standard) content of a layer one foot thick covering one acre,

         T = effective thickness of oil sand (or sands) in feet,

         P = effective porosity,

         c = connate water,

         s = shrinkage,

         r = residual oil.

Connate water, shrinkage, and residual oil may be combined into a convenient overall factor

$$F = (1-c) \ (1-s) \ (1-r).$$

[1] "Flow of Homogeneous Fluids," M. Muskat, McGraw-Hill Book Co., 1937, Chap. III.

[2] "Notes on valuation of Oil and Gas Properties," Corpus Christi Geologists' Study Group, South Texas Geological Soc., about 1940. With indexed bibliography.

Substituting the respective values given above for the Example Lease, gives

$$F = .85 \times .80 \times .75$$
$$= 51\% \text{ of the total pore space volume}$$
$$\text{occupied by recoverable oil}$$

Then, $\quad R = 7758 \times 35 \times .25 \times .51$
$$= 34620 \text{ bbls./acre.}$$

Recoverable reserve for the lease will then be

$$34620 \times 10{,}000 = 346{,}200{,}000 \text{ bbls.}$$

Deducting production to date, estimated at 50,000,000 bbls., leaves current recoverable reserve of 296,200,000 bbls.

Life At full prorated production, estimated at 10,000,000 bbls. per year, the present reserve would last 29.6 years from the valuation date. But since the lease now has but 100 wells, this output level will not be reached for two years. Production during the first year of development, with 200 wells coming in throughout the year, will be limited to 4,000,000 bbls.; and during the second year, to 8,000,000 bbls. This delay in reaching full output will increase the apparent life to 30.4 years, or, say, 30 years.

Actually, the life to depletion will be somewhat longer, as a decline in output may be expected in the late years. To allow for this, it is assumed that full production will be maintained through the 20th year and that, thereafter, the rate will fall off at 6.4% per year to the end of the 30th year, when normal operations are expected to cease.

It is possible that operation of the lease as a unit might be considered for a few years longer but with costs increasing and production declining, there is indication that continued operation would be more profitable if conducted in smaller units. The larger operator at that time will probably arrange to dispose of the lease to several small operators who would continue pumping until the wells decline to the point where only "stripper" production can continue.

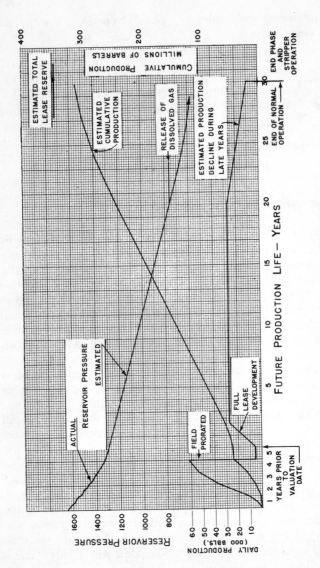

Fig. 48. Reservoir pressure vs. production—example oil lease.

These data are shown in Fig. 48, wherein reservoir pressure, lease production, and estimated reserves are plotted against years of life. Valuation date is indicated at the end of the fifth historical year, as assumed, by which time field production has been steadied under proration to conserve reservoir energy. Years of forward life start again with zero as of the valuation date, thus separating the past record from the present evaluation.

Cost of Development, Plant, and Equipment   As noted, the lease property now has 100 wells in operation. It will be assumed that these wells are so spaced as to fit in with the forward development program calling for 200 new wells during each of the first two years.

Cost per well is estimated at $30,000, including derrick, casing, valves, etc., but not including pumping equipment.

It will be assumed, further, that present wells will be paid for, as of the valuation date, at the same average price, namely, $30,000 per well to the respective owners. In this way the development account will be kept entirely separate from the land account.

Some plant and equipment will be needed to maintain production. No refining is contemplated. It is estimated that storage facilities, shops, trucks, pipe lines, office, laboratory, heating equipment, etc., will cost $1,000,000 and will be required by the end of the first operating year.

Flow vs. Pumping   With the oil sands at 3200 ft. below datum and with topography in the lease area at varying elevations of about 300 ft. above datum, back pressure on the wells will be at some figure near 1000 lb./in^2. Accurate calculation would depend upon determination of the gravity of the oil-gas mixture at various points in the well column. With gas release, the column will be lighter toward the top.

Inspection of the estimated pressure drop as shown in Fig. 48 indicates free flow for about another 10 years. This will vary among wells. It will be assumed, however, that preparations should be made to install pumping equipment during the ninth year, using central power with geared installations serving 9 to 11 wells per unit.

Estimated cost per well is $3000.

Royalty   In consolidating the acreage of the Example Lease, it has been found, let us say, that, on the average, the individual owners demand a ⅛ royalty for the original land holder plus an overriding ⅛ royalty for their own interests. This oil will be lifted free of charge and delivered to the pipe line for the accounts of the royalty owners. It will be assumed that royalty oil will pay its own taxes. Six barrels out of each eight produced, therefore, will have to carry the costs of the lease operator.

Operating Costs   A simple cost setup will be used here, although it is recognized that detailed analysis and itemized listings would usually be required in an investigation of this type.

Depreciation and depletion will not be included as costs, since development and plant will be set up as a separate account and depletion will be returned through the valuation formula.

For free-flowing oil, during the first 10 years, costs per barrel will be assumed as follows:—

Lifting	8¢
Overhead	12¢
Taxes	20¢
Field Transportation	10¢
Miscellaneous	6¢
	56¢

During the next 10 years, when some of the wells will be pumping, costs will be assumed at :—

Lifting	16¢
Overhead	12¢
Taxes	20¢
Field Transportation	10¢
Miscellaneous	5¢
	63¢

Costs will increase during the final 10 years and will be taken as :—

Lifting	32¢
Overhead	15¢
Taxes	24¢
Field Transportation	10¢
Miscellaneous	4¢
	85¢

Taxes, it will be noted, are assumed to increase, on a per barrel basis, during this late period. This point will bear careful investigation. Though levied on reserves or production, taxes may not drop in line with depletion or a declining rate of output.

Working Capital Working capital is required to keep a business going. This money is in the nature of a revolving fund, from which current operating expenses are paid out and to which replenishment is made upon receipts from sales. The total amount needed for smooth operation varies among businesses and is dependent to a large extent upon the time lag between production of a unit and receipt of payment for it. Wages, transportation charges, taxes, etc., must be paid; supplies bought; and other current items attended to during this period between production and income.

The operator is entitled to interest on working capital at the same rate, usually, as other moneys used in the business. No depletion is involved, as working capital is not consumed.

For operation of the Example Lease, it will be assumed that working capital should be sufficient in amount to cover approximately six-months' operating costs. Deferred costs need not be covered by working capital. To allow for this, two-thirds of the overhead charges will be excluded as long-range costs. Calculation of the interest as a cost-per-barrel will automatically adjust the item to varying rates of output.

Careful analysis of costs will give an accurate estimate of this item.

On the assumed basis, working capital required will be:—

> First 10-year period
> Production for six months   5,000,000 bbls. (approx.)
> Current costs
> Operator's oil, 3,750,000 at 48¢ = $1,800,000
> Royalty oil,   1,250,000 at 28¢ =   350,000
> Working capital $2,150,000
> Interest rate   8%
> Interest on W. C. per year $ 172,000
> Cost per bbl. operator's oil   2.3¢

A similar calculation for the second 10-year period gives working capital at $2,500,000, with a resulting interest charge of 2⅔¢ per bbl.

An approximation will be resorted to for the third 10-year period, during which production is declining. Using an average output of 3,600,000 bbls. for six months, and calculating as above, gives working capital of $2,480,000 with an interest charge of 3⅔¢ per barrel of operator's oil.

Selling Price   An estimate of selling price for a 30-year forward period is most difficult. It will involve not only statistical analysis of the past record and present supply-demand ratio, but also a long forward look at the overall situation. Some analysts use the current price rather than attempt such an estimate, on the grounds that profit spread will tend to remain constant.

Selling price, at pipe line or port, will be assumed at $1.20 per bbl. for crude of the gravity which the lease will produce.

Profit   Profit per barrel, taking into account the costs to the operator for lifting and delivering the royalty oil and including the costs figured above for interest on working capital, may be calculated as follows:—

	Yrs. 1–10		Period Yrs. 11–20		Yrs. 21–30	
Six bbls. will cost	at 56¢	$3.36	at 63¢	$3.78	at 85¢	$5.10
Two bbls. will cost	at 36¢	.72	at 43¢	.86	at 61¢	1.22
Total		$4.08		$4.64		$6.32
Selling price of operators, six barrels		7.20		7.20		7.20
Balance on operators, six bbls.		3.12		2.56		.88
Balance per bbl.		.52		.42⅔		.14⅔
Less Int. on W. C.		.023		.02⅔		.03⅔
Profit/bbl.		$.497		$.40		$.11
or		$.50				

Interest Rates   Depletion, or amortization of capital, will be covered by using a two-rate sinking-fund premise of the Hoskold type. Income, however, will not be uniform throughout the life and consequently the present value computation will involve summarizing the uneven series instead of by single calculation as in the case of uniform income.

Hoskold rates of 8% and 4% will be used.

Computation of Present Value Present value of the series of unequal annual profits may now be calculated by using the formula:

$$= \frac{(\text{Sum of } P_m R^{n-m} \text{ series})}{1 + r' \left(\dfrac{R^n - 1}{r} \right)}$$

wherein

P_m = respective yearly profits; as P_1, P_2, etc., to P_n,

n = years life,

r' = speculative rate of interest, 8%,

r = safe rate of interest 4%.

Computations will be simplified by setting up, as shown on the insert, a production schedule on which may be listed all of the individual items already discussed and the respective valuation factors to be applied.

Present value of $10,400,000, or $1040 per average acre in addition to the overriding royalty oil may be checked by calculating the value of the lease on the basis of full cash purchase of the overriding interest. On this basis, operator would get seven barrels of each eight. Using the same cost and production data as above, the present values would then be $38,500,000 for the operator's interest before deducting capital outlays and $11,300,000 for the overriding royalty interest. When carried to sufficient arithmetic accuracy, the difference between these two, considering capital outlays, will give the present worth as calculated for the example.

EXAMPLE LEASE — PRODUCTION SCHEDULE — PRORATED LIMIT 55 BBLS./WELL/DAY.

Period	Yr	Output First of Yr	Output Last of Yr	Average for Yr	Total Prod. Year	Total Prod. Cumulative	Recoverable Reserve End of Each Year	Operator's Share of Oil per Year	Profit per Bbl.	Profit per Year P_m	4% R^{-m} (From Table I, n=30, m=oper. year)	Product $P_m R^{-m}$	Money Available First of Year	Factor from Tab. II	Present Value @ 4% Discounted Value as of Valuation Date
PRE-VALUATION YEARS							346,200,000*								$16,865,275
1 OPENING YEAR FOR LEASE	1	0	11,000	5,500	2,007,500	2,007,500									
2 RAPID	2	11,000	36,000	23,500	8,577,500	10,585,000									
3 GROWTH OF	3	36,000	54,000	45,000	16,425,000	27,010,000									
4 OUTPUT	4	54,000	61,000	57,500	20,987,500	47,997,500									
5 FIELD PRORATED	5	54,000	5,500	5,500	2,007,500	50,005,000	296,200,000								
VALUATION DATE															
FUTURE OPERATING LIFE															
DEVELOPMENT PERIOD / LOW-COST PERIOD	1	5,500	16,500	11,000	4,000,000	54,000,000	292,200,000	3,000,000	$.50	$1,500,000	3.1187	4,678,050	$10,000,000	1.0000	10,000,000
	2	16,500	27,500	22,000	8,000,000	62,000,000	284,200,000	6,000,000		3,000,000	2.9997	8,996,100	6,000,000	.96154	5,769,240
	3	27,500	27,500	27,500	10,000,000	72,000,000	274,200,000	7,500,000		3,750,000	2.8834	10,812,750			
UNIFORM OUTPUT	4				10,000,000	82,000,000	264,200,000			3,750,000	2.7725	10,396,875			
	5					92,000,000	254,200,000				2.6658	9,996,750			
	6					102,000,000	244,200,000				2.5633	9,612,375			
	7					112,000,000	234,200,000				2.4647	9,242,625			
INSTALL PUMPING EQPT.	8					122,000,000	224,200,000				2.3699	8,887,125	1,500,000	.73069	1,096,035
	9					132,000,000	214,200,000				2.2788	8,545,500			
	10					142,000,000	204,200,000	7,500,000			2.1911	8,216,625			
MEDIUM-COST PERIOD	11					152,000,000	194,200,000		$.40	$3,000,000	2.1068	6,320,400			
	12					162,000,000	184,200,000				2.0258	6,077,400			
UNDER	13					172,000,000	174,200,000				1.9479	5,843,700			
	14					182,000,000	164,200,000				1.8730	5,619,000			
PRORATION	15					192,000,000	154,200,000				1.8009	5,402,700			
	16					202,000,000	144,200,000				1.7317	5,195,100			
	17					212,000,000	134,200,000				1.6651	4,995,300			
	18					222,000,000	124,200,000				1.6010	4,803,000			
	19					232,000,000	114,200,000				1.5395	4,618,500			
	20	27,500	27,500	27,500		242,000,000	104,200,000	7,500,000			1.4802	4,440,600			
HIGH-COST PERIOD / PRODUCTION DECLINE IN LATE YEARS ASSUMED AT 6.4% IN RATE PER YEAR	21	27,500	25,740	26,620	9,680,000	251,680,000	94,520,000	7,260,000	$.11	$798,600	1.4233	1,136,650			
	22	25,740	23,980	24,860	9,040,000	260,720,000	85,480,000	6,780,000		745,800	1.3686	1,020,700			
	23	23,980	22,220	23,100	8,400,000	269,120,000	77,080,000	6,300,000		693,000	1.3159	911,920			
	24	22,220	20,460	21,340	7,760,000	276,880,000	69,320,000	5,820,000		640,200	1.2653	810,045			
	25	20,460	18,700	19,580	7,120,000	284,000,000	62,200,000	5,340,000		587,400	1.2167	714,690			
	26	18,700	16,940	17,820	6,480,000	290,480,000	55,720,000	4,860,000		534,600	1.1699	625,430			
	27	16,940	15,180	16,060	5,840,000	296,320,000	49,880,000	4,380,000		481,800	1.1249	541,980			
	28	15,180	13,420	14,300	5,200,000	301,520,000	44,680,000	3,900,000		429,000	1.0816	464,010			
	29	13,420	11,660	12,540	4,560,000	306,080,000	40,120,000	3,420,000		376,200	1.0400	391,250			
END PHASE AND STRIPPER OPERATION	30	11,660	9,900	10,780	3,920,000	310,000,000	36,200,000#	2,940,000		323,400	1.0000	323,400			
								7,500,000				Σ 149,640,550	16,865,275		10,407,592

19.8 BBLS./WELL/DAY

#10.4% of *Original Reserve.

$$V_p = \frac{(\Sigma P_a R^{-m} \text{ Series})}{1 + r\left(\dfrac{1 - R^{-m}}{r}\right)}$$

Denominator $= 1 + .08(56.0849)$
$= 1 + 4.486792$
$= 5.486792$

Then $V_p = \dfrac{149,640,550}{5.486792} = 27,272,867$

Less V_p of Capital Outlays 16,865,275

10,407,592

Or $10,400,000

PART IV

OTHER VALUATION THEORIES

Timber Storage Underground.

CHAPTER 20

THE O'DONAHUE, MORKILL, AND GRIMES-CRAIGUE FORMULAS FOR MINE VALUATION

From time to time students of the subject of mine valuation have differed with the premises on which Hoskold's formulas are based. Such differences are the natural outcome of serious thought and are bound to result from individual analysis of any subject by various persons.

It is the contention of the author of this text that the Hoskold premises best express the practical considerations in the majority of mine valuations involving uniform, terminable incomes and logically combine the several factors entering into the calculations to suit best the average conditions. Nevertheless, it will be well, in closing, to discuss briefly three of the most important of the dissenting viewpoints and to point out the logic upon which they are founded. Wherever possible in these discussions, statements will be quoted directly from the originators of the formulas.

O'DONAHUE MODIFICATION OF THE HOSKOLD FORMULA — The premises of T. A. O'Donahue, set forth in 1906, differ from the Hoskold formula only in the treatment of deferred annuities. In all other respects O'Donahue is in agreement with Hoskold. O'Donahue's contention that "absurdly low present values are given by tables calculated at compound interest, when high remunerative rates of interest are necessary and the deferred period exceeds a few years"[1] is well founded and is worthy of serious consideration. The remunerative rate to which he refers corresponds with the term speculative, or hazard rate, as used in this text.

The Hoskold two-rate formula, as such, applies only to the active life of the annuity being valued. It is expressed as

$$V_p = \frac{A}{\dfrac{r}{R^n - 1} + r'}$$ and provides for simple interest to the

purchaser at the speculative rate r' and for the accumulation of a sinking fund at compound interest at the lower or safe rate r. When deferment was involved, Hoskold combined his basic equation with compound interest discount during the deferment period at the speculative rate r'. The combined

equation was stated[2] as $P_{t+n} = \dfrac{pM_n}{(1 + r')^t (1 + r'M_n)}$ which,

after conversion to the respective symbols used in this text

becomes $V_p = \dfrac{A}{\dfrac{r}{R^n - 1} + r'} \times \dfrac{1}{(1 + r')^m}$.

Hoskold apparently did not consider that a rate of discount other than the speculative rate might be advisable, under certain conditions, during the deferment period. If another rate is to be permitted, the combined formula would then be written, as it is in this text, as

$$V_p = \frac{A}{\dfrac{r}{R^n - 1} + r'} \times \frac{1}{(1 + r'')^m} .$$

[1] "The Valuation of Mineral Properties"—T. A. O'Donahue. Inst. of Min. & Met., Vol. 33, page 399.
[2] "Engineer's Valuing Assistant"—H. D. Hoskold. Longmans, Green & Co., 1st Ed. 1877, page 34.

O'Donahue's premise "allows interest at the stipulated rate (remunerative or speculative rate r') on the principal for the entire period (deferment period plus annuity life); but the accumulations of interest are assumed to increase at the lower rate (redemption rate r) of interest during the period of deferment and the annuity provides interest on the profits at the lower rate and not at the stipuated rate."[1]

O'Donahue stated his equation[2] for an annuity of \$1 per year as:

$$P \left(1 + S \frac{R^{n+d} - 1}{r}\right) = \frac{R^n - 1}{r}.$$

When converted into the symbols used here and applied to an annuity of \$A per year this would be:

$$V_p = \frac{\dfrac{(R^n - 1)}{r}}{1 + \dfrac{r'(R^{n+m} - 1)}{r}}.$$

Its derivation is as follows:

Let A = annuity to be valued,
  V_p = present value,
  n = annuity life,
  m = deferment period,
  r = safe rate of interest,
  r' = speculative rate of interest.

Then:

The amount of A per year for n years at r rate will be

$$A \frac{(1 + r)^n - 1}{r}.$$

[1] "Notes on the Valuation of Mineral Properties"—T. A. O'Donahue. Inst. of Min. & Met., Vol. 43, page 32.
[2] "Valuation of Mineral Properties"—T. A. O'Donahue. Inst. of Min. & Met., Vol. 32, page 416.

At the termination of the annuity life, after $m + n$ years, the purchaser is to have his original investment and his annual speculative return $V_p r'$ together with compound interest accrual at the safe rate r on the annual return, or

$$V_p + V_p r' \frac{[(1 + r)^{n+m} - 1]}{r}.$$

These may then be equated to give

$$V_p + V_p r' \left(\frac{R^{n+m} - 1}{r} \right) = \frac{A(R^n - 1)}{r},$$

and

$$V_p = \frac{\dfrac{A(R^n - 1)}{r}}{1 + r' \left(\dfrac{R^{n+m} - 1}{r} \right)}. \qquad (O'Donahue)$$

For a direct comparison between the two premises, the Hoskold formula combined with compound interest deferment may be written as

$$V_p = \frac{\dfrac{A(R^n - 1)}{r}}{1 + r' \left(\dfrac{R^n - 1}{r} \right)} \times \frac{1}{(1 + r'')^m}. \qquad (Hoskold)$$

To illustrate the actual difference between the use of the O'Donahue formula and the Hoskold, let the present worth of an annuity of \$1 per year for 10 years, after a deferment period of 5 years, be determined by both methods, allowing the purchaser 10% interest with redemption of capital at 4%.

By the Hoskold premise:

$$V_p = \frac{1}{\dfrac{r}{R^n - 1} + r} \times \frac{1}{(1 + r')^m}$$

$$= \frac{1}{\dfrac{.04}{1.04^{10} - 1} + .10} \times \frac{1}{1.10^5} = \frac{5.4558}{1.6105} = \underline{\$3.388.}$$

By the O'Donahue premise:

$$V_p = \frac{\dfrac{R^n - 1}{r}}{1 + r' \dfrac{R^{n+m} - 1}{r}} = \frac{\dfrac{\overline{1.04^{10}} - 1}{.04}}{1 + .10 \dfrac{\overline{1.04^{15}} - 1}{.04}}$$

$$= \frac{12.0061}{1 + .10(20.0236)} = \frac{12.0061}{3.0024} = \underline{\$3.999.}$$

Thus, the Hoskold formula gives an appreciably lower present worth than the O'Donahue, and this difference widens as the length of deferment increases.

O'Donahue, however, is not without opposition in his contention that "the rate of remuneration allowed during the deferred period should be identical with that during the annuity term, but should not be greater."[1] It has been pointed out that there is also the risk of not getting even the interest during the period of deferment, and that this risk is as great as that assumed by the capital. When such high remunerative rates of interest are involved, probably the best method of determining the present worth is by the use of hazard factors rather

---

[1] "Valuation of Mineral Properties" —— T. A. O'Donahue.
Inst. of Min. & Met., Vol. 32, page 418.

than by either the Hoskold or the O'Donahue deferment premises.

MORKILL FORMULA FOR MINE VALUATION — At variance also
with the Hoskold
premises are the views set forth in 1918 by D. B. Morkill.[1] He
disagrees upon the grounds that interest should not be received
by the investor upon the whole of the original capital throughout the entire annuity life, because this capital is being periodically returned to the investor. This is a logical contention.
Morkill's argument is as follows:

> "The theory on which the Hoskold formula is based
> is that the dividend received from a mining investment
> must be regarded by the investor as being composed of
> two constant parts, one representing interest on the orig-
> inal investment (at a rate which is considered commen-
> surate with the risk) and the other a return of capital,
> which latter must be of such amount that, when rein-
> vested at compound interest (security rate), it will equal
> the amount of the original investment when the mine is
> exhausted and the dividends cease."

Morkill agrees with the Hoskold theory of separating the
dividend into two such parts, but disagrees with Hoskold's
method of apportionment, and considers that the risk-rate of
interest should be expected only from the amount of capital
remaining unreturned and that, therefore, the two parts of
the dividend should not be constant but varying, the amount
of risk-rate interest annually decreasing and the returns of
capital correspondingly increasing in the investor's segregation
of dividend.

> "The formula here suggested is based on the assump-
> tion that the investor, while drawing risk-rate interest on
> the amount of capital remaining in the original venture,

---

[1] "Formulas for Mine Valuation" — D. B. Morkill.
  Min. & Scientific Press. Vol. 117, page 276.

is also entitled to security-rate interest on the portion that is considered to be returned, for it necessarily does not come into his use if it must be set aside as a sinking-fund.''

Morkill's formula may be derived by tabulating the income allocation as follows:

End of Year	Invested Capital	Dividend
1	V_p	A
2	$V_p(1+r')-A$	A
3	$V_p(1+r')^2-A(1+r')-A$	A
4	$V_p(1+r')^3-A(1+r')^2-A(1+r')-A$	A

End of Year	Interest on Capital	Redemption
1	$V_p r'$	$A-V_p r'$
2	$[V_p(1+r')-A]r'$	$(A-V_p r')(1+r')$
3	$[V_p(1+r')^2-A(1+r')-A]r'$	$(A-V_p r')(1+r')^2$
4	$[V_p(1+r')^3-A(1+r')^2-A(1+r')-A]r'$	$(A-V_p r')(1+r')^3$

and so forth, to n years, when the redemption fund would sum up to

$$(A-V_p r') \frac{(1+r')^n-1}{r'}.$$

As the redemption fund must replace the original investment, we would then have

$$V_p = (A-V_p r') \frac{(1+r')^n-1}{r'}$$

$$= \frac{A[(1+r')^n-1]}{(1+r')^n r'}. \quad (Morkill's\ formula)$$

It will be noted that Morkill's formula takes the same form as that given under Premise 4 for the present value of an annuity at a single rate of interest. Morkill feels that the investor is entitled to interest on the returned capital and that the interest so accrued should not be used to augment the sinking-fund total. In other words, his valuation premise takes into account only one rate of interest, the risk-rate.

In comparison, Morkill further states:

"The Hoskold formula provides for an income at risk-rate each year on the original capital, irrespective of the fact that an annually increasing amount of it has been removed from the venture on which the risk-rate should be paid. The new formula provides for an income at risk-rate on the unreturned capital and at security-rate (or, as the investor may elect) on the returned capital, the combined income varying from risk-rate to security-rate according as capital is removed from one class of investment to the other." [1]

This change in rate of return is most readily shown by comparing the income allocation by the two methods of a definite annuity of $1000 per year for 10 years, allowing interest to the investor at 10% and providing for redemption at 4%, as follows:

HOSKOLD.

Year	V_p	A	$V_p r'$	Actual % Return to Investor	A—$V_p r'$	Amount in Sinking Fund
1	$5455.81	$1000	$545.58	10	$454.42	$454.42
2	5455.81	1000	545.58	10	454.42	927.02
3	5455.81	1000	545.58	10	454.42	1418.52
4	5455.81	1000	545.58	10	454.42	1929.68
5	5455.81	1000	545.58	10	454.42	2461.28
6	5455.81	1000	545.58	10	454.42	3014.15
7	5455.81	1000	545.58	10	454.42	3589.15
8	5455.81	1000	545.58	10	454.42	4187.12
9	5455.81	1000	545.58	10	454.42	4809.03
10	5455.81	1000	545.58	10	454.42	5455.81
					$4544.20	

---

[1] "Formulas for Mine Valuation"—D. B. Morkill. Min. & Scientific Press, vol. 117, page 277.

MORKILL.

Year	V_p	A	$V_p r'$	Actual % Return to Investor	$A - V_p r'$	Amount in Sinking Fund
1	$6144.58	$1000	$614.46	10	$385.54	$385.54
2	5759.04	1000	575.90	9.62	424.10	809.64
3	5334.94	1000	533.49	9.21	466.51	1276.15
4	4868.43	1000	484.84	8.75	513.16	1789.31
5	4355.27	1000	435.52	8.24	564.48	2353.79
6	3790.79	1000	379.08	7.70	620.92	2974.71
7	3169.87	1000	316.99	7.09	683.01	3657.72
8	2486.86	1000	248.68	6.43	751.32	4409.04
9	1735.54	1000	173.55	5.69	826.45	5235.49
10	909.09	1000	90.91	4.89	909.09	6144.58
					$6144.58	

Morkill's formula, when applied to a uniform, terminable income, gives identically the same results as the ordinary single-rate compound-interest methods of valuation, although, of course, when adapted to a series of nonuniform income payments the allocation of the income and the present worth are individual to the Morkill premises alone.

GRIMES-CRAIGUE THREE-RATE VALUATION FORMULA —

"With this method of valuation the investor receives a speculative rate of interest on capital outstanding in the speculative enterprise at the beginning of each year. The capital outstanding in the speculative enterprise is the algebraic difference between the amount of the initial investment and the amount accumulated in the sinking fund at the beginning of the year. The sinking fund is invested to earn a safe rate of interest. The investor is paid a semispeculative rate of interest — a rate of interest intermediate between the speculative and safe rates — upon the amount of capital in the sinking fund at the beginning of the year. The theory accounting for the semispeculative rate of interest is that the possible diversion of the sinking fund to other purposes than the return of capital, without the consent of the investor, justifies a demand for a rate of interest higher than the safe rate but less than the speculative rate upon unreturned capital.[1]

"The effect of this method of valuation is a division of the total investment into two separate and distinct parts, one a speculative investment at a speculative rate of interest and the other a semispeculative investment at a semispeculative rate of interest. The total investment is constant, but the speculative and semispeculative portions vary from year to year."[2]

In the rest of this discussion the symbols used in this text will be substituted for the corresponding symbols used by Grimes and Craigue in the analyses of their premises.

"As in the case of all sinking-fund premises, the value (V_p) is the sum of the amounts contributed to the sinking fund plus interest earned at the rate (r) by each contribution. The amount contributed to the sinking fund in any year is the income for that year less interest paid to the investor. Interest is paid to the investor at one rate (r') on the portion of the initial investment not retired to the sinking fund, and at another rate (r'') on the portion of the initial investment retired to the sinking fund."[3]

A formula or equation which will satisfy the premises upon which Grimes and Craigue have based their method of valuation is determined most readily by allocating the yearly income

[1] "Principles of Valuation" — Grimes & Craigue.
     Prentice-Hall, Inc., 1928, page 46.
[2] Ibid.
[3] "Principles of Valuation"—Grimes & Craigue.
     Prentice-Hall, Inc., 1928, page 47.

to its various divisions. The following allocation chart is entirely similar to the one used by Grimes and Craigue in their text[1] with the exception that the symbols used here have been substituted for theirs in order to arrive at a formula which will be comparable with others previously stated. The formula, as developed, is for a uniform, terminable income, but the same method of allocating income may be used to formulate a series of nonuniform income payments. In the following derivation of the Grimes-Craigue formula for their Sinking Fund Valuation Method with Three Rates of Interest, let

V_p = present value,
A = annual income or annuity to be purchased,
r = safe rate of interest,
r' = speculative rate of interest,
r'' = semi-speculative rate of interest,
n = annuity life.

The itemized income allocation is as follows:

Year	Capital Invested in Speculative Enterprise	Income	Minus Interest to Investor on Capital at Speculative Rate r'
1	V_p	A	$V_p r'$
2	$V_p - (A - V_p r')$	A	$[V_p - (A - V_p r')] r'$
3	$V_p - 2(A - V_p r')$ $- (A - V_p r')(r' - r'' + r)$	A	$[V_p - 2(A - V_p r')$ $- (A - V_p r')(r' - r'' + r)] r'$
n		A	

Year	Minus Interest on Sinking Fund at Semispeculative Rate r''	Plus Interest Earned by Sinking Fund at Safe Rate r
1	O	O
2	$(A - V_p r') r''$	$(A - V_p r') r$
3	$[2(A - V_p r')$ $+ (A - V_p r')(r' - r'' + r)] r''$	$[2(A - V_p r')$ $+ (A - V_p r')(r' - r'' + r)] r$

---

[1] "Principles of Valuation"—Grimes & Craigue, page 48.

Year	Yearly Addition to Sinking Fund
1	$(A-V_p r')$
2	$[A-V_p r'][1+(r'-r''+r)]$
3	$[A-V_p r'][1+(r'-r''+r)]^2$
n	$[A-V_p r'][1+(r'-r''+r)]^{n-1}$

Since the premise upon which the method is based calls for redemption of capital, the yearly additions to the sinking fund must sum up to the present value. These sinking-fund payments, it will be noted, are in the form of a series such as

$$A + AR + AR^2 \cdots\cdots + AR^{n-1},$$

wherein $A = (A-V_p r')$,

$$R = (1+r'-r''+r),$$
$$r = (r'-r''+r).$$

The sum of such a series is $\dfrac{A(R^n-1)}{r}$,

or

$$\frac{(A-V_p r')[(1+r'-r''+r)^n-1]}{(r'-r''+r)} = V_p,$$

$$\frac{A[(1+r'-r''+r)^n-1]}{(r'-r''+r)} - \frac{V_p r'[(1+r'-r''+r)^n-1]}{(r'-r''+r)} = V_p,$$

$$\frac{A[(1+r'-r''+r)^n-1]}{(r'-r''+r)} = V_p + \frac{V_p r'[(1+r'-r''+r)^n-1]}{(r'-r''+r)},$$

$$A[(1+r'-r''+r)^n-1] = V_p(r'-r''+r) + V_p r'[(1+r'-r''+r)^n-1],$$

$$V_p = \frac{A[(1+r'-r''+r)^n-1]}{(r'-r''+r)+r'[(1+r'-r''+r)^n-1]}$$

or

$$= \frac{A[(1+r'-r''+r)^n-1]}{r'(1+r'-r''+r)^n-r'+(r'-r''+r)} \cdot \left(\begin{array}{c}\textit{Grimes-Craigue}\\ \textit{formula}\end{array}\right)$$

PART V

VALUATION TABLES

Tabulated factors for use in calculating compound interest improvements and discounts, and for computing the amounts and present values of various types of annuities, with or without allowance for capital redemption.

A table of six-place logarithms to assist in computing improvements and discounts for compound interest percentages not listed among the tabulations of factors.

PRINCIPAL IMPROVEMENT AND DISCOUNT AT COMPOUND INTEREST

TABLE 1

The sum to which \$1 will amount in n years at rates of 1, 1¼, 1½, 1¾, 2, 2¼, 2½, 2¾, 3, 3¼, 3½, 3¾, 4, 4¼, 4½, 4¾, 5, 5½, 6, 6½, 7, 7½, 8, 9, 10, 11, 12, 13, 14, 15, 16, 18, 20, 25, and 30 percent.

Calculated to 4 decimal places
and to 50 years.

The factors given in this table represent values of

$$(1 + r)^n,$$

or $R^n.$

If the principal sum accruing is other than unity, this principal is multiplied by the factor given in the table to obtain the desired amount.

$$S = P(1 + r)^n$$
$$= PR^n$$
$$= P \times \text{Table Factor.}$$

For instance, to what sum will \$50 amount in 14 years at 6% compound interest?

$$S = 50 \times 2.2609$$
$$= \$113.04.$$

PRINCIPAL IMPROVEMENT AND DISCOUNT

TABLE 1

Amount of \$1 in n years at the following rates percent, compound interest.

Years	1%	1¼%	1½%	1¾%	2%	2¼%	2½%
1	1.0100	1.0125	1.0150	1.0175	1.0200	1.0225	1.0250
2	1.0201	1.0252	1.0302	1.0353	1.0404	1.0455	1.0506
3	1.0303	1.0380	1.0457	1.0534	1.0612	1.0690	1.0769
4	1.0406	1.0509	1.0614	1.0719	1.0824	1.0931	1.1038
5	1.0510	1.0641	1.0773	1.0906	1.1041	1.1177	1.1314
6	1.0615	1.0774	1.0934	1.1097	1.1262	1.1428	1.1597
7	1.0721	1.0909	1.1098	1.1291	1.1487	1.1685	1.1887
8	1.0829	1.1045	1.1265	1.1489	1.1717	1.1948	1.2184
9	1.0937	1.1183	1.1434	1.1690	1.1951	1.2217	1.2489
10	1.1046	1.1323	1.1605	1.1894	1.2190	1.2492	1.2801
11	1.1157	1.1464	1.1779	1.2103	1.2434	1.2773	1.3121
12	1.1268	1.1608	1.1956	1.2314	1.2682	1.3060	1.3449
13	1.1381	1.1753	1.2136	1.2530	1.2936	1.3354	1.3785
14	1.1495	1.1900	1.2318	1.2749	1.3195	1.3655	1.4130
15	1.1610	1.2048	1.2502	1.2972	1.3459	1.3962	1.4483
16	1.1726	1.2199	1.2690	1.3199	1.3728	1.4276	1.4845
17	1.1843	1.2351	1.2880	1.3430	1.4002	1.4597	1.5216
18	1.1961	1.2506	1.3073	1.3665	1.4282	1.4926	1.5597
19	1.2081	1.2662	1.3270	1.3904	1.4568	1.5262	1.5987
20	1.2202	1.2820	1.3469	1.4148	1.4859	1.5605	1.6386
21	1.2324	1.2981	1.3671	1.4395	1.5157	1.5956	1.6796
22	1.2447	1.3143	1.3876	1.4647	1.5460	1.6315	1.7216
23	1.2572	1.3307	1.4084	1.4904	1.5769	1.6682	1.7646
24	1.2697	1.3474	1.4295	1.5164	1.6084	1.7058	1.8087
25	1.2824	1.3642	1.4509	1.5430	1.6406	1.7441	1.8539
26	1.2953	1.3812	1.4727	1.5700	1.6734	1.7834	1.9003
27	1.3082	1.3985	1.4948	1.5975	1.7069	1.8235	1.9478
28	1.3213	1.4160	1.5172	1.6254	1.7410	1.8645	1.9965
29	1.3345	1.4337	1.5400	1.6539	1.7758	1.9065	2.0464
30	1.3478	1.4516	1.5631	1.6828	1.8114	1.9494	2.0976
31	1.3613	1.4698	1.5865	1.7122	1.8476	1.9933	2.1500
32	1.3749	1.4881	1.6103	1.7422	1.8845	2.0381	2.2038
33	1.3887	1.5067	1.6345	1.7727	1.9222	2.0840	2.2589
34	1.4026	1.5256	1.6590	1.8037	1.9607	2.1308	2.3153
35	1.4166	1.5446	1.6839	1.8353	1.9999	2.1788	2.3732
36	1.4308	1.5639	1.7091	1.8674	2.0399	2.2278	2.4325
37	1.4451	1.5835	1.7348	1.9001	2.0807	2.2779	2.4933
38	1.4595	1.6033	1.7608	1.9333	2.1223	2.3292	2.5557
39	1.4741	1.6233	1.7872	1.9672	2.1647	2.3816	2.6196
40	1.4889	1.6436	1.8140	2.0016	2.2080	2.4352	2.6851
41	1.5038	1.6642	1.8412	2.0366	2.2522	2.4900	2.7522
42	1.5188	1.6850	1.8688	2.0723	2.2972	2.5460	2.8210
43	1.5340	1.7060	1.8969	2.1085	2.3432	2.6033	2.8915
44	1.5493	1.7274	1.9253	2.1454	2.3901	2.6619	2.9638
45	1.5648	1.7489	1.9542	2.1830	2.4379	2.7218	3.0379
46	1.5805	1.7708	1.9835	2.2212	2.4866	2.7830	3.1139
47	1.5963	1.7929	2.0133	2.2600	2.5363	2.8456	3.1917
48	1.6122	1.8154	2.0435	2.2996	2.5871	2.9096	3.2715
49	1.6283	1.8380	2.0741	2.3398	2.6388	2.9751	3.3533
50	1.6446	1.8610	2.1052	2.3808	2.6916	3.0420	3.4371

TABLE 1

Amount of $1 in n years at the following rates percent, compound interest.

Years	2¾%	3%	3¼%	3½%	3¾%	4%	4¼%
1	1.0275	1.0300	1.0325	1.0350	1.0375	1.0400	1.0425
2	1.0558	1.0609	1.0661	1.0712	1.0764	1.0816	1.0868
3	1.0848	1.0927	1.1007	1.1087	1.1168	1.1249	1.1330
4	1.1146	1.1255	1.1365	1.1475	1.1587	1.1699	1.1811
5	1.1453	1.1593	1.1734	1.1877	1.2021	1.2167	1.2313
6	1.1768	1.1941	1.2115	1.2293	1.2472	1.2653	1.2837
7	1.2091	1.2299	1.2509	1.2723	1.2939	1.3159	1.3382
8	1.2424	1.2668	1.2916	1.3168	1.3425	1.3686	1.3951
9	1.2765	1.3048	1.3336	1.3629	1.3928	1.4233	1.4544
10	1.3117	1.3439	1.3769	1.4106	1.4450	1.4802	1.5162
11	1.3477	1.3842	1.4216	1.4600	1.4992	1.5395	1.5807
12	1.3848	1.4258	1.4678	1.5111	1.5555	1.6010	1.6478
13	1.4229	1.4685	1.5155	1.5640	1.6138	1.6651	1.7179
14	1.4620	1.5126	1.5648	1.6187	1.6743	1.7317	1.7909
15	1.5022	1.5580	1.6157	1.6753	1.7371	1.8009	1.8670
16	1.5435	1.6047	1.6682	1.7340	1.8022	1.8730	1.9463
17	1.5860	1.6528	1.7224	1.7947	1.8698	1.9479	2.0291
18	1.6296	1.7024	1.7784	1.8575	1.9399	2.0258	2.1153
19	1.6744	1.7535	1.8362	1.9225	2.0127	2.1068	2.2052
20	1.7204	1.8061	1.8958	1.9898	2.0882	2.1911	2.2989
21	1.7677	1.8603	1.9575	2.0594	2.1665	2.2788	2.3966
22	1.8164	1.9161	2.0211	2.1315	2.2477	2.3699	2.4985
23	1.8663	1.9736	2.0868	2.2061	2.3320	2.4647	2.6047
24	1.9176	2.0328	2.1546	2.2833	2.4194	2.5633	2.7153
25	1.9704	2.0938	2.2246	2.3632	2.5102	2.6658	2.8308
26	2.0245	2.1566	2.2969	2.4460	2.6043	2.7725	2.9511
27	2.0802	2.2213	2.3715	2.5316	2.7020	2.8834	3.0765
28	2.1374	2.2879	2.4486	2.6202	2.8033	2.9987	3.2072
29	2.1962	2.3566	2.5282	2.7119	2.9084	3.1187	3.3435
30	2.2566	2.4273	2.6104	2.8068	3.0175	3.2434	3.4856
31	2.3187	2.5001	2.6952	2.9050	3.1306	3.3731	3.6338
32	2.3824	2.5751	2.7828	3.0067	3.2480	3.5081	3.7882
33	2.4479	2.6523	2.8732	3.1119	3.3698	3.6484	3.9492
34	2.5153	2.7319	2.9666	3.2209	3.4962	3.7943	4.1171
35	2.5844	2.8139	3.0630	3.3336	3.6273	3.9461	4.2920
36	2.6555	2.8983	3.1626	3.4503	3.7633	4.1039	4.4744
37	2.7285	2.9852	3.2654	3.5710	3.9045	4.2681	4.6646
38	2.8036	3.0748	3.3715	3.6960	4.0509	4.4388	4.8628
39	2.8807	3.1670	3.4811	3.8254	4.2028	4.6164	5.0695
40	2.9599	3.2620	3.5942	3.9593	4.3604	4.8010	5.2850
41	3.0413	3.3599	3.7110	4.0978	4.5239	4.9931	5.5096
42	3.1249	3.4607	3.8316	4.2413	4.6935	5.1928	5.7437
43	3.2108	3.5645	3.9561	4.3897	4.8695	5.4005	5.9878
44	3.2991	3.6715	4.0847	4.5433	5.0522	5.6165	6.2423
45	3.3899	3.7816	4.2175	4.7024	5.2416	5.8412	6.5076
46	3.4831	3.8950	4.3545	4.8669	5.4382	6.0748	6.7842
47	3.5789	4.0119	4.4961	5.0373	5.6421	6.3178	7.0725
48	3.6773	4.1323	4.6422	5.2136	5.8537	6.5705	7.3731
49	3.7784	4.2562	4.7931	5.3961	6.0732	6.8333	7.6865
50	3.8823	4.3839	4.9488	5.5849	6.3009	7.1067	8.0131

TABLE 1

Amount of $1 in n years at the following rates percent, compound interest.

Years	4½%	4¾%	5%	5½%	6%	6½%	7%
1	1.0450	1.0475	1.0500	1.0550	1.0600	1.0650	1.0700
2	1.0920	1.0973	1.1025	1.1130	1.1236	1.1342	1.1449
3	1.1412	1.1494	1.1576	1.1742	1.1910	1.2079	1.2250
4	1.1925	1.2040	1.2155	1.2388	1.2625	1.2865	1.3108
5	1.2462	1.2612	1.2763	1.3070	1.3382	1.3701	1.4026
6	1.3023	1.3211	1.3401	1.3788	1.4185	1.4591	1.5007
7	1.3609	1.3838	1.4071	1.4547	1.5036	1.5540	1.6058
8	1.4221	1.4495	1.4775	1.5347	1.5938	1.6550	1.7182
9	1.4861	1.5184	1.5513	1.6191	1.6895	1.7626	1.8385
10	1.5530	1.5905	1.6289	1.7081	1.7908	1.8771	1.9672
11	1.6229	1.6661	1.7103	1.8021	1.8983	1.9992	2.1049
12	1.6959	1.7452	1.7959	1.9012	2.0122	2.1291	2.2522
13	1.7722	1.8281	1.8856	2.0058	2.1329	2.2675	2.4098
14	1.8519	1.9149	1.9799	2.1161	2.2609	2.4149	2.5785
15	1.9353	2.0059	2.0789	2.2325	2.3966	2.5718	2.7590
16	2.0224	2.1012	2.1829	2.3553	2.5404	2.7390	2.9522
17	2.1134	2.2010	2.2920	2.4848	2.6928	2.9170	3.1588
18	2.2085	2.3055	2.4066	2.6215	2.8543	3.1067	3.3799
19	2.3079	2.4150	2.5270	2.7656	3.0256	3.3086	3.6165
20	2.4117	2.5298	2.6533	2.9178	3.2071	3.5236	3.8697
21	2.5202	2.6499	2.7860	3.0782	3.3996	3.7527	4.1406
22	2.6337	2.7758	2.9253	3.2475	3.6035	3.9966	4.4304
23	2.7522	2.9077	3.0715	3.4262	3.8197	4.2564	4.7405
24	2.8760	3.0458	3.2251	3.6146	4.0489	4.5331	5.0724
25	3.0054	3.1904	3.3864	3.8134	4.2919	4.8277	5.4274
26	3.1407	3.3420	3.5557	4.0231	4.5494	5.1415	5.8074
27	3.2820	3.5007	3.7335	4.2444	4.8223	5.4757	6.2139
28	3.4297	3.6670	3.9201	4.4778	5.1117	5.8316	6.6488
29	3.5840	3.8412	4.1161	4.7241	5.4184	6.2107	7.1143
30	3.7453	4.0237	4.3219	4.9840	5.7435	6.6144	7.6123
31	3.9139	4.2148	4.5380	5.2581	6.0881	7.0443	8.1451
32	4.0900	4.4150	4.7649	5.5473	6.4534	7.5022	8.7153
33	4.2740	4.6247	5.0032	5.8524	6.8406	7.9898	9.3253
34	4.4664	4.8444	5.2533	6.1742	7.2510	8.5092	9.9781
35	4.6673	5.0745	5.5160	6.5138	7.6861	9.0623	10.6766
36	4.8774	5.3155	5.7918	6.8721	8.1473	9.6513	11.4239
37	5.0969	5.5680	6.0814	7.2501	8.6361	10.2786	12.2236
38	5.3262	5.8325	6.3855	7.6488	9.1543	10.9467	13.0793
39	5.5659	6.1095	6.7048	8.0695	9.7035	11.6583	13.9948
40	5.8164	6.3997	7.0400	8.5133	10.2857	12.4161	14.9745
41	6.0781	6.7037	7.3920	8.9815	10.9029	13.2231	16.0227
42	6.3516	7.0221	7.7616	9.4755	11.5570	14.0826	17.1443
43	6.6374	7.3557	8.1497	9.9967	12.2505	14.9980	18.3444
44	6.9361	7.7051	8.5572	10.5465	12.9855	15.9729	19.6285
45	7.2482	8.0711	8.9850	11.1266	13.7646	17.0111	21.0025
46	7.5744	8.4544	9.4343	11.7385	14.5905	18.1168	22.4726
47	7.9153	8.8560	9.9060	12.3841	15.4659	19.2944	24.0457
48	8.2715	9.2767	10.4013	13.0653	16.3939	20.5485	25.7289
49	8.6437	9.7173	10.9213	13.7838	17.3775	21.8842	27.5299
50	9.0326	10.1789	11.4674	14.5420	18.4202	23.3067	29.4570

TABLE 1

Amount of $1 in n years at the following rates percent, compound interest.

Years	7½%	8%	9%	10%	11%	12%	13%
1	1.0750	1.0800	1.0900	1.1000	1.1100	1.1200	1.1300
2	1.1556	1.1664	1.1881	1.2100	1.2321	1.2544	1.2769
3	1.2423	1.2597	1.2950	1.3310	1.3676	1.4049	1.4429
4	1.3355	1.3605	1.4116	1.4641	1.5181	1.5735	1.6305
5	1.4356	1.4693	1.5386	1.6105	1.6851	1.7623	1.8424
6	1.5433	1.5869	1.6771	1.7716	1.8704	1.9738	2.0820
7	1.6590	1.7138	1.8280	1.9487	2.0762	2.2107	2.3526
8	1.7835	1.8509	1.9926	2.1436	2.3045	2.4760	2.6584
9	1.9172	1.9990	2.1719	2.3579	2.5580	2.7731	3.0040
10	2.0610	2.1589	2.3674	2.5937	2.8394	3.1058	3.3946
11	2.2156	2.3316	2.5804	2.8531	3.1518	3.4785	3.8359
12	2.3818	2.5182	2.8127	3.1384	3.4985	3.8960	4.3345
13	2.5604	2.7196	3.0658	3.4523	3.8833	4.3635	4.8980
14	2.7524	2.9372	3.3417	3.7975	4.3104	4.8871	5.5348
15	2.9589	3.1722	3.6425	4.1772	4.7846	5.4736	6.2543
16	3.1808	3.4259	3.9703	4.5950	5.3109	6.1304	7.0673
17	3.4194	3.7000	4.3276	5.0545	5.8951	6.8660	7.9861
18	3.6758	3.9960	4.7171	5.5599	6.5436	7.6900	9.0243
19	3.9515	4.3157	5.1417	6.1159	7.2633	8.6128	10.1974
20	4.2479	4.6610	5.6044	6.7275	8.0623	9.6463	11.5231
21	4.5664	5.0338	6.1088	7.4002	8.9492	10.8038	13.0211
22	4.9089	5.4365	6.6586	8.1403	9.9336	12.1003	14.7138
23	5.2771	5.8715	7.2579	8.9543	11.0263	13.5523	16.6266
24	5.6729	6.3412	7.9111	9.8497	12.2392	15.1786	18.7881
25	6.0983	6.8485	8.6231	10.8347	13.5855	17.0001	21.2305
26	6.5557	7.3964	9.3992	11.9182	15.0799	19.0401	23.9905
27	7.0474	7.9881	10.2451	13.1100	16.7386	21.3249	27.1093
28	7.5759	8.6271	11.1671	14.4210	18.5799	23.8839	30.6335
29	8.1441	9.3173	12.1722	15.8631	20.6237	26.7499	34.6158
30	8.7550	10.0627	13.2677	17.4494	22.8923	29.9599	39.1159
31	9.4116	10.8677	14.4618	19.1943	25.4104	33.5551	44.2010
32	10.1174	11.7371	15.7633	21.1138	28.2056	37.5817	49.9471
33	10.8763	12.6760	17.1820	23.2252	31.3082	42.0915	56.4402
34	11.6920	13.6901	18.7284	25.5477	34.7521	47.1425	63.7774
35	12.5689	14.7853	20.4140	28.1024	38.5749	52.7996	72.0685
36	13.5115	15.9682	22.2512	30.9127	42.8181	59.1356	81.4374
37	14.5249	17.2456	24.2538	34.0039	47.5281	66.2318	92.0243
38	15.6143	18.6253	26.4367	37.4043	52.7562	74.1797	103.987
39	16.7853	20.1153	28.8160	41.1448	58.5593	83.0812	117.506
40	18.0442	21.7245	31.4094	45.2593	65.0009	93.0510	132.782
41	19.3976	23.4625	34.2363	49.7852	72.1510	104.217	150.043
42	20.8524	25.3395	37.3175	54.7637	80.0876	116.723	169.549
43	22.4163	27.3666	40.6761	60.2401	88.8972	130.730	191.590
44	24.0975	29.5560	44.3370	66.2641	98.6759	146.418	216.497
45	25.9048	31.9204	48.3273	72.8905	109.530	163.988	244.641
46	27.8477	34.4741	52.6767	80.1795	121.579	183.666	276.445
47	29.9363	37.2320	57.4176	88.1975	134.952	205.706	312.383
48	32.1815	40.2106	62.5852	97.1072	149.797	230.391	352.992
49	34.5951	43.4274	68.2179	106.719	166.275	258.038	398.881
50	37.1897	46.9016	74.3575	117.391	184.565	289.002	450.736

TABLE 1

Amount of $1 in n years at the following rates percent, compound interest.

Years	14%	15%	16%	18%	20%	25%	30%
1	1.1400	1.1500	1.1600	1.1800	1.2000	1.2500	1.3000
2	1.2996	1.3225	1.3456	1.3924	1.4400	1.5625	1.6900
3	1.4815	1.5209	1.5609	1.6430	1.7280	1.9531	2.1970
4	1.6890	1.7490	1.8106	1.9388	2.0736	2.4414	2.8561
5	1.9254	2.0114	2.1003	2.2878	2.4883	3.0518	3.7129
6	2.1950	2.3131	2.4364	2.6996	2.9860	3.8147	4.8268
7	2.5023	2.6600	2.8262	3.1855	3.5832	4.7684	6.2749
8	2.8526	3.0590	3.2784	3.7589	4.2998	5.9605	8.1573
9	3.2519	3.5179	3.8030	4.4355	5.1598	7.4506	10.6045
10	3.7072	4.0456	4.4114	5.2338	6.1917	9.3132	13.7858
11	4.2262	4.6524	5.1173	6.1759	7.4301	11.6415	17.9216
12	4.8179	5.3503	5.9360	7.2876	8.9161	14.5519	23.2981
13	5.4924	6.1528	6.8858	8.5994	10.6993	18.1899	30.2875
14	6.2613	7.0757	7.9875	10.1472	12.8392	22.7374	39.3738
15	7.1379	8.1371	9.2655	11.9737	15.4070	28.4217	51.1859
16	8.1372	9.3576	10.7480	14.1290	18.4884	35.5271	66.5417
17	9.2765	10.7613	12.4677	16.6722	22.1861	44.4089	86.5041
18	10.5752	12.3755	14.4625	19.6733	26.6233	55.5112	112.455
19	12.0557	14.2318	16.7765	23.2144	31.9480	69.3889	146.192
20	13.7435	16.3665	19.4608	27.3930	38.3376	86.7362	190.050
21	15.6676	18.8215	22.5745	32.3238	46.0051	108.420	247.064
22	17.8610	21.6447	26.1864	38.1421	55.2061	135.525	321.184
23	20.3616	24.8915	30.3762	45.0076	66.2474	169.407	417.539
24	23.2122	28.6252	35.2364	53.1090	79.4968	211.758	542.801
25	26.4619	32.9190	40.8742	62.6686	95.3962	264.698	705.641
26	30.1666	37.8568	47.4141	73.9490	114.475	330.872	917.333
27	34.3899	43.5353	55.0004	87.2598	137.371	413.590	
28	39.2045	50.0656	63.8004	102.967	164.845	516.988	
29	44.6931	57.5755	74.0085	121.501	197.814	646.235	
30	50.9502	66.2118	85.8499	143.371	237.376	807.794	
31	58.0832	76.1435	99.5859	169.177	284.852		
32	66.2148	87.5651	115.520	199.629	341.822		
33	75.4849	100.700	134.003	235.563	410.186		
34	86.0528	115.805	155.443	277.964	492.224		
35	98.1002	133.176	180.314	327.997			
36	111.834	153.152	209.164	387.037			
37	127.491	176.125	242.631	456.703			
38	145.340	202.543	281.452	538.910			
39	165.687	232.925	326.484				
40	188.884	267.864	378.721				
41	215.327	308.043	439.317				
42	245.473	354.250	509.607				
43	279.839	407.387					
44	319.017	468.495					
45	363.679	538.769					
46	414.594	619.585					
47	472.637						
48	538.807						
49	614.239						
50	700.233						

PRESENT VALUE OF A UNIT PRINCIPAL AT COMPOUND INTEREST

TABLE 2

The present value of $1 due n years hence, at rates of 1, 1¼, 1½, 1¾, 2, 2¼, 2½, 2¾, 3, 3¼, 3½, 3¾, 4, 4¼, 4½, 4¾, 5, 5½, 6, 6½, 7, 7½, 8, 9, 10, 11, 12, 13, 14, 15, 16, 18, 20, 25, and 30 percent.

Calculated to 5 decimal places
and to 50 years.

The factors given in this table represent values of

$$\frac{1}{(1+r)^n},$$

or $$\frac{1}{R^n}.$$

The factors given in this table are reciprocals of the corresponding factors in Table 1.

$$1 \div R^n = \frac{1}{R^n}.$$

If the principal sum to be discounted is other than unity, this sum is multiplied by the factor given in the table to obtain the desired present value

$$V_p = \frac{P}{(1+r)^n}$$

$$= \frac{P}{R^n} = P \times \frac{1}{R^n}$$

$$= P \times \text{Table Factor.}$$

For instance, what is the present value of $50 due 14 years hence at 6% compound interest?

$$V_p = 50 \times .44230$$
$$= \$22.11.$$

TABLE 2

Present value of $1 due n years hence at the following rates percent, compound interest.

Years	1%	1¼%	1½%	1¾%	2%	2¼%	2½%
1	.99010	.98765	.98522	.98280	.98039	.97800	.97561
2	.98030	.97546	.97066	.96590	.96117	.95647	.95181
3	.97059	.96342	.95632	.94929	.94232	.93543	.92860
4	.96098	.95152	.94218	.93296	.92385	.91484	.90595
5	.95147	.93978	.92826	.91691	.90573	.89471	.88385
6	.94205	.92817	.91454	.90114	.88797	.87502	.86230
7	.93272	.91672	.90103	.88564	.87056	.85577	.84127
8	.92348	.90540	.88771	.87041	.85349	.83694	.82075
9	.91434	.89422	.87459	.85544	.83676	.81852	.80073
10	.90529	.88318	.86167	.84073	.82035	.80051	.78120
11	.89632	.87228	.84893	.82627	.80426	.78289	.76214
12	.88745	.86151	.83639	.81206	.78849	.76567	.74356
13	.87866	.85087	.82403	.79809	.77303	.74882	.72542
14	.86996	.84037	.81185	.78436	.75788	.73234	.70773
15	.86135	.82999	.79985	.77087	.74301	.71623	.69047
16	.85282	.81975	.78803	.75762	.72845	.70047	.67362
17	.84438	.80963	.77639	.74459	.71416	.68505	.65720
18	.83602	.79963	.76491	.73178	.70016	.66998	.64117
19	.82774	.78976	.75361	.71919	.68643	.65523	.62553
20	.81954	.78001	.74247	.70682	.67297	.64082	.61027
21	.81143	.77038	.73150	.69467	.65978	.62672	.59539
22	.80340	.76087	.72069	.68272	.64684	.61292	.58086
23	.79544	.75147	.71004	.67098	.63416	.59944	.56670
24	.78757	.74220	.69954	.65944	.62172	.58625	.55288
25	.77977	.73303	.68921	.64810	.60953	.57335	.53939
26	.77205	.72398	.67902	.63695	.59758	.56073	.52623
27	.76440	.71505	.66899	.62599	.58586	.54839	.51340
28	.75684	.70622	.65910	.61523	.57437	.53632	.50088
29	.74934	.69750	.64936	.60465	.56311	.52452	.48866
30	.74192	.68889	.63976	.59425	.55207	.51298	.47674
31	.73458	.68038	.63031	.58403	.54125	.50169	.46511
32	.72730	.67198	.62099	.57398	.53063	.49065	.45377
33	.72010	.66369	.61182	.56411	.52023	.47986	.44270
34	.71297	.65549	.60277	.55441	.51003	.46930	.43191
35	.70591	.64740	.59387	.54487	.50003	.45897	.42137
36	.69892	.63941	.58509	.53550	.49022	.44887	.41109
37	.69200	.63152	.57644	.52629	.48061	.43899	.40107
38	.68515	.62372	.56792	.51724	.47119	.42933	.39128
39	.67837	.61602	.55953	.50834	.46195	.41989	.38174
40	.67165	.60841	.55126	.49960	.45289	.41065	.37243
41	.66500	.60090	.54312	.49101	.44401	.40161	.36335
42	.65842	.59348	.53509	.48256	.43530	.39277	.35448
43	.65190	.58616	.52718	.47426	.42677	.38413	.34584
44	.64545	.57892	.51939	.46611	.41840	.37568	.33740
45	.63905	.57177	.51171	.45809	.41020	.36741	.32917
46	.63273	.56471	.50415	.45021	.40215	.35932	.32115
47	.62646	.55774	.49670	.44247	.39427	.35142	.31331
48	.62026	.55086	.48936	.43486	.38654	.34369	.30567
49	.61412	.54406	.48213	.42738	.37896	.33612	.29822
50	.60804	.53734	.47500	.42003	.37153	.32873	.29094

TABLE 2

Present value of $1 due n years hence at the following rates percent, compound interest.

Years	2¾%	3%	3¼%	3½%	3¾%	4%	4¼%
1	.97324	.97087	.96852	.96618	.96386	.96154	.95923
2	.94719	.94260	.93804	.93351	.92902	.92456	.92013
3	.92184	.91514	.90851	.90194	.89544	.88900	.88262
4	.89717	.88849	.87991	.87144	.86307	.85480	.84663
5	.87315	.86261	.85222	.84197	.83188	.82193	.81212
6	.84978	.83748	.82539	.81350	.80181	.79031	.77901
7	.82704	.81309	.79941	.78599	.77283	.75992	.74725
8	.80491	.78941	.77425	.75941	.74490	.73069	.71679
9	.78336	.76642	.74988	.73373	.71797	.70259	.68757
10	.76240	.74409	.72627	.70892	.69202	.67556	.65954
11	.74199	.72242	.70341	.68495	.66701	.64958	.63265
12	.72213	.70138	.68127	.66178	.64290	.62460	.60686
13	.70281	.68095	.65983	.63940	.61966	.60057	.58212
14	.68400	.66112	.63906	.61778	.59726	.57748	.55839
15	.66569	.64186	.61894	.59689	.57568	.55526	.53562
16	.64787	.62317	.59946	.57671	.55487	.53391	.51379
17	.63053	.60502	.58059	.55720	.53481	.51337	.49284
18	.61366	.58739	.56231	.53836	.51548	.49363	.47275
19	.59723	.57029	.54461	.52016	.49685	.47464	.45348
20	.58125	.55368	.52747	.50257	.47889	.45639	.43499
21	.56569	.53755	.51087	.48557	.46158	.43883	.41726
22	.55055	.52189	.49479	.46915	.44490	.42196	.40025
23	.53582	.50669	.47921	.45329	.42882	.40573	.38393
24	.52148	.49193	.46413	.43796	.41332	.39012	.36828
25	.50752	.47761	.44952	.42315	.39838	.37512	.35326
26	.49394	.46369	.43537	.40884	.38398	.36069	.33886
27	.48072	.45019	.42167	.39501	.37010	.34682	.32505
28	.46785	.43708	.40839	.38165	.35672	.33348	.31180
29	.45533	.42435	.39554	.36875	.34383	.32065	.29908
30	.44314	.41199	.38309	.35628	.33140	.30832	.28689
31	.43128	.39999	.37103	.34423	.31942	.29646	.27520
32	.41974	.38834	.35935	.33259	.30788	.28506	.26398
33	.40851	.37703	.34804	.32134	.29675	.27409	.25322
34	.39757	.36604	.33708	.31048	.28603	.26355	.24289
35	.38693	.35538	.32647	.29998	.27569	.25342	.23299
36	.37658	.34503	.31620	.28983	.26572	.24367	.22349
37	.36650	.33498	.30624	.28003	.25612	.23430	.21438
38	.35669	.32523	.29660	.27056	.24686	.22529	.20564
39	.34714	.31575	.28727	.26141	.23794	.21662	.19726
40	.33785	.30656	.27823	.25257	.22934	.20829	.18922
41	.32881	.29763	.26947	.24403	.22105	.20028	.18150
42	.32001	.28896	.26099	.23578	.21306	.19257	.17410
43	.31144	.28054	.25277	.22781	.20536	.18517	.16700
44	.30311	.27237	.24481	.22010	.19794	.17805	.16020
45	.29500	.26444	.23711	.21266	.19078	.17120	.15367
46	.28710	.25674	.22965	.20547	.18389	.16461	.14740
47	.27942	.24926	.22242	.19852	.17724	.15828	.14139
48	.27194	.24200	.21542	.19181	.17083	.15219	.13563
49	.26466	.23495	.20863	.18532	.16466	.14634	.13010
50	.25758	.22811	.20207	.17905	.15871	.14071	.12479

TABLE 2

Present value of $1 due n years hence at the following rates percent, compound interest.

Years	4½%	4¾%	5%	5½%	6%	6½%	7%
1	.95694	.95465	.95238	.94787	.94340	.93897	.93458
2	.91573	.91136	.90703	.89845	.89000	.88166	.87344
3	.87630	.87004	.86384	.85161	.83962	.82785	.81630
4	.83856	.83058	.82270	.80722	.79209	.77732	.76290
5	.80245	.79292	.78353	.76513	.74726	.72988	.71299
6	.76790	.75697	.74622	.72525	.70496	.68533	.66634
7	.73483	.72264	.71068	.68744	.66506	.64351	.62275
8	.70319	.68987	.67684	.65160	.62741	.60423	.58201
9	.67290	.65859	.64461	.61763	.59190	.56735	.54393
10	.64393	.62872	.61391	.58543	.55839	.53273	.50835
11	.61620	.60021	.58468	.55491	.52679	.50021	.47509
12	.58966	.57300	.55684	.52598	.49697	.46968	.44401
13	.56427	.54701	.53032	.49856	.46884	.44102	.41496
14	.53997	.52221	.50507	.47257	.44230	.41410	.38782
15	.51672	.49853	.48102	.44793	.41727	.38883	.36245
16	.49447	.47592	.45811	.42458	.39365	.36510	.33873
17	.47318	.45434	.43630	.40245	.37136	.34281	.31657
18	.45280	.43374	.41552	.38147	.35034	.32189	.29586
19	.43330	.41407	.39573	36158	.33051	.30224	.27651
20	.41464	.39529	.37689	.34273	.31180	.28380	.25842
21	.39679	.37737	.35894	.32486	.29416	.26648	.24151
22	.37970	.36026	.34185	.30793	.27751	.25021	.22571
23	.36335	.34392	.32557	.29187	.26180	.23494	.21095
24	.34770	.32832	.31007	.27666	.24698	.22060	.19715
25	.33273	.31344	.29530	.26223	.23300	.20714	.18425
26	.31840	.29922	.28124	.24856	.21981	.19450	.17220
27	.30469	.28565	.26785	.23560	.20737	.18263	.16093
28	.29157	.27270	.25509	.22332	.19563	.17148	.15040
29	.27902	.26034	.24295	.21168	.18456	.16101	.14056
30	.26700	.24853	.23138	.20064	.17411	.15119	.13137
31	.25550	.23726	.22036	.19018	.16425	.14196	.12277
32	.24450	.22650	.20987	.18027	.15496	.13329	.11474
33	.23397	.21623	.19987	.17087	.14619	.12516	.10723
34	.22390	.20643	.19035	.16196	.13791	.11752	.10022
35	.21425	.19706	.18129	.15352	.13011	.11035	.09366
36	.20503	.18813	.17266	.14552	.12274	.10361	.08754
37	.19620	.17960	.16444	.13793	.11579	.09729	.08181
38	.18775	.17145	.15661	.13074	.10924	.09135	.07646
39	.17967	.16368	.14915	.12392	.10306	.08578	.07146
40	.17193	.15626	.14205	.11746	.09722	.08054	.06678
41	.16453	.14917	.13528	.11134	.09172	.07563	.06241
42	.15744	.14241	.12884	.10554	.08653	.07101	.05833
43	.15066	.13595	.12270	.10003	.08163	.06668	.05451
44	.14417	.12978	.11686	.09482	.07701	.06261	.05095
45	.13796	.12390	.11130	.08988	.07265	.05879	.04761
46	.13202	.11828	.10600	.08519	.06854	.05520	.04450
47	.12634	.11292	.10095	.08075	.06466	.05183	.04159
48	.12090	.10780	.09614	.07654	.06100	.04867	.03887
49	.11569	.10291	.09156	.07255	.05755	.04570	.03632
50	.11071	.09824	.08720	.06877	.05429	.04291	.03395

VALUATION TABLES

TABLE 2

Present value of $1 due n years hence at the following rates percent, compound interest.

Years	7½%	8%	9%	10%	11%	12%	13%
1	.93023	.92593	.91743	.90909	.90090	.89286	.88496
2	.86533	.85734	.84168	.82645	.81162	.79719	.78315
3	.80496	.79383	.77218	.75131	.73119	.71178	.69305
4	.74880	.73503	.70843	.68301	.65873	.63552	.61332
5	.69656	.68058	.64993	.62092	.59345	.56743	.54276
6	.64796	.63017	.59627	.56447	.53464	.50663	.48032
7	.60275	.58349	.54703	.51316	.48166	.45235	.42506
8	.56070	.54027	.50187	.46651	.43393	.40388	.37616
9	.52158	.50025	.46043	.42410	.39092	.36061	.33288
10	.48519	.46319	.42241	.38554	.35218	.32197	.29459
11	.45134	.42888	.38753	.35049	.31728	.28748	.26070
12	.41985	.39711	.35553	.31863	.28584	.25668	.23071
13	.39056	.36770	.32618	.28966	.25751	.22917	.20416
14	.36331	.34046	.29925	.26333	.23199	.20462	.18068
15	.33797	.31524	.27454	.23939	.20900	.18270	.15989
16	.31439	.29189	.25187	.21763	.18829	.16312	.14150
17	.29245	.27027	.23107	.19784	.16963	.14564	.12522
18	.27205	.25025	.21199	.17986	.15282	.13004	.11081
19	.25307	.23171	.19449	.16351	.13768	.11611	.09806
20	.23541	.21455	.17843	.14864	.12403	.10367	.08678
21	.21899	.19866	.16370	.13513	.11174	.09256	.07680
22	.20371	.18394	.15018	.12285	.10067	.08264	.06796
23	.18950	.17032	.13778	.11168	.09069	.07379	.06014
24	.17628	.15770	.12640	.10153	.08170	.06588	.05323
25	.16398	.14602	.11597	.09230	.07361	.05882	.04710
26	.15254	.13520	.10639	.08391	.06631	.05252	.04168
27	.14190	.12519	.09761	.07628	.05974	.04689	.03689
28	.13200	.11591	.08955	.06934	.05382	.04187	.03264
29	.12279	.10733	.08215	.06304	.04849	.03738	.02889
30	.11422	.09938	.07537	.05731	.04368	.03338	.02557
31	.10625	.09202	.06915	.05210	.03935	.02980	.02262
32	.09884	.08520	.06344	.04736	.03545	.02661	.02002
33	.09194	.07889	.05820	.04306	.03194	.02376	.01772
34	.08553	.07305	.05339	.03914	.02878	.02121	.01568
35	.07956	.06763	.04899	.03558	.02592	.01894	.01388
36	.07401	.06262	.04494	.03235	.02335	.01691	.01228
37	.06885	.05799	.04123	.02941	.02104	.01510	.01087
38	.06404	.05369	.03783	.02673	.01896	.01348	.00962
39	.05958	.04971	.03470	.02430	.01708	.01204	.00851
40	.05542	.04603	.03184	.02209	.01538	.01075	.00753
41	.05155	.04262	.02921	.02009	.01386	.00960	.00666
42	.04796	.03946	.02680	.01826	.01249	.00857	.00590
43	.04461	.03654	.02458	.01660	.01125	.00765	.00522
44	.04150	.03383	.02255	.01509	.01013	.00683	.00462
45	.03860	.03133	.02069	.01372	.00913	.00610	.00409
46	.03591	.02901	.01898	.01247	.00823	.00544	.00362
47	.03340	.02686	.01742	.01134	.00741	.00486	.00320
48	.03107	.02487	.01598	.01031	.00668	.00434	.00283
49	.02891	.02303	.01466	.00937	.00601	.00388	.00251
50	.02689	.02132	.01345	.00852	.00542	.00346	.00222

TABLE 2

Present value of $1 due n years hence at the following rates percent, compound interest.

Years	14%	15%	16%	18%	20%	25%	30%
1	.87719	.86957	.86207	.84746	.83333	.80000	.76923
2	.76947	.75614	.74316	.71818	.69444	.64000	.59172
3	.67497	.65752	.64066	.60863	.57870	.51200	.45517
4	.59208	.57175	.55229	.51579	.48225	.40960	.35013
5	.51937	.49718	.47611	.43711	.40188	.32768	.26933
6	.45559	.43233	.41044	.37043	.33490	.26214	.20718
7	.39964	.37594	.35383	.31393	.27908	.20972	.15937
8	.35056	.32690	.30503	.26604	.23257	.16777	.12259
9	.30751	.28426	.26295	.22546	.19381	.13422	.09430
10	.26974	.24718	.22668	.19106	.16151	.10737	.07254
11	.23662	.21494	.19542	.16192	.13459	.08590	.05580
12	.20756	.18691	.16846	.13722	.11216	.06872	.04292
13	.18207	.16253	.14523	.11629	.09346	.05498	.03302
14	.15971	.14133	.12520	.09855	.07789	.04398	.02540
15	.14010	.12289	.10793	.08352	.06491	.03518	.01954
16	.12289	.10686	.09304	.07078	.05409	.02815	.01503
17	.10780	.09293	.08021	.05998	.04507	.02252	.01156
18	.09456	.08081	.06914	.05083	.03756	.01801	.00889
19	.08295	.07027	.05961	.04308	.03130	.01441	.00684
20	.07276	.06110	.05139	.03651	.02608	.01153	.00526
21	.06383	.05313	.04430	.03094	.02174	.00922	.00405
22	.05599	.04620	.03819	.02622	.01811	.00738	.00311
23	.04911	.04017	.03292	.02220	.01509	.00590	.00239
24	.04308	.03493	.02838	.01883	.01258	.00472	.00184
25	.03779	.03038	.02447	.01596	.01048	.00378	.00142
26	.03315	.02642	.02109	.01352	.00874	.00302	.00109
27	.02908	.02297	.01818	.01146	.00728	.00242	
28	.02551	.01997	.01567	.00971	.00607	.00193	
29	.02237	.01737	.01351	.00823	.00506	.00155	
30	.01963	.01510	.01165	.00697	.00421	.00124	
31	.01722	.01313	.01004	.00591	.00351		
32	.01510	.01142	.00866	.00501	.00293		
33	.01325	.00993	.00746	.00425	.00244		
34	.01162	.00864	.00643	.00360	.00203		
35	.01019	.00751	.00555	.00305			
36	.00894	.00653	.00478	.00258			
37	.00784	.00568	.00412	.00219			
38	.00688	.00494	.00355	.00186			
39	.00604	.00429	.00306				
40	.00529	.00373	.00264				
41	.00464	.00325	.00228				
42	.00407	.00282	.00196				
43	.00357	.00245					
44	.00313	.00213					
45	.00275	.00186					
46	.00241	.00161					
47	.00212						
48	.00186						
49	.00163						
50	.00143						

AMOUNT OF AN ANNUITY OF $1 PER YEAR AT COMPOUND INTEREST

TABLE 3

The sum to which $1 per year will amount in n years at rates of 1, 1¼, 1½, 1¾, 2, 2¼, 2½, 2¾, 3, 3¼, 3½, 3¾, 4, 4¼, 4½, 4¾, 5, 5½, 6, 6½, 7, 7½, 8, 9, 10, 11, 12, 13, 14, 15, 16, 18, 20, 25, and 30 percent.

Calculated to 4 decimal places
and to 50 years.

The factors given in this table represent values of

$$\frac{R^n - 1}{r},$$

$$\text{or} \quad \frac{(1 + r)^n - 1}{r}.$$

If the annuity is for a yearly payment other than unity, this payment is multiplied by the factor given in the table to obtain the desired amount.

$$S = \frac{A(R^n - 1)}{r}$$

$$= A \times \text{Table Factor.}$$

For instance, to what sum will an annuity of $50 per year for 14 years amount at 6% compound interest?

$$S = 50 \times 21.0151$$

$$= \underline{\$1050.75.}$$

Note. — If annuity payments are to be made at the beginning of each year (Annuity Due), use table factor for n + 1 years and subtract 1.

TABLE 3

Amount of $1 per year in n years at the following rates percent, compound interest. Payments made at the end of each year — Immediate Annuity.

Years	1%	1¼%	1½%	1¾%	2%	2¼%	2½%
1	1.0000	1.0000	1.0000	1.0000	1.0000	1.0000	1.0000
2	2.0100	2.0125	2.0150	2.0175	2.0200	2.0225	2.0250
3	3.0301	3.0377	3.0452	3.0528	3.0604	3.0680	3.0756
4	4.0604	4.0756	4.0909	4.1062	4.1216	4.1370	4.1525
5	5.1010	5.1266	5.1523	5.1781	5.2040	5.2301	5.2563
6	6.1520	6.1907	6.2296	6.2687	6.3081	6.3478	6.3877
7	7.2135	7.2680	7.3230	7.3784	7.4343	7.4906	7.5474
8	8.2857	8.3589	8.4328	8.5075	8.5830	8.6592	8.7361
9	9.3685	9.4634	9.5593	9.6564	9.7546	9.8540	9.9545
10	10.4622	10.5817	10.7027	10.8254	10.9497	11.0757	11.2034
11	11.5668	11.7139	11.8633	12.0148	12.1687	12.3249	12.4835
12	12.6825	12.8604	13.0412	13.2251	13.4121	13.6022	13.7956
13	13.8093	14.0211	14.2368	14.4565	14.6803	14.9083	15.1404
14	14.9474	15.1964	15.4504	15.7095	15.9739	16.2437	16.5190
15	16.0969	16.3863	16.6821	16.9844	17.2934	17.6092	17.9319
16	17.2579	17.5912	17.9324	18.2817	18.6393	19.0054	19.3802
17	18.4304	18.8111	19.2014	19.6016	20.0121	20.4330	20.8647
18	19.6147	20.0462	20.4894	20.9446	21.4123	21.8928	22.3863
19	20.8109	21.2968	21.7967	22.3112	22.8406	23.3853	23.9460
20	22.0190	22.5630	23.1237	23.7016	24.2974	24.9115	25.5447
21	23.2392	23.8450	24.4705	25.1164	25.7833	26.4720	27.1833
22	24.4716	25.1431	25.8376	26.5559	27.2990	28.0676	28.8629
23	25.7163	26.4574	27.2251	28.0207	28.8450	29.6992	30.5844
24	26.9735	27.7881	28.6335	29.5110	30.4219	31.3674	32.3490
25	28.2432	29.1354	30.0630	31.0275	32.0303	33.0732	34.1578
26	29.5256	30.4996	31.5140	32.5704	33.6709	34.8173	36.0117
27	30.8209	31.8809	32.9867	34.1404	35.3443	36.6007	37.9120
28	32.1291	33.2794	34.4815	35.7379	37.0512	38.4242	39.8598
29	33.4504	34.6954	35.9987	37.3633	38.7922	40.2888	41.8563
30	34.7849	36.1291	37.5387	39.0172	40.5681	42.1953	43.9027
31	36.1327	37.5807	39.1018	40.7000	42.3794	44.1447	46.0003
32	37.4941	39.0504	40.6883	42.4122	44.2270	46.1379	48.1503
33	38.8690	40.5384	42.2986	44.1544	46.1116	48.1760	50.3540
34	40.2577	42.0453	43.9331	45.9271	48.0338	50.2600	52.6129
35	41.6603	43.5709	45.5921	47.7308	49.9945	52.3908	54.9282
36	43.0769	45.1155	47.2760	49.5661	51.9944	54.5696	57.3014
37	44.5076	46.6794	48.9851	51.4335	54.0343	56.7974	59.7339
38	45.9527	48.2629	50.7199	53.3336	56.1149	59.0754	62.2273
39	47.4123	49.8662	52.4807	55.2670	58.2372	61.4046	64.7830
40	48.8864	51.4896	54.2679	57.2341	60.4020	63.7862	67.4026
41	50.3752	53.1332	56.0819	59.2357	62.6100	66.2214	70.0876
42	51.8790	54.7973	57.9231	61.2724	64.8622	68.7113	72.8398
43	53.3978	56.4823	59.7920	63.3446	67.1595	71.2574	75.6608
44	54.9318	58.1883	61.6889	65.4532	69.5027	73.8606	78.5523
45	56.4811	59.9157	63.6142	67.5986	71.8927	76.5225	81.5161
46	58.0459	61.6646	65.5684	69.7816	74.3306	79.2443	84.5540
47	59.6263	63.4354	67.5519	72.0027	76.8172	82.0273	87.6679
48	61.2226	65.2284	69.5652	74.2628	79.3535	84.8729	90.8596
49	62.8348	67.0437	71.6087	76.5624	81.9406	87.7825	94.1311
50	64.4632	68.8818	73.6828	78.9022	84.5794	90.7576	97.4843

TABLE 3

Amount of $1 per year in n years at the following rates percent, compound interest. Payments made at the end of each year — Immediate Annuity.

Years	2¾%	3%	3¼%	3½%	3¾%	4%	4¼%
1	1.0000	1.0000	1.0000	1.0000	1.0000	1.0000	1.0000
2	2.0275	2.0300	2.0325	2.0350	2.0375	2.0400	2.0425
3	3.0833	3.0909	3.0986	3.1062	3.1139	3.1216	3.1293
4	4.1680	4.1836	4.1993	4.2149	4.2307	4.2465	4.2623
5	5.2827	5.3091	5.3357	5.3625	5.3893	5.4163	5.4434
6	6.4279	6.4684	6.5091	6.5502	6.5914	6.6330	6.6748
7	7.6047	7.6625	7.7207	7.7794	7.8386	7.8983	7.9585
8	8.8138	8.8923	8.9716	9.0517	9.1326	9.2142	9.2967
9	10.0562	10.1591	10.2632	10.3685	10.4750	10.5828	10.6918
10	11.3328	11.4639	11.5967	11.7314	11.8678	12.0061	12.1462
11	12.6444	12.8078	12.9736	13.1420	13.3129	13.4864	13.6624
12	13.9921	14.1920	14.3953	14.6020	14.8121	15.0258	15.2431
13	15.3769	15.6178	15.8631	16.1130	16.3676	16.6268	16.8909
14	16.7998	17.0863	17.3787	17.6770	17.9814	18.2919	18.6088
15	18.2618	18.5989	18.9435	19.2957	19.6557	20.0236	20.3997
16	19.7640	20.1569	20.5592	20.9710	21.3927	21.8245	22.2666
17	21.3075	21.7616	22.2273	22.7050	23.1950	23.6975	24.2130
18	22.8934	23.4144	23.9497	24.4997	25.0648	25.6454	26.2420
19	24.5230	25.1169	25.7281	26.3572	27.0047	27.6712	28.3573
20	26.1974	26.8704	27.5642	28.2797	29.0174	29.7781	30.5625
21	27.9178	28.6765	29.4601	30.2695	31.1055	31.9692	32.8614
22	29.6856	30.5368	31.4175	32.3289	33.2720	34.2480	35.2580
23	31.5019	32.4529	33.4386	34.4604	35.5197	36.6179	37.7565
24	33.3682	34.4265	35.5254	36.6665	37.8517	39.0826	40.3611
25	35.2858	36.4593	37.6799	38.9499	40.2711	41.6459	43.0765
26	37.2562	38.5530	39.9045	41.3131	42.7813	44.3117	45.9072
27	39.2808	40.7096	42.2014	43.7591	45.3856	47.0842	48.8583
28	41.3610	42.9309	44.5730	46.2906	48.0875	49.9676	51.9348
29	43.4984	45.2189	47.0216	48.9108	50.8908	52.9663	55.1420
30	45.6946	47.5754	49.5498	51.6227	53.7992	56.0849	58.4855
31	47.9512	50.0027	52.1602	54.4295	56.8167	59.3283	61.9712
32	50.2699	52.5028	54.8554	57.3345	59.9473	62.7015	65.6049
33	52.6523	55.0778	57.6382	60.3412	63.1954	66.2095	69.3931
34	55.1002	57.7302	60.5114	63.4532	66.5652	69.8579	73.3424
35	57.6155	60.4621	63.4780	66.6740	70.0614	73.6522	77.4594
36	60.1999	63.2759	66.5411	70.0076	73.6887	77.5983	81.7514
37	62.8554	66.1742	69.7037	73.4579	77.4520	81.7022	86.2259
38	65.5839	69.1594	72.9690	77.0289	81.3565	85.9703	90.8905
39	68.3875	72.2342	76.3405	80.7249	85.4073	90.4091	95.7533
40	71.2681	75.4013	79.8216	84.5503	89.6101	95.0255	100.823
41	74.2280	78.6633	83.4158	88.5095	93.9705	99.8265	106.108
42	77.2693	82.0232	87.1268	92.6074	98.4944	104.820	111.617
43	80.3942	85.4839	90.9584	96.8486	103.188	110.012	117.361
44	83.6050	89.0484	94.9146	101.238	108.057	115.413	123.349
45	86.9042	92.7199	98.9993	105.782	113.110	121.029	129.591
46	90.2940	96.5015	103.217	110.484	118.351	126.871	136.099
47	93.7771	100.397	107.571	115.351	123.789	132.945	142.883
48	97.3560	104.408	112.067	120.388	129.431	139.263	149.956
49	101.033	108.541	116.710	125.602	135.285	145.834	157.329
50	104.812	112.797	121.503	130.998	141.358	152.667	165.015

TABLE 3

Amount of $1 per year in n years at the following rates percent, compound interest. Payments made at the end of each year — Immediate Annuity.

Years	4½%	4¾%	5%	5½%	6%	6½%	7%
1	1.0000	1.0000	1.0000	1.0000	1.0000	1.0000	1.0000
2	2.0450	2.0475	2.0500	2.0550	2.0600	2.0650	2.0700
3	3.1370	3.1448	3.1525	3.1680	3.1836	3.1992	3.2149
4	4.2782	4.2941	4.3101	4.3423	4.3746	4.4072	4.4399
5	5.4707	5.4981	5.5256	5.5811	5.6371	5.6936	5.7507
6	6.7169	6.7593	6.8019	6.8881	6.9753	7.0637	7.1533
7	8.0192	8.0803	8.1420	8.2669	8.3938	8.5229	8.6540
8	9.3800	9.4641	9.5491	9.7216	9.8975	10.0769	10.2598
9	10.8021	10.9137	11.0266	11.2563	11.4913	11.7319	11.9780
10	12.2882	12.4321	12.5779	12.8754	13.1808	13.4944	13.8164
11	13.8412	14.0226	14.2068	14.5835	14.9716	15.3716	15.7836
12	15.4640	15.6887	15.9171	16.3856	16.8699	17.3707	17.8885
13	17.1599	17.4339	17.7130	18.2868	18.8821	19.4998	20.1406
14	18.9321	19.2620	19.5986	20.2926	21.0151	21.7673	22.5505
15	20.7841	21.1770	21.5786	22.4087	23.2760	24.1822	25.1290
16	22.7193	23.1829	23.6575	24.6411	25.6725	26.7540	27.8881
17	24.7417	25.2840	25.8404	26.9964	28.2129	29.4930	30.8402
18	26.8551	27.4850	28.1324	29.4812	30.9057	32.4101	33.9990
19	29.0636	29.7906	30.5390	32.1027	33.7600	35.5167	37.3790
20	31.3714	32.2056	33.0660	34.8683	36.7856	38.8253	40.9955
21	33.7831	34.7354	35.7193	37.7861	39.9927	42.3490	44.8652
22	36.3034	37.3853	38.5052	40.8643	43.3923	46.1016	49.0057
23	38.9370	40.1611	41.4305	44.1118	46.9958	50.0982	53.4361
24	41.6892	43.0688	44.5020	47.5380	50.8156	54.3546	58.1767
25	44.5652	46.1146	47.7271	51.1526	54.8645	58.8877	63.2490
26	47.5706	49.3050	51.1135	54.9660	59.1564	63.7154	68.6765
27	50.7113	52.6470	54.6691	58.9891	63.7058	68.8569	74.4838
28	53.9933	56.1477	58.4026	63.2335	68.5281	74.3326	80.6977
29	57.4230	59.8147	62.3227	67.7114	73.6398	80.1642	87.3465
30	61.0071	63.6559	66.4388	72.4355	79.0582	86.3749	94.4608
31	64.7524	67.6796	70.7608	77.4194	84.8017	92.9892	102.073
32	68.6662	71.8944	75.2988	82.6775	90.8898	100.034	110.218
33	72.7562	76.3094	80.0638	88.2248	97.3432	107.536	118.933
34	77.0303	80.9341	85.0670	94.0771	104.184	115.526	128.259
35	81.4966	85.7784	90.3203	100.251	111.435	124.035	138.237
36	86.1640	90.8529	95.8363	106.765	119.121	133.097	148.913
37	91.0413	96.1684	101.628	113.637	127.268	142.748	160.337
38	96.1382	101.736	107.710	120.887	135.904	153.027	172.561
39	101.464	107.569	114.095	128.536	145.058	163.974	185.640
40	107.030	113.678	120.800	136.606	154.762	175.632	199.635
41	112.847	120.078	127.840	145.119	165.048	188.048	214.610
42	118.925	126.782	135.232	154.100	175.951	201.271	230.632
43	125.276	133.804	142.993	163.576	187.508	215.354	247.776
44	131.914	141.160	151.143	173.573	199.758	230.352	266.121
45	138.850	148.865	159.700	184.119	212.744	246.325	285.749
46	146.098	156.936	168.685	195.246	226.508	263.336	306.752
47	153.673	165.390	178.119	206.984	241.099	281.453	329.224
48	161.588	174.246	188.025	219.368	256.565	300.747	353.270
49	169.859	183.523	198.427	232.434	272.958	321.295	378.999
50	178.503	193.240	209.348	246.217	290.336	343.180	406.529

TABLE 3

Amount of $1 per year in n years at the following rates percent, compound interest. Payments made at the end of each year — Immediate Annuity.

Years	7½%	8%	9%	10%	11%	12%	13%
1	1.0000	1.0000	1.0000	1.0000	1.0000	1.0000	1.0000
2	2.0750	2.0800	2.0900	2.1000	2.1100	2.1200	2.1300
3	3.2306	3.2464	3.2781	3.3100	3.3421	3.3744	3.4069
4	4.4729	4.5061	4.5731	4.6410	4.7097	4.7793	4.8498
5	5.8084	5.8666	5.9847	6.1051	6.2278	6.3528	6.4803
6	7.2440	7.3359	7.5233	7.7156	7.9129	8.1152	8.3227
7	8.7873	8.9228	9.2004	9.4872	9.7833	10.0890	10.4047
8	10.4464	10.6366	11.0285	11.4359	11.8594	12.2997	12.7573
9	12.2298	12.4876	13.0210	13.5795	14.1640	14.7757	15.4157
10	14.1471	14.4866	15.1929	15.9374	16.7220	17.5487	18.4197
11	16.2081	16.6455	17.5603	18.5312	19.5614	20.6546	21.8143
12	18.4237	18.9771	20.1407	21.3843	22.7132	24.1331	25.6502
13	20.8055	21.4953	22.9534	24.5227	26.2116	28.0291	29.9847
14	23.3659	21.2149	26.0192	27.9750	30.0949	32.3926	34.8827
15	26.1184	27.1521	29.3609	31.7725	34.4054	37.2797	40.4175
16	29.0772	30.3243	33.0034	35.9497	39.1899	42.7533	46.6717
17	32.2580	33.7502	36.9737	40.5447	44.5008	48.8837	53.7391
18	35.6774	37.4502	41.3013	45.5992	50.3959	55.7497	61.7251
19	39.3532	41.4463	46.0185	51.1591	56.9395	63.4397	70.7494
20	43.3047	45.7620	51.1601	57.2750	64.2028	72.0524	80.9468
21	47.5525	50.4229	56.7645	64.0025	72.2651	81.6987	92.4699
22	52.1190	55.4568	62.8733	71.4027	81.2143	92.5026	105.491
23	57.0279	60.8933	69.5319	79.5430	91.1479	104.603	120.205
24	62.3050	66.7648	76.7898	88.4973	102.174	118.155	136.831
25	67.9779	73.1059	84.7009	98.3471	114.413	133.334	155.620
26	74.0762	79.9544	93.3240	109.182	127.999	150.334	176.850
27	80.6319	87.3508	102.723	121.100	143.079	169.374	200.841
28	87.6793	95.3388	112.968	134.210	159.817	190.699	227.950
29	95.2553	103.966	124.135	148.631	178.397	214.583	258.583
30	103.399	113.283	136.308	164.494	199.021	241.333	293.199
31	112.154	123.346	149.575	181.943	221.913	271.293	332.315
32	121.566	134.214	164.037	201.138	247.324	304.848	376.516
33	131.683	145.951	179.800	222.252	275.529	342.429	426.463
34	142.560	158.627	196.982	245.477	306.837	384.521	482.903
35	154.252	172.317	215.711	271.024	341.590	431.663	546.681
36	166.820	187.102	236.125	299.127	380.164	484.463	618.749
37	180.332	203.070	258.376	330.039	422.982	543.599	700.187
38	194.857	220.316	282.630	364.043	470.511	609.831	792.211
39	210.471	238.941	309.066	401.448	523.267	684.010	896.198
40	227.257	259.057	337.882	442.593	581.826	767.091	1013.70
41	245.301	280.781	369.292	487.852	646.827	860.142	1146.49
42	264.698	304.244	403.528	537.637	718.978	964.359	1296.53
43	285.551	329.583	440.846	592.401	799.065	1081.08	1466.08
44	307.967	356.950	481.522	652.641	887.963	1211.81	1657.67
45	332.065	386.506	525.859	718.905	986.639	1358.23	1874.16
46	357.969	418.426	574.186	791.795	1096.17	1522.22	2118.81
47	385.817	452.900	626.863	871.975	1217.75	1705.88	2395.25
48	415.753	490.132	684.280	960.172	1352.70	1911.59	2707.63
49	447.935	530.343	746.866	1057.19	1502.50	2141.98	3060.63
50	482.530	573.770	815.084	1163.91	1668.77	2400.02	3459.51

TABLE 3

Amount of $1 per year in n years at the following rates percent, compound interest. Payments made at the end of each year — Immediate Annuity.

Years	14%	15%	16%	18%	20%	25%	30%
1	1.0000	1.0000	1.0000	1.0000	1.0000	1.0000	1.0000
2	2.1400	2.1500	2.1600	2.1800	2.2000	2.2500	2.3000
3	3.4396	3.4725	3.5056	3.5724	3.6400	3.8125	3.9900
4	4.9211	4.9934	5.0665	5.2154	5.3680	5.7656	6.1870
5	6.6101	6.7424	6.8771	7.1542	7.4416	8.2070	9.0431
6	8.5355	8.7537	8.9775	9.4420	9.9299	11.2588	12.7560
7	10.7305	11.0668	11.4139	12.1415	12.9159	15.0735	17.5828
8	13.2328	13.7268	14.2401	15.3270	16.4991	19.8418	23.8577
9	16.0853	16.7858	17.5185	19.0859	20.7989	25.8023	32.0150
10	19.3373	20.3037	21.3215	23.5213	25.9587	33.2529	42.6195
11	23.0445	24.3493	25.7329	28.7551	32.1504	42.5661	56.4053
12	27.2707	29.0017	30.8502	34.9311	39.5805	54.2077	74.3270
13	32.0887	34.3519	36.7862	42.2187	48.4966	68.7596	97.6250
14	37.5811	40.5047	43.6720	50.8180	59.1959	86.9495	127.913
15	43.8424	47.5804	51.6595	60.9653	72.0351	109.687	167.286
16	50.9804	55.7175	60.9250	72.9390	87.4421	138.109	218.472
17	59.1176	65.0751	71.6730	87.0680	105.931	173.636	285.014
18	68.3941	75.8364	84.1407	103.740	128.117	218.045	371.518
19	78.9692	88.2118	98.6032	123.414	154.740	273.556	483.973
20	91.0249	102.444	115.380	146.628	186.688	342.945	630.165
21	104.768	118.810	134.841	174.021	225.026	429.681	
22	120.436	137.632	157.415	206.345	271.031	538.101	
23	138.297	159.276	183.601	244.487	326.237	673.626	
24	158.659	184.168	213.978	289.494	392.484	843.033	
25	181.871	212.793	249.214	342.603	471.981	1054.79	
26	208.333	245.712	290.088	405.272	567.377		
27	238.499	283.569	337.502	479.221	681.853		
28	272.889	327.104	392.503	566.481	819.223		
29	312.094	377.170	456.303	669.447	984.068		
30	356.787	434.745	530.312	790.948	1181.88		
31	407.737	500.957	616.162	934.319			
32	465.820	577.100	715.747	1103.50			
33	532.035	664.666	831.267	1303.13			
34	607.520	765.365	965.270	1538.69			
35	693.573	881.170	1120.71	1816.65			
36	791.673	1014.35	1301.03				
37	903.507	1167.50	1510.19				
38	1031.00	1343.62	1752.82				
39	1176.34	1546.17	2034.27				
40	1342.03	1779.09	2360.76				
41	1530.91	2046.95					
42	1746.24	2355.00					
43	1991.71	2709.25					
44	2271.55	3116.63					
45	2590.56	3585.13					
46	2954.24						
47	3368.84						
48	3841.48						
49	4380.28						
50	4994.52						

**PRESENT VALUE OF AN ANNUITY OF $1
PER YEAR AT COMPOUND INTEREST**

TABLE 4

The present value (or "years' purchase" factor) of an annuity of $1 per year for n years at rates of 1, $1\frac{1}{4}$, $1\frac{1}{2}$, $1\frac{3}{4}$, 2, $2\frac{1}{4}$, $2\frac{1}{2}$, $2\frac{3}{4}$, 3, $3\frac{1}{4}$, $3\frac{1}{2}$, $3\frac{3}{4}$, 4, $4\frac{1}{4}$, $4\frac{1}{2}$, $4\frac{3}{4}$, 5, $5\frac{1}{2}$, 6, $6\frac{1}{2}$, 7, $7\frac{1}{2}$, 8, 9, 10, 11, 12, 13, 14, 15, 16, 18, 20, 25, and 30 percent.

Calculated to 4 decimal places,
and to 50 years.

The factors listed in this table represent values of

$$\frac{R^n - 1}{R^n r},$$

$$\text{or} \quad \frac{\dfrac{R^n - 1}{r}}{R^n}.$$

These factors have been obtained either by multiplying the factors of Table 3 by the corresponding factors of Table 2,

$$\frac{R^n - 1}{r} \times \frac{1}{R^n} = \frac{R^n - 1}{R^n r},$$

or by dividing the factors of Table 3 by the corresponding factors of Table 1,

$$\frac{R^n - 1}{r} \div R^n = \frac{R^n - 1}{R^n r}.$$

If the annuity is for a yearly payment other than unity, this payment is multiplied by the factor given in the table to obtain the present value:

$$V_p = \frac{A(R^n - 1)}{R^n r}$$

$$= A \times \text{Table Factor}.$$

For instance, what is the present value or purchase price of an annuity of $50 per year for 14 years at 6% compound interest?

$$V_p = 50 \times 9.2950$$
$$= \$464.75.$$

Note. — If the annuity payments are to be made at the beginning of each year (Annuity Due), use table factor for n — 1 years and add 1.

TABLE 4

Present value of an annuity of $1 per year for n years at the following rates percent, compound interest. Payments made at the end of each year — Immediate Annuity.

Years	1%	1¼%	1½%	1¾%	2%	2¼%	2½%
1	.9901	.9877	.9852	.9828	.9804	.9780	.9756
2	1.9704	1.9631	1.9559	1.9487	1.9416	1.9345	1.9274
3	2.9410	2.9265	2.9122	2.8980	2.8839	2.8699	2.8560
4	3.9020	3.8781	3.8544	3.8309	3.8077	3.7847	3.7620
5	4.8534	4.8178	4.7826	4.7479	4.7135	4.6795	4.6458
6	5.7955	5.7460	5.6972	5.6490	5.6014	5.5545	5.5081
7	6.7282	6.6627	6.5982	6.5346	6.4720	6.4102	6.3494
8	7.6517	7.5681	7.4859	7.4051	7.3255	7.2472	7.1701
9	8.5660	8.4623	8.3605	8.2605	8.1622	8.0657	7.9709
10	9.4713	9.3455	9.2222	9.1012	8.9826	8.8662	8.7521
11	10.3676	10.2178	10.0711	9.9275	9.7868	9.6491	9.5142
12	11.2551	11.0793	10.9075	10.7395	10.5753	10.4148	10.2578
13	12.1337	11.9302	11.7315	11.5376	11.3484	11.1636	10.9832
14	13.0037	12.7706	12.5434	12.3220	12.1062	11.8959	11.6909
15	13.8651	13.6005	13.3432	13.0929	12.8493	12.6122	12.3814
16	14.7179	14.4203	14.1313	13.8505	13.5777	13.3126	13.0550
17	15.5623	15.2299	14.9076	14.5951	14.2919	13.9977	13.7122
18	16.3983	16.0295	15.6726	15.3269	14.9920	14.6677	14.3534
19	17.2260	16.8193	16.4262	16.0461	15.6785	15.3229	14.9789
20	18.0456	17.5993	17.1686	16.7529	16.3514	15.9637	15.5892
21	18.8570	18.3697	17.9001	17.4475	17.0112	16.5904	16.1845
22	19.6604	19.1306	18.6208	18.1303	17.6580	17.2034	16.7654
23	20.4558	19.8820	19.3309	18.8012	18.2922	17.8028	17.3321
24	21.2434	20.6242	20.0304	19.4607	18.9139	18.3890	17.8850
25	22.0232	21.3573	20.7196	20.1088	19.5235	18.9624	18.4244
26	22.7952	22.0813	21.3986	20.7457	20.1210	19.5231	18.9506
27	23.5596	22.7963	22.0676	21.3717	20.7069	20.0715	19.4640
28	24.3164	23.5025	22.7267	21.9870	21.2813	20.6078	19.9649
29	25.0658	24.2000	23.3761	22.5916	21.8444	21.1323	20.4535
30	25.8077	24.8889	24.0158	23.1858	22.3965	21.6453	20.9303
31	26.5423	25.5693	24.6461	23.7699	22.9377	22.1470	21.3954
32	27.2696	26.2413	25.2671	24.3439	23.4683	22.6377	21.8492
33	27.9897	26.9050	25.8790	24.9080	23.9886	23.1175	22.2919
34	28.7027	27.5605	26.4817	25.4624	24.4986	23.5868	22.7238
35	29.4086	28.2079	27.0756	26.0073	24.9986	24.0458	23.1452
36	30.1075	28.8473	27.6607	26.5428	25.4888	24.4947	23.5563
37	30.7995	29.4788	28.2371	27.0690	25.9695	24.9337	23.9573
38	31.4847	30.1025	28.8051	27.5863	26.4406	25.3630	24.3486
39	32.1630	30.7185	29.3646	28.0946	26.9026	25.7829	24.7303
40	32.8347	31.3269	29.9158	28.5942	27.3555	26.1935	25.1028
41	33.4997	31.9278	30.4590	29.0852	27.7995	26.5951	25.4661
42	34.1581	32.5213	30.9941	29.5678	28.2348	26.9879	25.8206
43	34.8100	33.1075	31.5212	30.0421	28.6616	27.3720	26.1664
44	35.4555	33.6864	32.0406	30.5082	29.0800	27.7477	26.5038
45	36.0945	34.2582	32.5523	30.9663	29.4902	28.1151	26.8330
46	36.7272	34.8229	33.0565	31.4165	29.8923	28.4744	27.1542
47	37.3537	35.3806	33.5532	31.8589	30.2866	28.8259	27.4675
48	37.9740	35.9315	34.0426	32.2938	30.6731	29.1695	27.7732
49	38.5881	36.4755	34.5247	32.7212	31.0521	29.5057	28.0714
50	39.1961	37.0129	34.9997	33.1412	31.4236	29.8344	28.3623

ANNUITY IMPROVEMENT AND DISCOUNT

TABLE 4

Present value of an annuity of $1 per year for n years at lowing rates percent, compound interest. Payments made at the of each year — Immediate Annuity.

Years	2¾%	3%	3¼%	3½%	3¾%	4%	4¼%
1	.9732	.9709	.9685	.9662	.9639	.9615	.9592
2	1.9204	1.9135	1.9066	1.8997	1.8929	1.8861	1.8794
3	2.8423	2.8286	2.8151	2.8016	2.7883	2.7751	2.7620
4	3.7394	3.7171	3.6950	3.6731	3.6514	3.6299	3.6086
5	4.6126	4.5797	4.5472	4.5151	4.4833	4.4518	4.4207
6	5.4624	5.4172	5.3726	5.3286	5.2851	5.2421	5.1997
7	6.2894	6.2303	6.1720	6.1145	6.0579	6.0021	5.9470
8	7.0943	7.0197	6.9462	6.8740	6.8028	6.7327	6.6638
9	7.8777	7.7861	7.6961	7.6077	7.5208	7.4353	7.3513
10	8.6401	8.5302	8.4224	8.3166	8.2128	8.1109	8.0109
11	9.3821	9.2526	9.1258	9.0016	8.8798	8.7605	8.6435
12	10.1042	9.9540	9.8071	9.6633	9.5227	9.3851	9.2504
13	10.8070	10.6350	10.4669	10.3027	10.1424	9.9856	9.8325
14	11.4910	11.2961	11.1060	10.9205	10.7396	10.5631	10.3909
15	12.1567	11.9379	11.7249	11.5174	11.3153	11.1184	10.9265
16	12.8046	12.5611	12.3244	12.0941	11.8702	11.6523	11.4403
17	13.4351	13.1661	12.9049	12.6513	12.4050	12.1657	11.9332
18	14.0488	13.7535	13.4673	13.1897	12.9205	12.6593	12.4059
19	14.6460	14.3238	14.0119	13.7098	13.4173	13.1339	12.8594
20	15.2273	14.8775	14.5393	14.2124	13.8962	13.5903	13.2944
21	15.7929	15.4150	15.0502	14.6980	14.3578	14.0292	13.7116
22	16.3435	15.9369	15.5450	15.1671	14.8027	14.4511	14.1119
23	16.8793	16.4436	16.0242	15.6204	15.2315	14.8568	14.4958
24	17.4008	16.9355	16.4883	16.0584	15.6448	15.2470	14.8641
25	17.9083	17.4131	16.9379	16.4815	16.0432	15.6221	15.2173
26	18.4023	17.8768	17.3732	16.8904	16.4272	15.9828	15.5562
27	18.8830	18.3270	17.7949	17.2854	16.7973	16.3296	15.8812
28	19.3508	18.7641	18.2033	17.6670	17.1540	16.6631	16.1930
29	19.8062	19.1885	18.5988	18.0358	17.4978	16.9837	16.4921
30	20.2493	19.6004	18.9819	18.3920	17.8292	17.2920	16.7790
31	20.6806	20.0004	19.3529	18.7363	18.1487	17.5885	17.0542
32	21.1003	20.3888	19.7123	19.0689	18.4565	17.8736	17.3182
33	21.5088	20.7658	20.0603	19.3902	18.7533	18.1476	17.5714
34	21.9064	21.1318	20.3974	19.7007	19.0393	18.4112	17.8143
35	22.2933	21.4872	20.7239	20.0007	19.3150	18.6646	18.0473
36	22.6699	21.8323	21.0401	20.2905	19.5807	18.9083	18.2708
37	23.0364	22.1672	21.3463	20.5705	19.8369	19.1426	18.4852
38	23.3931	22.4925	21.6429	20.8411	20.0837	19.3679	18.6908
39	23.7402	22.8082	21.9302	21.1025	20.3217	19.5845	18.8881
40	24.0781	23.1148	22.2084	21.3551	20.5510	19.7928	19.0773
41	24.4069	23.4124	22.4779	21.5991	20.7720	19.9931	19.2588
42	24.7269	23.7014	22.7389	21.8349	20.9851	20.1856	19.4329
43	25.0384	23.9819	22.9917	22.0627	21.1905	20.3708	19.5999
44	25.3415	24.2543	23.2365	22.2828	21.3884	20.5488	19.7601
45	25.6365	24.5187	23.4736	22.4955	21.5792	20.7200	19.9137
46	25.9236	24.7754	23.7032	22.7009	21.7631	20.8847	20.0611
47	26.2030	25.0247	23.9256	22.8994	21.9403	21.0429	20.2025
48	26.4749	25.2667	24.1411	23.0912	22.1111	21.1951	20.3382
49	26.7396	25.5017	24.3497	23.2766	22.2758	21.3415	20.4683
50	26.9972	25.7298	24.5518	23.4556	22.4345	21.4822	20.5931

TABLE 4

Present value of an annuity of $1 per year for n years at the following rates percent, compound interest. Payments made at the end of each year — Immediate Annuity.

Years	4½%	4¾%	5%	5½%	6%	6½%	7%
1	.9569	.9547	.9524	.9479	.9434	.9390	.9346
2	1.8727	1.8660	1.8594	1.8463	1.8334	1.8206	1.8080
3	2.7490	2.7361	2.7232	2.6979	2.6730	2.6485	2.6243
4	3.5875	3.5666	3.5460	3.5052	3.4651	3.4258	3.3872
5	4.3900	4.3596	4.3295	4.2703	4.2124	4.1557	4.1002
6	5.1579	5.1165	5.0757	4.9955	4.9173	4.8410	4.7665
7	5.8927	5.8392	5.7864	5.6830	5.5824	5.4845	5.3893
8	6.5959	6.5290	6.4632	6.3346	6.2098	6.0888	5.9713
9	7.2688	7.1876	7.1078	6.9522	6.8017	6.6561	6.5152
10	7.9127	7.8163	7.7217	7.5376	7.3601	7.1888	7.0236
11	8.5289	8.4166	8.3064	8.0925	7.8869	7.6890	7.4987
12	9.1186	8.9896	8.8633	8.6185	8.3838	8.1587	7.9427
13	9.6829	9.5366	9.3936	9.1171	8.8527	8.5997	8.3577
14	10.2228	10.0588	9.8986	9.5896	9.2950	9.0138	8.7455
15	10.7395	10.5573	10.3797	10.0376	9.7122	9.4027	9.1079
16	11.2340	11.0332	10.8378	10.4622	10.1059	9.7678	9.4466
17	11.7072	11.4876	11.2741	10.8646	10.4773	10.1106	9.7632
18	12.1600	11.9213	11.6896	11.2461	10.8276	10.4325	10.0591
19	12.5933	12.3354	12.0853	11.6077	11.1581	10.7347	10.3356
20	13.0079	12.7307	12.4622	11.9504	11.4699	11.0185	10.5940
21	13.4047	13.1080	12.8212	12.2752	11.7641	11.2850	10.8355
22	13.7844	13.4683	13.1630	12.5832	12.0416	11.5352	11.0612
23	14.1478	13.8122	13.4886	12.8750	12.3034	11.7701	11.2722
24	14.4955	14.1405	13.7986	13.1517	12.5504	11.9907	11.4693
25	14.8282	14.4540	14.0939	13.4139	12.7834	12.1979	11.6536
26	15.1466	14.7532	14.3752	13.6625	13.0032	12.3924	11.8258
27	15.4513	15.0389	14.6430	13.8981	13.2105	12.5750	11.9867
28	15.7429	15.3116	14.8981	14.1214	13.4062	12.7465	12.1371
29	16.0219	15.5719	15.1411	14.3331	13.5907	12.9075	12.2777
30	16.2889	15.8204	15.3725	14.5337	13.7648	13.0587	12.4090
31	16.5444	16.0577	15.5928	14.7239	13.9291	13.2006	12.5318
32	16.7889	16.2842	15.8027	14.9042	14.0840	13.3339	12.6466
33	17.0229	16.5004	16.0025	15.0751	14.2302	13.4591	12.7538
34	17.2468	16.7068	16.1929	15.2370	14.3681	13.5766	12.8540
35	17.4610	16.9039	16.3742	15.3906	14.4982	13.6870	12.9477
36	17.6660	17.0920	16.5469	15.5361	14.6210	13.7906	13.0352
37	17.8622	17.2716	16.7113	15.6740	14.7368	13.8879	13.1170
38	18.0500	17.4431	16.8679	15.8047	14.8460	13.9792	13.1935
39	18.2297	17.6068	17.0170	15.9287	14.9491	14.0650	13.2649
40	18.4016	17.7630	17.1591	16.0461	15.0463	14.1455	13.3317
41	18.5661	17.9122	17.2944	16.1575	15.1380	14.2212	13.3941
42	18.7235	18.0546	17.4232	16.2630	15.2245	14.2922	13.4524
43	18.8742	18.1905	17.5459	16.3630	15.3062	14.3588	13.5070
44	19.0184	18.3203	17.6628	16.4579	15.3832	14.4214	13.5579
45	19.1563	18.4442	17.7741	16.5477	15.4558	14.4802	13.6055
46	19.2884	18.5625	17.8801	16.6329	15.5244	14.5354	13.6500
47	19.4147	18.6754	17.9810	16.7137	15.5890	14.5873	13.6916
48	19.5356	18.7832	18.0772	16.7902	15.6500	14.6359	13.7305
49	19.6513	18.8861	18.1687	16.8628	15.7076	14.6816	13.7668
50	19.7620	18.9844	18.2559	16.9315	15.7619	14.7245	13.8007

TABLE 4

Present value of an annuity of $1 per year for n years at the following rates percent, compound interest. Payments made at the end of each year — Immediate Annuity.

Years	7½%	8%	9%	10%	11%	12%	13%
1	.9302	.9259	.9174	.9091	.9009	.8929	.8850
2	1.7956	1.7833	1.7591	1.7355	1.7125	1.6901	1.6681
3	2.6005	2.5771	2.5313	2.4869	2.4437	2.4018	2.3612
4	3.3493	3.3121	3.2397	3.1699	3.1024	3.0373	2.9745
5	4.0459	3.9927	3.8897	3.7908	3.6959	3.6048	3.5172
6	4.6938	4.6229	4.4859	4.3553	4.2305	4.1114	3.9975
7	5.2966	5.2064	5.0330	4.8684	4.7122	4.5638	4.4226
8	5.8573	5.7466	5.5348	5.3349	5.1461	4.9676	4.7988
9	6.3789	6.2469	5.9952	5.7590	5.5370	5.3282	5.1317
10	6.8641	6.7101	6.4177	6.1446	5.8892	5.6502	5.4262
11	7.3154	7.1390	6.8052	6.4951	6.2065	5.9377	5.6869
12	7.7353	7.5361	7.1607	6.8137	6.4924	6.1944	5.9176
13	8.1258	7.9038	7.4869	7.1034	6.7499	6.4235	6.1218
14	8.4892	8.2442	7.7862	7.3667	6.9819	6.6282	6.3025
15	8.8271	8.5595	8.0607	7.6061	7.1909	6.8109	6.4624
16	9.1415	8.8514	8.3126	7.8237	7.3792	6.9740	6.6039
17	9.4340	9.1216	8.5436	8.0216	7.5488	7.1196	6.7291
18	9.7060	9.3719	8.7556	8.2014	7.7016	7.2497	6.8399
19	9.9591	9.6036	8.9501	8.3649	7.8393	7.3658	6.9380
20	10.1945	9.8181	9.1285	8.5136	7.9633	7.4694	7.0248
21	10.4135	10.0168	9.2922	8.6487	8.0751	7.5620	7.1016
22	10.6172	10.2007	9.4424	8.7715	8.1757	7.6446	7.1695
23	10.8067	10.3711	9.5802	8.8832	8.2664	7.7184	7.2297
24	10.9830	10.5288	9.7066	8.9847	8.3481	7.7843	7.2829
25	11.1469	10.6748	9.8226	9.0770	8.4217	7.8431	7.3300
26	11.2995	10.8100	9.9290	9.1609	8.4881	7.8957	7.3717
27	11.4414	10.9352	10.0266	9.2372	8.5478	7.9426	7.4086
28	11.5734	11.0511	10.1161	9.3066	8.6016	7.9844	7.4412
29	11.6962	11.1584	10.1983	9.3696	8.6501	8.0218	7.4701
30	11.8104	11.2578	10.2737	9.4269	8.6938	8.0552	7.4957
31	11.9166	11.3498	10.3428	9.4790	8.7331	8.0850	7.5183
32	12.0155	11.4350	10.4062	9.5264	8.7686	8.1116	7.5383
33	12.1074	11.5139	10.4644	9.5694	8.8005	8.1354	7.5560
34	12.1929	11.5869	10.5178	9.6086	8.8293	8.1566	7.5717
35	12.2725	11.6546	10.5668	9.6442	8.8552	8.1755	7.5856
36	12.3465	11.7172	10.6118	9.6765	8.8786	8.1924	7.5979
37	12.4154	11.7752	10.6530	9.7059	8.8996	8.2075	7.6087
38	12.4794	11.8289	10.6908	9.7327	8.9186	8.2210	7.6183
39	12.5390	11.8786	10.7255	9.7570	8.9357	8.2330	7.6268
40	12.5944	11.9246	10.7574	9.7791	8.9511	8.2438	7.6344
41	12.6460	11.9672	10.7866	9.7991	8.9649	8.2534	7.6410
42	12.6939	12.0067	10.8134	9.8174	8.9774	8.2619	7.6469
43	12.7385	12.0432	10.8380	9.8340	8.9886	8.2696	7.6522
44	12.7800	12.0771	10.8605	9.8491	8.9988	8.2764	7.6568
45	12.8186	12.1084	10.8812	9.8628	9.0079	8.2825	7.6609
46	12.8545	12.1374	10.9002	9.8753	9.0161	8.2880	7.6645
47	12.8879	12.1643	10.9176	9.8866	9.0235	8.2928	7.6677
48	12.9190	12.1891	10.9336	9.8969	9.0302	8.2972	7.6705
49	12.9479	12.2122	10.9482	9.9063	9.0362	8.3010	7.6730
50	12.9748	12.2335	10.9617	9.9148	9.0417	8.3045	7.6752

TABLE 4

Present value of an annuity of $1 per year for n years at the following rates percent, compound interest. Payments made at the end of each year — Immediate Annuity.

Years	14%	15%	16%	18%	20%	25%	30%
1	.8772	.8696	.8621	.8475	.8333	.8000	.7692
2	1.6467	1.6257	1.6052	1.5656	1.5278	1.4400	1.3609
3	2.3216	2.2832	2.2459	2.1743	2.1065	1.9520	1.8161
4	2.9137	2.8550	2.7982	2.6901	2.5887	2.3616	2.1662
5	3.4331	3.3522	3.2743	3.1272	2.9906	2.6893	2.4356
6	3.8887	3.7845	3.6847	3.4976	3.3255	2.9514	2.6427
7	4.2883	4.1604	4.0386	3.8115	3.6046	3.1611	2.8021
8	4.6389	4.4873	4.3436	4.0776	3.8372	3.3289	2.9247
9	4.9464	4.7716	4.6065	4.3030	4.0310	3.4631	3.0190
10	5.2161	5.0188	4.8332	4.4941	4.1925	3.5705	3.0915
11	5.4527	5.2337	5.0286	4.6560	4.3271	3.6564	3.1473
12	5.6603	5.4206	5.1971	4.7932	4.4392	3.7251	3.1903
13	5.8424	5.5831	5.3423	4.9095	4.5327	3.7801	3.2233
14	6.0021	5.7245	5.4675	5.0081	4.6106	3.8241	3.2487
15	6.1422	5.8474	5.5755	5.0916	4.6755	3.8593	3.2682
16	6.2651	5.9542	5.6685	5.1624	4.7296	3.8874	3.2832
17	6.3729	6.0472	5.7487	5.2223	4.7746	3.9099	3.2948
18	6.4674	6.1280	5.8178	5.2732	4.8122	3.9279	3.3037
19	6.5504	6.1982	5.8775	5.3162	4.8435	3.9424	3.3105
20	6.6231	6.2593	5.9288	5.3527	4.8696	3.9539	3.3158
21	6.6870	6.3125	5.9731	5.3837	4.8913	3.9631	
22	6.7429	6.3587	6.0113	5.4099	4.9094	3.9705	
23	6.7921	6.3988	6.0442	5.4321	4.9245	3.9764	
24	6.8351	6.4338	6.0726	5.4509	4.9371	3.9811	
25	6.8729	6.4641	6.0971	5.4669	4.9476	3.9849	
26	6.9061	6.4906	6.1182	5.4804	4.9563		
27	6.9352	6.5135	6.1364	5.4919	4.9636		
28	6.9607	6.5335	6.1520	5.5016	4.9697		
29	6.9830	6.5509	6.1656	5.5098	4.9747		
30	7.0027	6.5660	6.1772	5.5168	4.9789		
31	7.0199	6.5791	6.1872	5.5227			
32	7.0350	6.5905	6.1959	5.5277			
33	7.0482	6.6005	6.2034	5.5320			
34	7.0599	6.6091	6.2098	5.5356			
35	7.0700	6.6166	6.2153	5.5386			
36	7.0790	6.6231	6.2201				
37	7.08C8	6.6288	6.2242				
38	7.0937	6.6338	6.2278				
39	7.0997	6.6380	6.2309				
40	7.1050	6.6418	6.2335				
41	7.1097	6.6450					
42	7.1138	6.6478					
43	7.1173	6.6503					
44	7.1205	6.6524					
45	7.1232	6.6543					
46	7.1256						
47	7.1277						
48	7.1296						
49	7.1312						
50	7.1327						

PRESENT VALUE AT COMPOUND INTEREST OF EACH $1 OF TOTAL ANNUITY INCOME

TABLE 5

The present value of each $1 of total operating profit (or total income) when receivable as an annuity of $A per year for n years at rates of 1, 2, 3, 4, 5, 6, 7, 8, 9, 10, 12, 15, 20, and 25 percent compound interest.

Calculated to 5 decimal places
and to 50 years.

The factors listed in this table represent values of

$$\frac{R^n - 1}{R^n r} \div n$$

or

$$\frac{R^n - 1}{R^n r \, n}.$$

These factors have been calculated by dividing each factor of Table 4 by its respective period of years n. To use this table the total income receivable as a uniform annuity over the given period of years is multiplied by the respective table factor to give the present value.

For instance, what is the present value of an annuity of $50 per year for 14 years at 6% compound interest?

$$V_p = 50 \times 14 \times .66393$$
$$= 700 \times .66393$$
$$= \$464.75.$$

TABLE 5

Present value of each $1 of total income receivable as a uniform annuity for n years at the following rates percent, compound interest.

Years	1%	2%	3%	4%	5%	6%	7%
1	.99010	.98039	.97087	.96154	.95238	.94340	.93458
2	.98520	.97078	.95673	.94305	.92970	.91669	.90401
3	.98033	.96129	.94287	.92503	.90775	.89100	.87477
4	.97549	.95019	.92927	.90747	.88649	.86628	.84680
5	.97069	.94269	.91594	.89036	.86590	.84247	.82004
6	.96591	.93357	.90287	.87369	.84595	.81955	.79442
7	.96103	.92457	.89004	.85744	.82662	.79748	.76990
8	.95646	.91569	.87746	.84159	.80790	.77622	.74642
9	.95178	.90692	.86512	.82615	.78976	.75574	.72391
10	.94713	.89826	.85302	.81109	.77217	.73601	.70236
11	.94251	.88971	.84115	.79641	.75513	.71699	.68170
12	.93792	.88128	.82950	.78209	.73860	.69865	.66189
13	.93336	.87295	.81807	.76813	.72258	.68098	.64290
14	.92884	.86473	.80686	.75451	.70705	.66393	.62468
15	.92434	.85662	.79586	.74123	.69198	.64748	.60719
16	.91987	.84861	.78507	.72827	.67736	.63162	.59042
17	.91543	.84070	.77448	.71563	.66318	.61631	.57432
18	.91101	.83289	.76408	.70329	.64942	.60153	.55884
19	.90663	.82518	.75388	.69126	.63607	.58727	.54398
20	.90228	.81757	.74387	.67952	.62311	.57349	.52970
21	.89795	.81006	.73405	.66806	.61053	.56019	.51598
22	.89365	.80264	.72441	.65687	.59832	.54735	.50278
23	.88938	.79531	.71494	.64595	.58646	.53493	.49010
24	.88514	.78808	.70565	.63529	.57494	.52293	.47789
25	.88033	.78094	.69653	.62488	.56376	.51133	.46614
26	.87674	.77389	.68757	.61472	.55289	.50012	.45484
27	.87258	.76692	.67878	.60480	.54233	.48928	.44395
28	.86844	.76005	.67015	.59511	.53208	.47879	.43347
29	.86434	.75325	.66167	.58565	.52210	.46865	.42337
30	.86026	.74655	.65335	.57640	.51241	.45883	.41363
31	.85620	.73993	.64518	.56737	.50299	.44933	.40425
32	.85217	.73339	.63715	.55855	.49383	.44013	.39521
33	.84817	.72693	.62927	.54993	.48493	.43122	.38648
34	.84420	.72055	.62152	.54151	.47626	.42259	.37806
35	.84025	.71425	.61392	.53327	.46783	.41424	.36991
36	.83632	.70802	.60645	.52523	.45963	.40614	.36205
37	.83242	.70188	.59911	.51737	.45166	.39829	.35454
38	.82854	.69581	.59191	.50968	.44389	.39068	.34720
39	.82469	.68981	.58483	.50217	.43633	.38331	.34013
40	.82087	.68389	.57787	.49482	.42898	.37616	.33328
41	.81707	.67804	.57103	.48764	.42181	.36922	.32666
42	.81329	.67226	.56432	.48061	.41484	.36249	.32032
43	.80954	.66655	.55772	.47374	.40804	.35596	.31417
44	.80581	.66091	.55123	.46702	.40143	.34962	.30816
45	.80210	.65534	.54486	.46045	.39498	.34346	.30231
46	.79842	.64983	.53860	.45401	.38870	.33749	.29675
47	.79476	.64440	.53244	.44772	.38257	.33168	.29133
48	.79112	.63902	.52639	.44157	.37661	.32604	.28609
49	.78751	.63372	.52044	.43554	.37079	.32056	.28099
50	.78392	.62847	.51460	.42964	.36512	.31524	.27607

TABLE 5

Present value of each $1 of total income receivable as a uniform annuity for n years at the following rates percent, compound interest.

Years	8%	9%	10%	12%	15%	20%	25%
1	.92593	.91743	.90909	.89286	.86957	.83333	.80000
2	.89163	.87956	.86777	.84502	.81285	.76389	.72000
3	.85903	.84376	.82895	.80061	.76108	.70216	.65067
4	.82803	.80993	.79247	.75934	.71374	.64718	.59040
5	.79854	.77793	.75816	.72096	.67043	.59812	.53786
6	.77048	.74765	.72588	.68523	.63075	.55425	.49190
7	.74377	.71899	.69549	.65197	.59435	.51494	.45159
8	.71833	.69185	.66687	.62095	.56092	.47965	.41611
9	.69410	.66614	.63989	.59203	.53018	.44789	.38479
10	.67101	.64177	.61446	.56502	.50188	.41925	.35705
11	.64900	.61865	.59046	.53979	.47579	.39337	.33240
12	.62801	.59673	.56781	.51620	.45172	.36993	.31043
13	.60798	.57592	.54641	.49412	.42947	.34867	.29078
14	.58887	.55615	.52619	.47344	.40889	.32933	.27315
15	.57063	.53738	.50707	.45406	.38982	.31170	.25728
16	.55321	.51953	.48898	.43587	.37214	.29560	.24296
17	.53657	.50256	.47186	.41880	.35572	.28086	.23000
18	.52066	.48642	.45563	.40276	.34044	.26734	.21822
19	.50545	.47106	.44026	.38767	.32622	.25492	.20749
20	.49091	.45643	.42568	.37347	.31297	.24348	.19769
21	.47699	.44249	.41185	.36010	.30059	.23292	.18872
22	.46367	.42920	.39871	.34748	.28903	.22316	.18048
23	.45092	.41653	.38623	.33558	.27821	.21411	.17289
24	.43870	.40444	.37436	.32435	.26807	.20571	.16588
25	.42699	.39290	.36308	.31373	.25857	.19790	.15940
26	.41577	.38188	.35234	.30368	.24964	.19063	.15338
27	.40501	.37135	.34212	.29417	.24124	.18384	.14779
28	.39468	.36127	.33238	.28516	.23334	.17749	.14258
29	.38477	.35166	.32309	.27661	.22589	.17154	.13772
30	.37526	.34246	.31423	.26851	.21887	.16596	.13317
31	.36612	.33364	.30577	.26081	.21223	.16072	.12890
32	.35734	.32519	.29770	.25349	.20595	.15579	.12490
33	.34891	.31710	.28998	.24653	.20001	.15115	.12114
34	.34079	.30935	.28261	.23990	.19439	.14676	.11759
35	.33299	.30191	.27555	.23359	.18905	.14262	.11424
36	.32548	.29477	.26879	.22757	.18398	.13869	.11108
37	.31825	.28792	.26232	.22182	.17916	.13498	.10808
38	.31129	.28134	.25612	.21634	.17457	.13145	.10524
39	.30458	.27501	.25018	.21110	.17021	.12810	.10255
40	.29812	.26893	.24448	.20609	.16604	.12491	.09999
41	.29188	.26309	.23900	.20130	.16207	.12188	.09755
42	.28587	.25746	.23375	.19671	.15828	.11899	.09523
43	.28008	.25205	.22870	.19232	.15466	.11623	.09302
44	.27448	.24683	.22384	.18810	.15119	.11360	.09090
45	.26908	.24180	.21917	.18406	.14787	.11108	.08889
46	.26386	.23696	.21468	.18017	.14469	.10867	.08695
47	.25881	.23229	.21035	.17644	.14164	.10636	.08510
48	.25394	.22778	.20619	.17286	.13872	.10415	.08333
49	.24923	.22343	.20217	.16941	.13591	.10203	.08163
50	.24467	.21923	.19830	.16609	.13321	.09998	.08000

UNIT REDEMPTION FUND PAYMENTS AT COMPOUND INTEREST

TABLE 6

The annual payment necessary to produce $1 in n years, if invested at rates of 1, 1¼, 1½, 1¾, 2, 2¼, 2½, 2¾, 3, 3¼, 3½, 3¾, 4, 4¼, 4½, 4¾, 5, 5½, 6, 6½, 7, 7½, and 8 percent, compound interest.

Calculated to 5 decimal places
and to 50 years.

The factors listed in this table represent the yearly annuity payments required to produce $1 in n years at r rate percent compound interest and are, therefore, values of

$$s = \frac{r}{R^n - 1}.$$

The values given in this table are reciprocals of the values listed in Table 3, because

$$\frac{r}{R^n - 1} = 1 \div \frac{R^n - 1}{r}.$$

If the sum to be produced (fund to be redeemed) is other than unity, the annual redemption payment is obtained by multiplying this sum by the factor given in the table.

$$A = S \times s$$

$$= \frac{Sr}{R^n - 1}$$

$$= S \times \text{Table Factor.}$$

For instance, what annual redemption fund payment at 6% compound interest is necessary to produce $50 in 14 years?

$$A = 50 \times .04758$$

$$= \$2.38.$$

TABLE 6

Redemption fund payment per year required to produce **$1 in n years** at the following rates percent, compound interest.

Years	1%	1¼%	1½%	1¾%	2%	2¼%	2½%
1	1.00000	1.00000	1.00000	1.00000	1.00000	1.00000	1.00000
2	.49751	.49689	.49628	.49566	.49505	.49444	.49383
3	.33002	.32920	.32838	.32757	.32675	.32594	.32514
4	.24628	.24536	.24444	.24353	.24262	.24172	.24082
5	.19604	.19506	.19409	.19312	.19216	.19120	.19025
6	.16255	.16153	.16053	.15952	.15853	.15753	.15655
7	.13863	.13759	.13656	.13553	.13451	.13350	.13250
8	.12069	.11963	.11858	.11754	.11651	.11548	.11447
9	.10674	.10567	.10461	.10356	.10252	.10148	.10046
10	.09558	.09450	.09343	.09238	.09133	.09029	.08926
11	.08645	.08537	.08429	.08323	.08218	.08114	.08011
12	.07885	.07776	.07668	.07561	.07456	.07352	.07249
13	.07241	.07132	.07024	.06917	.06812	.06708	.06605
14	.06690	.06581	.06472	.06366	.06260	.06156	.06054
15	.06212	.06103	.05994	.05888	.05783	.05679	.05577
16	.05794	.05685	.05577	.05670	.05365	.05262	.05160
17	.05426	.05316	.05208	.05102	.04997	.04894	.04793
18	.05098	.04988	.04881	.04774	.04670	.04568	.04467
19	.04805	.04696	.04588	.04482	.04378	.04276	.04176
20	.04542	.04432	.04325	.04219	.04116	.04014	.03915
21	.04303	.04194	.04087	.03981	.03878	.03778	.03679
22	.04086	.03977	.03870	.03766	.03663	.03563	.03465
23	.03889	.03780	.03673	.03569	.03467	.03367	.03270
24	.03707	.03599	.03492	.03389	.03287	.03188	.03091
25	.03541	.03432	.03326	.03223	.03122	.03024	.02928
26	.03387	.03279	.03173	.03070	.02970	.02872	.02777
27	.03245	.03137	.03032	.02929	.02829	.02732	.02638
28	.03112	.03005	.02900	.02798	.02699	.02603	.02509
29	.02990	.02882	.02778	.02676	.02578	.02482	.02389
30	.02875	.02768	.02664	.02563	.02465	.02370	.02278
31	.02768	.02661	.02557	.02457	.02360	.02265	.02174
32	.02667	.02561	.02458	.02358	.02261	.02167	.02077
33	.02573	.02467	.02364	.02265	.02169	.02076	.01986
34	.02484	.02378	.02276	.02177	.02082	.01990	.01901
35	.02400	.02295	.02193	.02095	.02000	.01909	.01821
36	.02321	.02217	.02115	.02018	.01923	.01833	.01745
37	.02247	.02142	.02041	.01944	.01851	.01761	.01674
38	.02176	.02072	.01972	.01875	.01782	.01693	.01607
39	.02109	.02005	.01905	.01809	.01717	.01629	.01544
40	.02046	.01942	.01843	.01747	.01656	.01568	.01484
41	.01985	.01882	.01783	.01688	.01597	.01510	.01427
42	.01928	.01825	.01726	.01632	.01542	.01455	.01373
43	.01873	.01770	.01672	.01579	.01489	.01403	.01322
44	.01820	.01719	.01621	.01528	.01439	.01354	.01273
45	.01771	.01669	.01572	.01479	.01391	.01307	.01227
46	.01723	.01622	.01525	.01433	.01345	.01262	.01183
47	.01677	.01576	.01480	.01389	.01302	.01219	.01141
48	.01633	.01533	.01437	.01347	.01260	.01178	.01101
49	.01591	.01492	.01396	.01306	.01220	.01139	.01062
50	.01551	.01452	.01357	.01267	.01182	.01102	.01026

TABLE 6

Redemption fund payment per year required to produce $1 in n years at the following rates percent, compound interest.

Years	2¾%	3%	3¼%	3½%	3¾%	4%	4¼%
1	1.00000	1.00000	1.00000	1.00000	1.00000	1.00000	1.00000
2	.49322	.49261	.49200	.49140	.49080	.49020	.48960
3	.32433	.32353	.32273	.32193	.32114	.32035	.31956
4	.23992	.23903	.23814	.23725	.23637	.23549	.23462
5	.18930	.18835	.18742	.18648	.18555	.18463	.18371
6	.15557	.15460	.15363	.15267	.15171	.15076	.14982
7	.13150	.13051	.12952	.12854	.12757	.12661	.12565
8	.11346	.11246	.11146	.11048	.10950	.10853	.10756
9	.09944	.09843	.09744	.09645	.09547	.09449	.09353
10	.08824	.08723	.08623	.08524	.08426	.08329	.08233
11	.07909	.07808	.07708	.07609	.07512	.07415	.07319
12	.07147	.07046	.06947	.06848	.06751	.06655	.06560
13	.06503	.06403	.06304	.06206	.06110	.06014	.05920
14	.05952	.05853	.05754	.05657	.05561	.05467	.05374
15	.05476	.05377	.05279	.05183	.05088	.04994	.04902
16	.05060	.04961	.04864	.04768	.04674	.04582	.04491
17	.04693	.04595	.04499	.04404	.04311	.04220	.04130
18	.04368	.04271	.04175	.04082	.03990	.03899	.03811
19	.04078	.03981	.03887	.03794	.03703	.03614	.03526
20	.03817	.03722	.03628	.03536	.03446	.03358	.03272
21	.03582	.03487	.03394	.03304	.03215	.03128	.03043
22	.03369	.03275	.03183	.03093	.03006	.02920	.02836
23	.03174	.03081	.02991	.02902	.02815	.02731	.02649
24	.02997	.02905	.02815	.02727	.02642	.02559	.02478
25	.02834	.02743	.02654	.02567	.02483	.02401	.02321
26	.02684	.02594	.02506	.02421	.02337	.02257	.02178
27	.02546	.02456	.02370	.02285	.02203	.02124	.02047
28	.02418	.02329	.02244	.02160	.02080	.02001	.01925
29	.02299	.02211	.02127	.02045	.01965	.01888	.01813
30	.02188	.02102	.02018	.01937	.01859	.01783	.01710
31	.02085	.02000	.01917	.01837	.01760	.01686	.01614
32	.01989	.01905	.01823	.01744	.01668	.01595	.01524
33	.01899	.01816	.01735	.01657	.01582	.01510	.01441
34	.01815	.01732	.01653	.01576	.01502	.01431	.01363
35	.01736	.01654	.01575	.01500	.01427	.01358	.01291
36	.01661	.01580	.01503	.01428	.01357	.01289	.01223
37	.01591	.01511	.01435	.01361	.01291	.01224	.01160
38	.01525	.01446	.01370	.01298	.01229	.01163	.01100
39	.01462	.01384	.01310	.01239	.01171	.01106	.01044
40	.01403	.01326	.01253	.01183	.01116	.01052	.00992
41	.01347	.01271	.01199	.01130	.01064	.01002	.00942
42	.01294	.01219	.01148	.01080	.01015	.00954	.00896
43	.01244	.01170	.01099	.01033	.00969	.00909	.00852
44	.01196	.01123	.01054	.00988	.00925	.00866	.00811
45	.01151	.01079	.01010	.00945	.00884	.00826	.00772
46	.01107	.01036	.00969	.00905	.00845	.00788	.00735
47	.01066	.00996	.00930	.00867	.00808	.00752	.00700
48	.01027	.00958	.00892	.00831	.00773	.00718	.00667
49	.00990	.00921	.00857	.00796	.00739	.00686	.00636
50	.00954	.00887	.00823	.00763	.00707	.00655	.00606

TABLE 6

Redemption fund payment per year required to produce $1 in n years at the following rates percent, compound interest.

Years	4½%	4¾%	5%	5½%	6%	6½%	7%
1	1.00000	1.00000	1.00000	1.00000	1.00000	1.00000	1.00000
2	.48900	.48840	.48780	.48662	.48544	.48426	.48309
3	.31877	.31799	.31721	.31565	.31411	.31258	.31105
4	.23374	.23288	.23201	.23029	.22859	.22690	.22523
5	.18279	.18188	.18097	.17918	.17740	.17563	.17389
6	.14887	.14795	.14702	.14518	.14336	.14157	.13980
7	.12470	.12376	.12282	.12096	.11914	.11733	.11555
8	.10661	.10567	.10472	.10286	.10104	.09924	.09747
9	.09257	.09163	.09069	.08884	.08702	.08524	.08349
10	.08138	.08044	.07950	.07767	.07587	.07410	.07238
11	.07225	.07131	.07039	.06857	.06679	.06506	.06336
12	.06467	.06374	.06283	.06103	.05928	.05757	.05590
13	.05828	.05736	.05646	.05468	.05296	.05128	.04965
14	.05282	.05192	.05102	.04928	.04758	.04594	.04434
15	.04811	.04722	.04634	.04463	.04296	.04135	.03979
16	.04402	.04314	.04227	.04058	.03895	.03738	.03586
17	.04042	.03955	.03870	.03704	.03544	.03391	.03243
18	.03724	.03638	.03555	.03392	.03236	.03085	.02941
19	.03441	.03357	.03275	.03115	.02962	.02816	.02675
20	.03188	.03105	.03024	.02868	.02718	.02576	.02439
21	.02960	.02879	.02800	.02646	.02500	.02361	.02229
22	.02755	.02675	.02597	.02447	.02305	.02169	.02041
23	.02568	.02490	.02414	.02267	.02128	.01996	.01871
24	.02399	.02322	.02247	.02104	.01968	.01840	.01719
25	.02244	.02169	.02095	.01955	.01823	.01698	.01581
26	.02102	.02028	.01956	.01819	.01690	.01569	.01456
27	.01972	.01899	.01829	.01695	.01570	.01452	.01343
28	.01852	.01781	.01712	.01581	.01459	.01345	.01239
29	.01741	.01672	.01605	.01477	.01358	.01247	.01145
30	.01639	.01571	.01505	.01381	.01265	.01158	.01059
31	.01544	.01478	.01413	.01292	.01179	.01075	.00980
32	.01456	.01391	.01328	.01210	.01100	.01000	.00907
33	.01374	.01310	.01249	.01133	.01027	.00930	.00841
34	.01298	.01236	.01176	.01063	.00960	.00866	.00780
35	.01227	.01166	.01107	.00997	.00897	.00806	.00723
36	.01161	.01101	.01043	.00937	.00839	.00751	.00672
37	.01098	.01040	.00984	.00880	.00786	.00701	.00624
38	.01040	.00983	.00928	.00827	.00736	.00653	.00580
39	.00986	.00930	.00876	.00778	.00689	.00610	.00539
40	.00934	.00880	.00828	.00732	.00646	.00569	.00501
41	.00886	.00833	.00782	.00689	.00606	.00532	.00466
42	.00841	.00789	.00739	.00649	.00568	.00497	.00434
43	.00798	.00747	.00699	.00611	.00533	.00464	.00404
44	.00758	.00708	.00662	.00576	.00501	.00434	.00376
45	.00720	.00672	.00626	.00543	.00470	.00406	.00350
46	.00684	.00637	.00593	.00512	.00441	.00380	.00326
47	.00651	.00605	.00561	.00483	.00415	.00355	.00304
48	.00619	.00574	.00532	.00456	.00390	.00333	.00283
49	.00589	.00545	.00504	.00430	.00366	.00311	.00264
50	.00560	.00517	.00478	.00406	.00344	.00291	.00246

TABLE 6

Redemption fund payment per year required to produce $1 in n years at the following rates percent, compound interest.

Years	7½%	8%
1	1.00000	1.00000
2	.48193	.48077
3	.30954	.30803
4	.22357	.22192
5	.17216	.17046
6	.13804	.13632
7	.11380	.11207
8	.09573	.09401
9	.08177	.08008
10	.07069	.06903
11	.06170	.06008
12	.05428	.05270
13	.04806	.04652
14	.04280	.04130
15	.03829	.03683
16	.03439	.03298
17	.03100	.02963
18	.02803	.02670
19	.02541	.02413
20	.02309	.02185
21	.02103	.01983
22	.01919	.01803
23	.01754	.01642
24	.01605	.01498
25	.01471	.01368
26	.01350	.01251
27	.01240	.01145
28	.01141	.01049
29	.01050	.00962
30	.00967	.00883
31	.00892	.00811
32	.00823	.00745
33	.00759	.00685
34	.00701	.00630
35	.00648	.00580
36	.00599	.00534
37	.00555	.00492
38	.00513	.00454
39	.00475	.00419
40	.00440	.00386
41	.00408	.00356
42	.00378	.00329
43	.00350	.00303
44	.00325	.00280
45	.00301	.00259
46	.00279	.00239
47	.00259	.00221
48	.00241	.00204
49	.00223	.00189
50	.00207	.00174

PRESENT VALUE OF UNIT REDEMPTION ANNUITIES

TABLE 7

MINE VALUATION
VALUATION OF DEPLETING RESERVES
REDEMPTION ANNUITIES

The present value (or "years' purchase" factor) of an annuity of $1 per year for n years, allowing interest to the purchaser on his invested capital at rates of 2, 3, 4, 5, 6, 7, 8, 9, 10, 11, 12, 15, 18, 20, and 25 percent per annum, with redemption of capital allowed at the expiration of the n year period by annually investing the dividend overplus at the practicable rates of 2, 3, 4, 5, or 6 percent per annum.

Calculated to 4 decimal places
and to 50 years.

The factors listed in this table represent the present value, or "years' purchase," of an annuity of $1 per year for n years which will return interest on invested capital at r' rate per annum and will allow redemption of capital by annually investing the dividend overplus at a safe practicable rate of r percent.

$$V_p = \frac{1}{\dfrac{r}{R^n - 1} + r'}$$

$$= \frac{1}{s + r'}.$$

If the annuity to be purchased pays an amount other than unity per year, the present value is found by multiplying the yearly payment by the factor given in the table.

$$V_p = \frac{A}{\dfrac{r}{R^n - 1} + r'} = \frac{A}{s + r'}$$

$$= A \times \text{Table Factor.}$$

For instance, what is the present value or purchase price of an annuity income of $50 per year for 14 years, if the purchaser desires interest on his investment at 8% per annum and redemption of his capital by annually investing the dividend overplus at 3% per annum?

$$V_p = 50 \times 7.2188$$
$$= \$360.94.$$

TABLE 7

Present value of $1 per year. Redemption of capital at 2% with interest to the purchaser at the following rates percent.

Years	2%	3%	4%	5%	6%	7%	8%
1	.9804	.9709	.9615	.9524	.9434	.9346	.9259
2	1.9416	1.9046	1.8690	1.8347	1.8016	1.7698	1.7390
3	2.8839	2.8030	2.7266	2.6542	2.5856	2.5204	2.4585
4	3.8077	3.6681	3.5383	3.4174	3.3044	3.1987	3.0900
5	4.7135	4.5013	4.3074	4.1295	3.9658	3.8145	3.6743
6	5.6014	5.3043	5.0371	4.7956	4.5761	4.3759	4.1924
7	6.4720	6.0786	5.7303	5.4197	5.1411	4.8897	4.6617
8	7.3255	6.8255	6.3894	6.0057	5.6654	5.3616	5.0888
9	8.1622	7.5463	7.0168	6.5567	6.1533	5.7966	5.4790
10	8.9826	8.2422	7.6146	7.0758	6.6082	6.1986	5.8368
11	9.7868	8.9144	8.1848	7.5656	7.0334	6.5713	6.1661
12	10.5753	9.5639	8.7291	8.0283	7.4317	6.9176	6.4700
13	11.3484	10.1918	9.2491	8.4661	7.8053	7.2402	6.7514
14	12.1062	10.7989	9.7464	8.8808	8.1565	7.5414	7.0125
15	12.8493	11.3862	10.2223	9.2742	8.4871	7.8232	7.2556
16	13.5777	11.9546	10.6780	9.6478	8.7989	8.0873	7.4822
17	14.2919	12.5047	11.1148	10.0030	9.0934	8.3354	7.6941
18	14.9920	13.0375	11.5337	10.3410	9.3719	8.5688	7.8925
19	15.6785	13.5535	11.9358	10.6631	9.6356	8.7888	8.0787
20	16.3514	14.0535	12.3218	10.9701	9.8857	8.9963	8.2538
21	17.0112	14.5381	12.6928	11.2632	10.1230	9.1925	8.4186
22	17.6580	15.0079	13.0495	11.5432	10.3486	9.3781	8.5740
23	18.2922	15.4636	13.3926	11.8108	10.5632	9.5540	8.7208
24	18.9139	15.9056	13.7229	12.0669	10.7676	9.7209	8.8597
25	19.5235	16.3344	14.0409	12.3122	10.9625	9.8794	8.9912
26	20.1210	16.7506	14.3474	12.5472	11.1484	10.0302	9.1158
27	20.7069	17.1547	14.6428	12.7725	11.3259	10.1737	9.2342
28	21.2813	17.5470	14.9277	12.9888	11.4956	10.3104	9.3467
29	21.8444	17.9281	15.2026	13.1964	11.6580	10.4408	9.4537
30	22.3965	18.2983	15.4679	13.3959	11.8134	10.5652	9.5557
31	22.9377	18.6580	15.7242	13.5876	11.9622	10.6842	9.6528
32	23.4683	19.0076	15.9717	13.7721	12.1050	10.7979	9.7456
33	23.9886	19.3474	16.2110	13.9496	12.2419	10.9067	9.8341
34	24.4986	19.6778	16.4423	14.1206	12.3734	11.0110	9.9188
35	24.9986	19.9991	16.6661	14.2853	12.4997	11.1108	9.9998
36	25.4888	20.3116	16.8825	14.4440	12.6210	11.2066	10.0773
37	25.9695	20.6157	17.0920	14.5971	12.7378	11.2986	10.1516
38	26.4406	20.9115	17.2949	14.7448	12.8501	11.3869	10.2228
39	26.9026	21.1994	17.4913	14.8873	12.9582	11.4717	10.2911
40	27.3555	21.4796	17.6817	15.0250	13.0624	11.5532	10.3567
41	27.7995	21.7524	17.8663	15.1580	13.1629	11.6317	10.4197
42	28.2348	22.0180	18.0449	15.2865	13.2596	11.7072	10.4803
43	28.6616	22.2767	18.2183	15.4107	13.3529	11.7800	10.5385
44	29.0800	22.5286	18.3864	15.5309	13.4430	11.8500	10.5946
45	29.4902	22.7741	18.5496	15.6471	13.5300	11.9176	10.6485
46	29.8923	23.0131	18.7079	15.7596	13.6141	11.9827	10.7005
47	30.2866	23.2461	18.8615	15.8685	13.6953	12.0456	10.7506
48	30.6731	23.4732	19.0107	15.9740	13.7738	12.1063	10.7989
49	31.0521	23.6945	19.1556	16.0761	13.8497	12.1649	10.8455
50	31.4236	23.9102	19.2964	16.1752	13.9231	12.2215	10.8905

TABLE 7

Present value of $1 per year. Redemption of capital at 2% with interest to the purchaser at the following rates percent.

Years	9%	10%	11%	12%	15%	18%	20%
1	.9174	.9091	.9009	.8929	.8696	.8475	.8333
2	1.7093	1.6805	1.6528	1.6259	1.5503	1.4814	1.4387
3	2.3995	2.3433	2.2896	2.2384	2.0975	1.9733	1.8984
4	3.0064	2.9187	2.8359	2.7577	2.5470	2.3662	2.2593
5	3.5441	3.4228	3.3095	3.2035	2.9226	2.6870	2.5500
6	4.0237	3.8681	3.7240	3.5903	3.2412	2.9540	2.7892
7	4.4541	4.2642	4.0898	3.9291	3.5148	3.1795	2.9894
8	4.8424	4.6187	4.4148	4.2282	3.7522	3.3726	3.1595
9	5.1944	4.9379	4.7055	4.4941	3.9602	3.5396	3.3056
10	5.5149	5.2267	4.9671	4.7320	4.1438	3.6856	3.4326
11	5.8079	5.4891	5.2035	4.9461	4.3070	3.8142	3.5439
12	6.0768	5.7287	5.4183	5.1398	4.4532	3.9284	3.6422
13	6.3244	5.9482	5.6142	5.3158	4.5847	4.0303	3.7297
14	6.5530	6.1500	5.7937	5.4764	4.7036	4.1220	3.8080
15	6.7647	6.3361	5.9586	5.6235	4.8117	4.2048	3.8786
16	6.9614	6.5083	6.1106	5.7587	4.9104	4.2799	3.9424
17	7.1444	6.6680	6.2512	5.8834	5.0008	4.3484	4.0005
18	7.3152	6.8165	6.3815	5.9987	5.0838	4.4111	4.0535
19	7.4749	6.9550	6.5027	6.1057	5.1604	4.4686	4.1020
20	7.6245	7.0843	6.6156	6.2051	5.2313	4.5217	4.1467
21	7.7649	7.2054	6.7211	6.2978	5.2970	4.5707	4.1879
22	7.8969	7.3190	6.8198	6.3844	5.3582	4.6161	4.2260
23	8.0213	7.4257	6.9124	6.4655	5.4151	4.6585	4.2613
24	8.1386	7.5261	6.9993	6.5415	5.4683	4.6977	4.2942
25	8.2494	7.6208	7.0811	6.6129	5.5181	4.7344	4.3249
26	8.3543	7.7101	7.1582	6.6801	5.5649	4.7687	4.3535
27	8.4536	7.7947	7.2310	6.7434	5.6087	4.8009	4.3803
28	8.5478	7.8747	7.2998	6.8032	5.6500	4.8312	4.4055
29	8.6372	7.9505	7.3649	6.8597	5.6890	4.8596	4.4291
30	8.7222	8.0225	7.4267	6.9132	5.7257	4.8864	4.4514
31	8.8031	8.0909	7.4852	6.9640	5.7605	4.9117	4.4723
32	8.8802	8.1559	7.5409	7.0121	5.7934	4.9356	4.4921
33	8.9536	8.2178	7.5938	7.0578	5.8246	4.9582	4.5109
34	9.0238	8.2769	7.6442	7.1013	5.8542	4.9796	4.5286
35	9.0907	8.3332	7.6922	7.1427	5.8823	4.9999	4.5454
36	9.1548	8.3869	7.7380	7.1822	5.9090	5.0193	4.5614
37	9.2160	8.4383	7.7817	7.2199	5.9345	5.0376	4.5765
38	9.2747	8.4875	7.8235	7.2558	5.9587	5.0551	4.5909
39	9.3309	8.5345	7.8634	7.2902	5.9819	5.0717	4.6047
40	9.3848	8.5796	7.9017	7.3230	6.0040	5.0876	4.6177
41	9.4365	8.6228	7.9383	7.3545	6.0251	5.1028	4.6302
42	9.4861	8.6642	7.9734	7.3846	6.0453	5.1173	4.6422
43	9.5338	8.7040	8.0071	7.4135	6.0647	5.1311	4.6535
44	9.5797	8.7422	8.0394	7.4411	6.0832	5.1444	4.6644
45	9.6327	8.7789	8.0704	7.4677	6.1009	5.1570	4.6749
46	9.6662	8.8142	8.1002	7.4933	6.1180	5.1692	4.6849
47	9.7070	8.8482	8.1289	7.5178	6.1343	5.1809	4.6944
48	9.7464	8.8809	8.1565	7.5414	6.1500	5.1921	4.7036
49	9.7844	8.9123	8.1830	7.5641	6.1651	5.2028	4.7124
50	9.8209	8.9427	8.2086	7.5859	6.1796	5.2131	4.7209

PRESENT VALUE OF REDEMPTION ANNUITIES

TABLE 7

Present value of $1 per year. Redemption of capital at 2% with interest to the purchaser at the following rates percent.

Years 25%

Years	Value
1	.8000
2	1.3422
3	1.7338
4	2.0299
5	2.2616
6	2.4478
7	2.6007
8	2.7284
9	2.8368
10	2.9297
11	3.0104
12	3.0811
13	3.1435
14	3.1990
15	3.2486
16	3.2933
17	3.3337
18	3.3704
19	3.4039
20	3.4346
21	3.4628
22	3.4888
23	3.5129
24	3.5352
25	3.5559
26	3.5753
27	3.5933
28	3.6102
29	3.6261
30	3.6410
31	3.6550
32	3.6682
33	3.6807
34	3.6925
35	3.7037
36	3.7143
37	3.7243
38	3.7338
39	3.7429
40	3.7516
41	3.7598
42	3.7677
43	3.7752
44	3.7823
45	3.7892
46	3.7957
47	3.8020
48	3.8080
49	3.8138
50	3.8194

TABLE 7

Present value of $1 per year. Redemption of capital at 3% with interest to the purchaser at the following rates percent.

Years	3%	4%	5%	6%	7%	8%	9%
1	.9709	.9615	.9524	.9434	.9346	.9259	.9174
2	1.9135	1.8775	1.8429	1.8096	1.7774	1.7464	1.7164
3	2.8286	2.7508	2.6772	2.6074	2.5411	2.4781	2.4182
4	3.7171	3.5839	3.4599	3.3442	3.2360	3.1345	3.0393
5	4.5797	4.3792	4.1954	4.0265	3.8706	3.7264	3.5925
6	5.4172	5.1388	4.8876	4.6599	4.4524	4.2626	4.0883
7	6.2303	5.8649	5.5400	5.2492	4.9874	4.7505	4.5350
8	7.0197	6.5593	6.1555	5.7986	5.4808	5.1960	4.9393
9	7.7861	7.2237	6.7370	6.3118	5.9370	5.6043	5.3069
10	8.5302	7.8597	7.2870	6.7921	6.3601	5.9798	5.6424
11	9.2526	8.4690	7.8078	7.2423	6.7532	6.3260	5.9496
12	9.9540	9.0529	8.3014	7.6651	7.1194	6.6462	6.2320
13	10.6350	9.6127	8.7697	8.0626	7.4610	6.9430	6.4923
14	11.2961	10.1496	9.2144	8.4369	7.7805	7.2188	6.7328
15	11.9379	10.6648	9.6370	8.7899	8.0797	7.4757	6.9557
16	12.5611	11.1594	10.0391	9.1232	8.3604	7.7154	7.1628
17	13.1661	11.6343	10.4218	9.4382	8.6242	7.9395	7.3555
18	13.7535	12.0906	10.7865	9.7363	8.8724	8.1494	7.5353
19	14.3238	12.5291	11.1341	10.0186	9.1063	8.3463	7.7033
20	14.8775	12.9507	11.4658	10.2864	9.3270	8.5313	7.8607
21	15.4150	13.3562	11.7825	10.5405	9.5355	8.7054	8.0082
22	15.9369	13.7462	12.0850	10.7820	9.7236	8.8694	8.1468
23	16.4436	14.1215	12.3741	11.0115	9.9193	9.0241	8.2772
24	16.9355	14.4828	12.6506	11.2300	10.0962	9.1703	8.4000
25	17.4131	14.8307	12.9152	11.4380	10.2640	9.3086	8.5159
26	17.8768	15.1657	13.1686	11.6363	10.4234	9.4395	8.6253
27	18.3270	15.4885	13.4113	11.8253	10.5748	9.5635	8.7287
28	18.7641	15.7995	13.6438	12.0058	10.7189	9.6812	8.8267
29	19.1885	16.0993	13.8668	12.1781	10.8560	9.7929	8.9194
30	19.6004	16.3883	14.0807	12.3427	10.9867	9.8991	9.0074
31	20.0004	16.6670	14.2859	12.5002	11.1112	10.0001	9.0910
32	20.3888	16.9358	14.4830	12.6508	11.2301	10.0963	9.1704
33	20.7658	17.1951	14.6722	12.7949	11.3435	10.1879	9.2459
34	21.1318	17.4453	14.8540	12.9329	11.4519	10.2752	9.3178
35	21.4872	17.6868	15.0287	13.0652	11.5554	10.3585	9.3862
36	21.8323	17.9199	15.1967	13.1920	11.6545	10.4380	9.4515
37	22.1672	18.1450	15.3582	13.3135	11.7493	10.5140	9.5137
38	22.4925	18.3623	15.5137	13.4301	11.8400	10.5866	9.5731
39	22.8082	18.5722	15.6632	13.5421	11.9269	10.6560	9.6298
40	23.1148	18.7750	15.8072	13.6496	12.0102	10.7224	9.6841
41	23.4124	18.9709	15.9458	13.7528	12.0901	10.7860	9.7359
42	23.7014	19.1601	16.0793	13.8520	12.1667	10.8470	9.7855
43	23.9819	19.3431	16.2080	13.9474	12.2402	10.9054	9.8330
44	24.2543	19.5199	16.3319	14.0391	12.3107	10.9613	9.8785
45	24.5187	19.6908	16.4514	14.1273	12.3785	11.0150	9.9221
46	24.7754	19.8560	16.5666	14.2121	12.4436	11.0665	9.9639
47	25.0247	20.0158	16.6776	14.2938	12.5062	11.1160	10.0040
48	25.2667	20.1703	16.7848	14.3724	12.5663	11.1635	10.0424
49	25.5017	20.3198	16.8881	14.4481	12.6242	11.2091	10.0793
50	25.7298	20.4643	16.9879	14.5211	12.6798	11.2530	10.1148

TABLE 7

Present value of $1 per year. Redemption of capital at 3% with interest to the purchaser at the following rates percent.

Years	10%	11%	12%	15%	18%	20%	25%
1	.9091	.9009	.8929	.8696	.8547	.8333	.8000
2	1.6874	1.6594	1.6324	1.5562	1.4867	1.4438	1.3466
3	2.3611	2.3066	2.2546	2.1118	1.9860	1.9101	1.7436
4	2.9496	2.8651	2.7853	2.5705	2.3865	2.2778	2.0449
5	3.4680	3.3517	3.2430	2.9555	2.7148	2.5750	2.2813
6	3.9278	3.7793	3.6417	3.2830	2.9887	2.8201	2.4716
7	4.3383	4.1579	3.9919	3.5650	3.2205	3.0257	2.6281
8	4.7068	4.4953	4.3019	3.8102	3.4193	3.2004	2.7590
9	5.0395	4.7977	4.5780	4.0252	3.5915	3.3508	2.8700
10	5.3410	5.0702	4.8255	4.2153	3.7421	3.4815	2.9653
11	5.6155	5.3170	5.0485	4.3845	3.8748	3.5961	3.0481
12	5.8664	5.5413	5.2504	4.5359	3.9926	3.6974	3.1205
13	6.0965	5.7462	5.4339	4.6723	4.0979	3.7875	3.1844
14	6.3081	5.9338	5.6014	4.7956	4.1924	3.8681	3.2412
15	6.5034	6.1063	5.7548	4.9076	4.2778	3.9406	3.2920
16	6.6840	6.2652	5.8958	5.0097	4.3552	4.0062	3.3377
17	6.8515	6.4122	6.0258	5.1033	4.4257	4.0658	3.3789
18	7.0073	6.5484	6.1460	5.1892	4.4902	4.1202	3.4164
19	7.1524	6.6749	6.2573	5.2683	4.5493	4.1699	3.4505
20	7.2878	6.7928	6.3607	5.3414	4.6037	4.2156	3.4817
21	7.4144	6.9027	6.4570	5.4092	4.6539	4.2576	3.5104
22	7.5331	7.0054	6.5468	5.4720	4.7004	4.2965	3.5367
23	7.6444	7.1016	6.6347	5.5305	4.7435	4.3325	3.5611
24	7.7491	7.1918	6.7093	5.5851	4.7836	4.3659	3.5836
25	7.8476	7.2765	6.7830	5.6361	4.8210	4.3970	3.6045
26	7.9404	7.3563	6.8522	5.6838	4.8558	4.4260	3.6240
27	8.0280	7.4314	6.9173	5.7286	4.8884	4.4531	3.6421
28	8.1107	7.5023	6.9787	5.7706	4.9190	4.4784	3.6591
29	8.1890	7.5692	7.0366	5.8101	4.9477	4.5022	3.6749
30	8.2631	7.6325	7.0912	5.8473	4.9746	4.5245	3.6898
31	8.3334	7.6924	7.1429	5.8824	5.0000	4.5455	3.7017
32	8.4001	7.7491	7.1918	5.9155	5.0239	4.5652	3.7168
33	8.4634	7.8030	7.2382	5.9469	5.0465	4.5839	3.7292
34	8.5236	7.8541	7.2822	5.9765	5.0679	4.6015	3.7408
35	8.5808	7.9027	7.3239	6.0046	5.0880	4.6181	3.7518
36	8.6353	7.9489	7.3636	6.0312	5.1072	4.6338	3.7622
37	8.6872	7.9929	7.4013	6.0565	5.1253	4.6487	3.7720
38	8.7367	8.0348	7.4372	6.0805	5.1425	4.6629	3.7813
39	8.7840	8.0747	7.4714	6.1034	5.1588	4.6763	3.7901
40	8.8291	8.1128	7.5040	6.1251	5.1743	4.6891	3.7985
41	8.8721	8.1491	7.5351	6.1458	5.1891	4.7012	3.8064
42	8.9133	8.1839	7.5648	6.1655	5.2031	4.7127	3.8140
43	8.9527	8.2171	7.5931	6.1844	5.2165	4.7237	3.8212
44	8.9904	8.2488	7.6202	6.2023	5.2293	4.7342	3.8280
45	9.0265	8.2792	7.6461	6.2195	5.2415	4.7442	3.8346
46	9.0610	8.3082	7.6709	6.2359	5.2531	4.7537	3.8408
47	9.0942	8.3361	7.6946	6.2515	5.2643	4.7628	3.8467
48	9.1259	8.3628	7.7174	6.2665	5.2749	4.7715	3.8524
49	9.1564	8.3883	7.7392	6.2809	5.2850	4.7798	3.8578
50	9.1856	8.4129	7.7600	6.2946	5.2948	4.7878	3.8630

TABLE 7

Present value of $1 per year. Redemption of capital at 4% with interest to the purchaser at the following rates percent.

Years	4%	5%	6%	7%	8%	9%	10%
1	.9615	.9524	.9434	.9346	.9259	.9174	.9091
2	1.8861	1.8512	1.8175	1.7859	1.7538	1.7236	1.6944
3	2.7751	2.7002	2.6292	2.5618	2.4978	2.4370	2.3790
4	3.6299	3.5027	3.3842	3.2735	3.1697	3.0723	2.9807
5	4.4518	4.2621	4.0879	3.9273	3.7789	3.6413	3.5134
6	5.2421	4.9810	4.7447	4.5298	4.3335	4.1531	3.9878
7	6.0021	5.6622	5.3588	5.0865	4.8400	4.6166	4.4129
8	6.7327	6.3080	5.9337	5.6014	5.3043	5.0371	4.7955
9	7.4353	6.9208	6.4728	6.0794	5.7309	5.4203	5.1416
10	8.1109	7.5024	6.9788	6.5235	6.1240	5.7707	5.4558
11	8.7605	8.0548	7.4544	6.9377	6.4872	6.0920	5.7422
12	9.3851	8.5798	7.9019	7.3233	6.8235	6.3874	6.0041
13	9.9856	9.0790	8.3234	7.6839	7.1355	6.6603	6.2444
14	10.5631	9.5539	8.7208	8.0213	7.4256	6.9123	6.4654
15	11.1184	10.0059	9.0958	8.3374	7.6958	7.1459	6.6693
16	11.6523	10.4362	9.4500	8.6341	7.9479	7.3627	6.8578
17	12.1657	10.8462	9.7849	8.8128	8.1834	7.5644	7.0324
18	12.6593	11.2368	10.1017	9.1749	8.4038	7.7523	7.1946
19	13.1339	11.6092	10.4016	9.4216	8.6104	7.9278	7.3455
20	13.5903	11.9643	10.6858	9.6542	8.8042	8.0918	7.4861
21	14.0292	12.3031	10.9553	9.8736	8.9863	8.2454	7.6173
22	14.4511	12.6265	11.2109	10.0808	9.1576	8.3893	7.7400
23	14.8568	12.9351	11.4536	10.2765	9.3189	8.5245	7.8549
24	15.2470	13.2298	11.6840	10.4617	9.4709	8.6515	7.9626
25	15.6221	13.5113	11.9031	10.6369	9.6143	8.7710	8.0637
26	15.9828	13.7803	12.1113	10.8029	9.7497	8.8836	8.1588
27	16.3296	14.0374	12.3094	10.9602	9.8777	8.9897	8.2482
28	16.6631	14.2831	12.4980	11.1095	9.9987	9.0898	8.3324
29	16.9837	14.5180	12.6775	11.2511	10.1133	9.1844	8.4118
30	17.2920	14.7427	12.8485	11.3856	10.2218	9.2738	8.4868
31	17.5885	14.9577	13.0115	11.5134	10.3247	9.3584	8.5576
32	17.8736	15.1633	13.1668	11.6348	10.4222	9.4385	8.6245
33	18.1476	15.3601	13.3149	11.7504	10.5149	9.5144	8.6878
34	18.4112	15.5485	13.4563	11.8603	10.6028	9.5864	8.7478
35	18.6646	15.7289	13.5911	11.9650	10.6863	9.6546	8.8046
36	18.9083	15.9016	13.7199	12.0646	10.7658	9.7194	8.8584
37	19.1426	16.0670	13.8428	12.1596	10.8413	9.7810	8.9095
38	19.3679	16.2254	13.9603	12.2501	10.9132	9.8394	8.9580
39	19.5845	16.3771	14.0725	12.3364	10.9817	9.8950	9.0041
40	19.7928	16.5225	14.1797	12.4187	11.0469	9.9479	9.0479
41	19.9931	16.6618	14.2822	12.4973	11.1090	9.9983	9.0895
42	20.1856	16.7954	14.3802	12.5722	11.1682	10.0462	9.1291
43	20.3708	16.9234	14.4739	12.6438	11.2246	10.0918	9.1668
44	20.5488	17.0461	14.5636	12.7122	11.2785	10.1354	9.2026
45	20.7200	17.1637	14.6493	12.7775	11.3298	10.1768	9.2368
46	20.8847	17.2765	14.7314	12.8399	11.3789	10.2164	9.2694
47	21.0429	17.3847	14.8100	12.8996	11.4257	10.2541	9.3004
48	21.1951	17.4884	14.8852	12.9566	11.4704	10.2901	9.3300
49	21.3415	17.5879	14.9573	13.0111	11.5132	10.3245	9.3583
50	21.4822	17.6834	15.0263	13.0633	11.5540	10.3573	9.3852

TABLE 7

Present value of $1 per year. Redemption of capital at 4% with interest to the purchaser at the following rates percent.

Years	11%	12%	15%	18%	20%	25%
1	.9009	.8929	.8696	.8476	.8333	.8000
2	1.6661	1.6388	1.5620	1.4921	1.4489	1.3510
3	2.3237	2.2709	2.1261	1.9986	1.9218	1.7533
4	2.8944	2.8130	2.5941	2.4068	2.2963	2.0598
5	3.3941	3.2827	2.9884	2.7425	2.5999	2.3008
6	3.8349	3.6933	3.3249	3.0233	2.8509	2.4952
7	4.2264	4.0550	3.6152	3.2615	3.0618	2.6553
8	4.5761	4.3758	3.8681	3.4659	3.2412	2.7892
9	4.8901	4.6622	4.0901	3.6431	3.3957	2.9028
10	5.1735	4.9191	4.2865	3.7981	3.5299	3.0004
11	5.4304	5.1507	4.4613	3.9347	3.6477	3.0850
12	5.6641	5.3604	4.6178	4.0559	3.7516	3.1590
13	5.8774	5.5511	4.7586	4.1642	3.8440	3.2243
14	6.0728	5.7251	4.8859	4.2613	3.9267	3.2823
15	6.2523	5.8844	5.0015	4.3489	4.0009	3.3340
16	6.4177	6.0306	5.1067	4.4283	4.0680	3.3804
17	6.5704	6.1653	5.2030	4.5005	4.1288	3.4223
18	6.7117	6.2896	5.2912	4.5663	4.1242	3.4603
19	6.8428	6.4046	5.3723	4.6267	4.2348	3.4948
20	6.9647	6.5112	5.4472	4.6820	4.2812	3.5263
21	7.0781	6.6103	5.5163	4.7331	4.3238	3.5552
22	7.1840	6.7025	5.5804	4.7801	4.3630	3.5817
23	7.2828	6.7884	5.6399	4.8237	4.3993	3.6061
24	7.3753	6.8688	5.6952	4.8641	4.4329	3.6286
25	7.4620	6.9438	5.7467	4.9017	4.4640	3.6495
26	7.5433	7.0142	5.7948	4.9366	4.4930	3.6688
27	7.6197	7.0802	5.8398	4.9692	4.5200	3.6868
28	7.6915	7.1422	5.8819	4.9997	4.5452	3.7035
29	7.7592	7.2005	5.9214	5.0282	4.5687	3.7191
30	7.8229	7.2553	5.9585	5.0548	4.5907	3.7337
31	7.8830	7.3070	5.9932	5.0799	4.6114	3.7473
32	7.9397	7.3557	6.0260	5.1034	4.6307	3.7601
33	7.9934	7.4017	6.0568	5.1255	4.6489	3.7721
34	8.0441	7.4452	6.0859	5.1463	4.6660	3.7834
35	8.0921	7.4863	6.1133	5.1659	4.6821	3.7940
36	8.1376	7.5252	6.1392	5.1844	4.6973	3.8039
37	8.1807	7.5620	6.1637	5.2018	4.7117	3.8133
38	8.2215	7.5969	6.1869	5.2183	4.7252	3.8222
39	8.2603	7.6300	6.2088	5.2339	4.7380	3.8305
40	8.2971	7.6615	6.2296	5.2487	4.7501	3.8384
41	8.3321	7.6913	6.2493	5.2627	4.7615	3.8459
42	8.3654	7.7196	6.2680	5.2759	4.7724	3.8530
43	8.3970	7.7465	6.2858	5.2885	4.7826	3.8597
44	8.4271	7.7721	6.3026	5.3004	4.7924	3.8660
45	8.4558	7.7965	6.3186	5.3117	4.8016	3.8720
46	8.4831	7.8197	6.3338	5.3225	4.8104	3.8777
47	8.5091	7.8418	6.3483	5.3327	4.8188	3.8832
48	8.5338	7.8628	6.3621	5.3424	4.8267	3.8883
49	8.5575	7.8829	6.3752	5.3517	4.8343	3.8932
50	8.5800	7.9020	6.3877	5.3605	4.8414	3.8979

VALUATION TABLES

TABLE 7

Present value of $1 per year. Redemption of capital at 5% with interest to the purchaser at the following rates percent.

Years	5%	6%	7%	8%	9%	10%	11%
1	.9524	.9434	.9346	.9259	.9174	.9091	.9009
2	1.8594	1.8255	1.7927	1.7612	1.7307	1.7012	1.6725
3	2.7232	2.6510	2.5826	2.5175	2.4557	2.3969	2.3408
4	3.5460	3.4245	3.3111	3.2050	3.1055	3.0119	2.9238
5	4.3295	4.1498	3.9845	3.8318	3.6904	3.5590	3.4367
6	5.0757	4.8305	4.6079	4.4049	4.2191	4.0483	3.8908
7	5.7864	5.4699	5.1862	4.9305	4.6988	4.4879	4.2952
8	6.4632	6.0708	5.7234	5.4135	5.1355	4.8846	4.6572
9	7.1078	6.6362	6.2231	5.8586	5.5344	5.2441	4.9828
10	7.7217	7.1682	6.6888	6.2694	5.8995	5.5709	5.2769
11	8.3064	7.6693	7.1231	6.6494	6.2348	5.8689	5.5436
12	8.8633	8.1416	7.5287	7.0015	6.5434	6.1416	5.7862
13	9.3936	8.5869	7.9079	7.3284	6.8280	6.3916	6.0076
14	9.8986	9.0070	8.2628	7.6322	7.0910	6.6215	6.2103
15	10.3797	9.4036	8.5953	7.9150	7.3345	6.8333	6.3962
16	10.8378	9.7781	8.9071	8.1786	7.5603	7.0290	6.5673
17	11.2741	10.1318	9.1997	8.4247	7.7701	7.2099	6.7250
18	11.6896	10.4661	9.4745	8.6545	7.9652	7.3776	6.8707
19	12.0853	10.7823	9.7328	8.8696	8.1470	7.5332	7.0055
20	12.4622	11.0812	9.9758	9.0709	8.3165	7.6780	7.1305
21	12.8212	11.3641	10.2045	9.2596	8.4749	7.8127	7.2466
22	13.1630	11.6319	10.4199	9.4366	8.6229	7.9384	7.3545
23	13.4886	11.8854	10.6228	9.6028	8.7614	8.0556	7.4551
24	13.7986	12.1255	10.8142	9.7589	8.8912	8.1652	7.5488
25	14.0939	12.3529	10.9948	9.9057	9.0129	8.2677	7.6364
26	14.3752	12.5684	11.1652	10.0438	9.1271	8.3637	7.7182
27	14.6430	12.7727	11.3261	10.1738	9.2343	8.4537	7.7947
28	14.8981	12.9664	11.4781	10.2963	9.3351	8.5381	7.8664
29	15.1411	13.1500	11.6218	10.4117	9.4299	8.6173	7.9336
30	15.3725	13.3242	11.7576	10.5206	9.5191	8.6918	7.9967
31	15.5928	13.4894	11.8861	10.6234	9.6032	8.7618	8.0559
32	15.8027	13.6462	12.0076	10.7204	9.6824	8.8277	8.1116
33	16.0025	13.7950	12.1227	10.8120	9.7570	8.8897	8.1639
34	16.1929	13.9362	12.2316	10.8985	9.8275	8.9481	8.2132
35	16.3742	14.0703	12.3348	10.9804	9.8940	9.0032	8.2596
36	16.5469	14.1976	12.4325	11.0577	9.9567	9.0551	8.3033
37	16.7113	14.3185	12.5251	11.1309	10.0160	9.1042	8.3445
38	16.8679	14.4333	12.6128	11.2002	10.0721	9.1505	8.3833
39	17.0170	14.5424	12.6961	11.2657	10.1251	9.1942	8.4200
40	17.1591	14.6460	12.7750	11.3278	10.1752	9.2355	8.4546
41	17.2944	14.7444	12.8498	11.3866	10.2226	9.2745	8.4874
42	17.4232	14.8380	12.9208	11.4423	10.2675	9.3114	8.5183
43	17.5459	14.9269	12.9881	11.4951	10.3100	9.3464	8.5475
44	17.6628	15.0114	13.0521	11.5452	10.3502	9.3794	8.5751
45	17.7741	15.0917	13.1127	11.5926	10.3883	9.4107	8.6013
46	17.8801	15.1680	13.1703	11.6376	10.4245	9.4404	8.6260
47	17.9810	15.2406	13.2250	11.6803	10.4587	9.4684	8.6495
48	18.0772	15.3096	13.2770	11.7208	10.4912	9.4950	8.6716
49	18.1687	15.3752	13.3263	11.7592	10.5219	9.5202	8.6927
50	18.2559	15.4376	13.3731	11.7957	10.5511	9.5441	8.7126

TABLE 7

Present value of $1 per year. Redemption of capital at 5% with interest to the purchaser at the following rates percent.

Years	12%	15%	18%	20%	25%
1	.8929	.8696	.8476	.8333	.8000
2	1.6453	1.5679	1.4974	1.4539	1.3554
3	2.2872	2.1404	2.0112	1.9335	1.7630
4	2.8408	2.6177	2.4271	2.3148	2.0746
5	3.3225	3.0214	2.7703	2.6248	2.3203
6	3.7451	3.3668	3.0579	2.8817	2.5188
7	4.1182	3.6654	3.3023	3.0977	2.6823
8	4.4499	3.9258	3.5122	3.2817	2.8191
9	4.7463	4.1548	3.6943	3.4401	2.9352
10	5.0124	4.3572	3.8535	3.5778	3.0349
11	5.2524	4.5374	3.9938	3.6984	3.1212
12	5.4697	4.6987	4.1182	3.8048	3.1967
13	5.6671	4.8437	4.2291	3.8993	3.2631
14	5.8471	4.9745	4.3286	3.9837	3.3220
15	6.0117	5.0931	4.4181	4.0594	3.3745
16	6.1626	5.2010	4.4990	4.1277	3.4215
17	6.3012	5.2994	4.5725	4.1893	3.4638
18	6.4290	5.3895	4.6394	4.2455	3.5021
19	6.5469	5.4721	4.7005	4.2965	3.5368
20	6.6559	5.5481	4.7564	4.3432	3.5683
21	6.7569	5.6181	4.8078	4.3860	3.5972
22	6.8507	5.6828	4.8551	4.4254	3.6236
23	6.9379	5.7426	4.8987	4.4616	3.6478
24	7.0190	5.7981	4.9390	4.4950	3.6701
25	7.0946	5.8496	4.9763	4.5259	3.6907
26	7.1652	5.8975	5.0109	4.5545	3.7097
27	7.2311	5.9421	5.0431	4.5810	3.7273
28	7.2927	5.9836	5.0730	4.6057	3.7436
29	7.3505	6.0224	5.1009	4.6287	3.7588
30	7.4046	6.0587	5.1269	4.6500	3.7729
31	7.4553	6.0927	5.1511	4.6700	3.7860
32	7.5030	6.1244	5.1738	4.6887	3.7982
33	7.5477	6.1542	5.1951	4.7061	3.8097
34	7.5898	6.1822	5.2150	4.7224	3.8204
35	7.6294	6.2084	5.2336	4.7377	3.8304
36	7.6667	6.2331	5.2512	4.7521	3.8397
37	7.7018	6.2563	5.2676	4.7655	3.8485
38	7.7349	6.2781	5.2831	4.7782	3.8568
39	7.7661	6.2986	5.2976	4.7901	3.8645
40	7.7956	6.3180	5.3113	4.8013	3.8718
41	7.8234	6.3362	5.3242	4.8118	3.8786
42	7.8496	6.3535	5.3363	4.8217	3.8851
43	7.8744	6.3697	5.3478	4.8311	3.8912
44	7.8979	6.3850	5.3586	4.8399	3.8969
45	7.9201	6.3995	5.3688	4.8482	3.9023
46	7.9410	6.4132	5.3784	4.8561	3.9073
47	7.9609	6.4261	5.3875	4.8635	3.9121
48	7.9797	6.4384	5.3961	4.8705	3.9167
49	7.9975	6.4500	5.4042	4.8771	3.9210
50	8.0143	6.4609	5.4119	4.8824	3.9250

TABLE 7

Present value of $1 per year. Redemption of capital at 6% with interest to the purchaser at the following rates percent.

Years	6%	7%	8%	9%	10%	11%	12%
1	.9434	.9346	.9259	.9174	.9091	.9009	.8929
2	1.8334	1.8004	1.7685	1.7378	1.7081	1.6794	1.6517
3	2.6730	2.6034	2.5374	2.4746	2.4148	2.3579	2.3036
4	3.4651	3.3491	3.2405	3.1388	3.0433	2.9534	2.8687
5	4.2124	4.0421	3.8851	3.7398	3.6049	3.4795	3.3625
6	4.9173	4.6869	4.4770	4.2852	4.1091	3.9469	3.7970
7	5.5824	5.2872	5.0217	4.7816	4.5634	4.3642	4.1817
8	6.2098	5.8467	5.5238	5.2346	4.9742	4.7385	4.5242
9	6.8017	6.3685	5.9872	5.6490	5.3470	5.0756	4.8304
10	7.3601	6.8555	6.4157	6.0289	5.6861	5.3802	5.1055
11	7.8869	7.3103	6.8123	6.3778	5.9955	5.6563	5.3535
12	8.3838	7.7353	7.1799	6.6990	6.2784	5.9075	5.5780
13	8.8527	8.1327	7.5211	6.9950	6.5377	6.1365	5.7817
14	9.2950	8.5045	7.8379	7.2682	6.7758	6.3458	5.9671
15	9.7122	8.8525	8.1325	7.5209	6.9948	6.5375	6.1364
16	10.1059	9.1783	8.4067	7.7548	7.1967	6.7136	6.2912
17	10.4773	9.4836	8.6621	7.9716	7.3831	6.8755	6.4332
18	10.8276	9.7698	8.9002	8.1728	7.5554	7.0246	6.5636
19	11.1581	10.0381	9.1224	8.3597	7.7148	7.1623	6.6836
20	11.4699	10.2897	9.3297	8.5335	7.8626	7.2894	6.7942
21	11.7641	10.5258	9.5234	8.6953	7.9997	7.4072	6.8963
22	12.0416	10.7474	9.7044	8.8460	8.1271	7.5162	6.9908
23	12.3034	10.9555	9.8738	8.9865	8.2455	7.6174	7.0782
24	12.5504	11.1509	10.0322	9.1175	8.3557	7.7113	7.1593
25	12.7834	11.3344	10.1805	9.2399	8.4583	7.7987	7.2345
26	13.0032	11.5069	10.3195	9.3542	8.5540	7.8800	7.3044
27	13.2105	11.6690	10.4496	9.4610	8.6433	7.9556	7.3694
28	13.4062	11.8214	10.5717	9.5609	8.7266	8.0262	7.4298
29	13.5907	11.9646	10.6861	9.6544	8.8044	8.0920	7.4862
30	13.7648	12.0994	10.7934	9.7419	8.8771	8.1534	7.5387
31	13.9291	12.2261	10.8942	9.8239	8.9452	8.2107	7.5877
32	14.0840	12.3453	10.9887	9.9008	9.0088	8.2643	7.6335
33	14.2302	12.4575	11.0775	9.9728	9.0684	8.3144	7.6762
34	14.3681	12.5631	11.1609	10.0403	9.1242	8.3613	7.7161
35	14.4982	12.6624	11.2393	10.1037	9.1765	8.4052	7.7535
36	14.6210	12.7559	11.3129	10.1631	9.2255	8.4463	7.7885
37	14.7368	12.8440	11.3821	10.2189	9.2715	8.4848	7.8212
38	14.8460	12.9269	11.4471	10.2714	9.3146	8.5209	7.8519
39	14.9491	13.0050	11.5083	10.3206	9.3551	8.5548	7.8806
40	15.0463	13.0785	11.5658	10.3668	9.3931	8.5865	7.9075
41	15.1380	13.1477	11.6200	10.4103	9.4287	8.6163	7.9328
42	15.2245	13.2129	11.6709	10.4511	9.4622	8.6443	7.9565
43	15.3062	13.2744	11.7188	10.4895	9.4937	8.6705	7.9787
44	15.3832	13.3323	11.7639	10.5256	9.5233	8.6952	7.9996
45	15.4558	13.3868	11.8063	10.5596	9.5511	8.7184	8.0192
46	15.5244	13.4382	11.8463	10.5916	9.5772	8.7401	8.0376
47	15.5890	13.4866	11.8839	10.6216	9.6018	8.7606	8.0549
48	15.6500	13.5322	11.9193	10.6499	9.6249	8.7798	8.0712
49	15.7076	13.5752	11.9526	10.6765	9.6466	8.7979	8.0865
50	15.7619	13.6158	11.9840	10.7016	9.6670	8.8149	8.1008

TABLE 7

Present value of $1 per year. Redemption of capital at 6% with interest to the purchaser at the following rates percent.

Years	15%	18%	20%	25%
1	.8696	.8476	.8333	.8000
2	1.5737	1.5028	1.4589	1.3597
3	2.1547	2.0238	1.9451	1.7727
4	2.6414	2.4474	2.3332	2.0895
5	3.0544	2.7980	2.6497	2.3397
6	3.4088	3.0925	2.9124	2.5422
7	3.7156	3.3430	3.1335	2.7090
8	3.9835	3.5583	3.3219	2.8487
9	4.2190	3.7450	3.4841	2.9672
10	4.4274	3.9083	3.6249	3.0687
11	4.6127	4.0520	3.7482	3.1566
12	4.7784	4.1793	3.8569	3.2333
13	4.9271	4.2926	3.9532	3.3008
14	5.0611	4.3940	4.0390	3.3604
15	5.1823	4.4851	4.1159	3.4134
16	5.2923	4.5672	4.1849	3.4608
17	5.3924	4.6416	4.2473	3.5033
18	5.4838	4.7091	4.3037	3.5416
19	5.5673	4.7705	4.3550	3.5763
20	5.6438	4.8266	4.4017	3.6077
21	5.7141	4.8779	4.4444	3.6363
22	5.7788	4.9250	4.4834	3.6624
23	5.8384	4.9682	4.5192	3.6862
24	5.8935	5.0080	4.5521	3.7081
25	5.9444	5.0447	4.5824	3.7282
26	5.9915	5.0786	4.6103	3.7467
27	6.0351	5.1099	4.6361	3.7637
28	6.0756	5.1389	4.6600	3.7794
29	6.1132	5.1658	4.6821	3.7939
30	6.1482	5.1908	4.7026	3.8074
31	6.1808	5.2140	4.7216	3.8198
32	6.2111	5.2355	4.7393	3.8314
33	6.2394	5.2556	4.7557	3.8421
34	6.2657	5.2743	4.7710	3.8521
35	6.2903	5.2917	4.7853	3.8614
36	6.3133	5.3080	4.7986	3.8700
37	6.3348	5.3232	4.8110	3.8781
38	6.3549	5.3374	4.8226	3.8856
39	6.3737	5.3506	4.8334	3.8927
40	6.3913	5.3630	4.8435	3.8992
41	6.4078	5.3746	4.8530	3.9054
42	6.4233	5.3855	4.8618	3.9111
43	6.4378	5.3957	4.8701	3.9165
44	6.4514	5.4052	4.8779	3.9215
45	6.4641	5.4142	4.8852	3.9262
46	6.4761	5.4226	4.8920	3.9306
47	6.4873	5.4304	4.8984	3.9347
48	6.4978	5.4378	4.9044	3.9386
49	6.5077	5.4447	4.9101	3.9422
50	6.5170	5.4512	4.9154	3.9456

PRESENT VALUE OF EACH $1 OF TOTAL UNIT REDEMPTION ANNUITY INCOME

TABLE 8

The present value of each $1 of total operating profit (or total income) when receivable as an annuity of $A per year, which will allow interest to the purchaser on his invested capital at rates of 2, 3, 4, 5, 6, 7, 8, 9, 10, 11, 12, 15, 18, 20, and 25 percent per annum, and, at the same time, the redemption of his capital at the expiration of the annuity life by annual investment of the dividend overplus at the practicable rates of 2, 3, 4, 5, or 6 percent.

Calculated to 5 decimal places
and to 50 years.

The factors listed in this table represent values of

$$\frac{1}{\dfrac{r}{R^n - 1} + r'} \div n, \qquad \text{or} \qquad \frac{1}{s + r'} \div n.$$

These factors have been calculated by dividing each factor of Table 7 by its respective period of years n. To use this table, the total income receivable as a uniform unity over the given period of years is multiplied by the respective table factor to give the present value. For instance, what is the present value of a redemption (Hoskold type) annuity of $5000 per year for 14 years, allowing the purchaser 8% on his investment, and the redemption of his capital at the expiration of the 14-year period by annual investment of the dividend overplus at 3% compound interest?

$$
\begin{aligned}
V_p &= 5000 \times 14 \times .51563 \\
&= 70000 \times .51563 \\
&= \$36094.10.
\end{aligned}
$$

TABLE 8

Present value of each $1 of total income receivable as a uniform annuity for n years. Redemption of capital at 2% with interest to the purchaser at the following rates percent.

Years	2%	3%	4%	5%	6%	7%	8%
1	.98039	.97087	.96154	.95238	.94340	.93458	.92593
2	.97078	.95229	.93449	.91735	.90082	.88488	.86949
3	.96129	.93435	.90887	.88475	.86187	.84015	.81949
4	.95193	.91701	.88457	.85434	.82611	.79968	.77250
5	.94269	.90026	.86148	.82591	.79315	.76290	.73487
6	.93357	.88405	.83952	.79926	.76269	.72931	.69874
7	.92457	.86837	.81861	.77424	.73444	.69853	.66596
8	.91569	.85319	.79867	.75071	.70818	.67021	.63610
9	.90692	.83848	.77964	.72852	.68370	.64407	.60878
10	.89826	.82422	.76146	.70758	.66082	.61986	.58368
11	.88971	.81040	.74407	.68778	.63940	.59739	.56055
12	.88128	.79699	.72742	.66902	.61930	.57646	.53917
13	.87295	.78398	.71147	.65124	.60041	.55694	.51934
14	.86473	.77135	.69617	.63435	.58261	.53867	.50089
15	.85662	.75908	.68149	.61828	.56581	.52154	.48370
16	.84861	.74716	.66738	.60299	.54993	.50546	.46764
17	.84070	.73557	.65381	.58841	.53491	.49032	.45259
18	.83289	.72430	.64076	.57450	.52066	.47605	.43847
19	.82518	.71334	.62820	.56121	.50714	.46257	.42520
20	.81757	.70267	.61609	.54851	.49428	.44982	.41269
21	.81006	.69229	.60442	.53634	.48205	.43774	.40089
22	.80264	.68218	.59316	.52469	.47039	.42628	.38973
23	.79531	.67233	.58229	.51351	.45927	.41539	.37917
24	.78808	.66273	.57179	.50279	.44865	.40504	.36915
25	.78094	.65338	.56164	.49249	.43850	.39518	.35965
26	.77389	.64426	.55182	.48258	.42878	.38578	.35061
27	.76692	.63536	.54232	.47306	.41948	.37680	.34201
28	.76005	.62668	.53313	.46388	.41056	.36823	.33381
29	.75325	.61821	.52423	.45505	.40200	.36003	.32599
30	.74655	.60994	.51560	.44653	.39378	.35217	.31852
31	.73993	.60187	.50723	.43831	.38588	.34465	.31138
32	.73339	.59399	.49912	.43038	.37828	.33743	.30455
33	.72693	.58628	.49124	.42272	.37097	.33051	.29800
34	.72055	.57876	.48360	.41531	.36392	.32385	.29173
35	.71425	.57140	.47617	.40815	.35713	.31745	.28571
36	.70802	.56421	.46896	.40122	.35058	.31130	.27993
37	.70188	.55718	.46195	.39452	.34426	.30537	.27437
38	.69581	.55030	.45513	.38802	.33816	.29965	.26902
39	.68981	.54357	.44850	.38173	.33226	.29415	.26387
40	.68389	.53699	.44204	.37562	.32656	.28883	.25892
41	.67804	.53055	.43576	.36971	.32105	.28370	.25414
42	.67226	.52424	.42964	.36396	.31570	.27874	.24953
43	.66655	.51806	.42368	.35839	.31053	.27395	.24508
44	.66091	.51201	.41787	.35297	.30552	.26932	.24079
45	.65534	.50609	.41221	.34771	.30067	.26484	.23663
46	.64983	.50029	.40669	.34260	.29596	.26049	.23262
47	.64440	.49460	.40131	.33763	.29139	.25629	.22874
48	.63902	.48902	.39606	.33279	.28695	.25221	.22498
49	.63372	.48356	.39093	.32808	.28265	.24826	.22134
50	.62847	.47820	.38593	.32350	.27846	.24443	.21781

TABLE 8

Present value of each $1 of total income receivable as a uniform annuity for n years. Redemption of capital at 2% with interest to the purchaser at the following rates percent.

Years	9%	10%	11%	12%	15%	18%	20%
1	.91743	.90909	.90090	.89286	.86956	.84746	.83333
2	.85463	.84027	.82638	.81294	.77513	.74069	.71937
3	.79983	.78109	.76320	.74612	.69917	.65778	.63281
4	.75160	.72966	.70897	.68942	.63674	.59154	.56481
5	.70882	.68456	.66190	.64070	.58452	.53741	.51000
6	.67062	.64468	.62067	.59839	.54020	.49233	.46487
7	.63630	.60917	.58425	.56130	.50211	.45422	.42706
8	.60530	.57734	.55185	.52852	.46903	.42157	.39493
9	.57715	.54866	.52284	.49934	.44002	.39329	.36729
10	.55149	.52267	.49671	.47320	.41438	.36856	.34326
11	.52800	.49901	.47305	.44965	.39155	.34675	.32217
12	.50640	.47739	.45153	.42832	.37110	.32736	.30352
13	.48649	.45755	.43186	.40891	.35267	.31003	.28690
14	.46807	.43928	.41383	.39117	.33597	.29443	.27200
15	.45098	.42241	.39724	.37490	.32078	.28032	.25857
16	.43508	.40677	.38191	.35992	.30690	.26749	.24640
17	.42026	.39224	.36772	.34608	.29416	.25579	.23532
18	.40640	.37870	.35453	.33326	.28243	.24506	.22519
19	.39341	.36605	.34225	.32135	.27160	.23519	.21590
20	.38122	.35422	.33078	.31026	.26157	.22608	.20733
21	.36976	.34311	.32005	.29990	.25224	.21765	.19942
22	.35895	.33268	.30999	.29020	.24355	.20982	.19209
23	.34875	.32285	.30054	.28111	.23544	.20254	.18528
24	.33911	.31359	.29164	.27256	.22785	.19574	.17893
25	.32998	.30483	.28325	.26451	.22073	.18938	.17300
26	.32132	.29654	.27532	.25693	.21403	.18341	.16744
27	.31310	.28869	.26782	.24976	.20773	.17781	.16223
28	.30528	.28124	.26071	.24297	.20179	.17254	.15734
29	.29783	.27415	.25396	.23654	.19617	.16757	.15273
30	.29074	.26742	.24756	.23044	.19086	.16288	.14838
31	.28397	.26100	.24146	.22464	.18582	.15844	.14427
32	.27750	.25487	.23565	.21913	.18104	.15424	.14038
33	.27132	.24903	.23011	.21387	.17650	.15025	.13699
34	.26540	.24344	.22483	.20886	.17218	.14646	.13319
35	.25974	.23809	.21978	.20408	.16807	.14286	.12987
36	.25430	.23297	.21494	.19951	.16414	.13942	.12670
37	.24908	.22806	.21032	.19513	.16039	.13615	.12369
38	.24407	.22335	.20588	.19094	.15681	.13303	.12081
39	.23925	.21883	.20163	.18693	.15338	.13004	.11807
40	.23462	.21449	.19754	.18308	.15010	.12719	.11544
41	.23016	.21031	.19362	.17938	.14695	.12446	.11293
42	.22586	.20629	.18984	.17582	.14394	.12184	.11053
43	.22172	.20242	.18621	.17241	.14104	.11933	.10822
44	.21772	.19869	.18271	.16912	.13825	.11692	.10601
45	.21486	.19509	.17934	.16595	.13558	.11460	.10389
46	.21013	.19161	.17609	.16290	.13300	.11237	.10184
47	.20653	.18826	.17296	.15995	.13052	.11023	.09988
48	.20305	.18502	.16993	.15711	.12812	.10817	.09799
49	.19968	.18188	.16700	.15437	.12582	.10618	.09617
50	.19642	.17885	.16417	.15172	.12359	.10426	.09442

TABLE 8

Present value of each $1 of total income receivable as a uniform annuity for n years. Redemption of capital at 2% with interest to the purchaser at the following rates percent.

Years	25%
1	.80000
2	.67110
3	.57794
4	.50749
5	.45233
6	.40797
7	.37153
8	.34106
9	.31520
10	.29297
11	.27368
12	.25676
13	.24181
14	.22850
15	.21657
16	.20583
17	.19610
18	.18724
19	.17915
20	.17173
21	.16489
22	.15858
23	.15273
24	.14730
25	.14224
26	.13751
27	.13309
28	.12894
29	.12504
30	.12137
31	.11790
32	.11463
33	.11154
34	.10860
35	.10582
36	.10317
37	.10066
38	.09826
39	.09597
40	.09379
41	.09170
42	.08971
43	.08779
44	.08596
45	.08420
46	.08252
47	.08089
48	.07933
49	.07783
50	.07639

TABLE 8

Present value of each $1 of total income receivable as a uniform annuity for n years. Redemption of capital at 3% with interest to the purchaser at the following rates percent.

Years	3%	4%	5%	6%	7%	8%	9%
1	.97087	.96154	.95238	.94340	.93458	.92593	.91743
2	.95673	.93877	.92147	.90480	.88871	.87319	.85821
3	.94287	.91693	.89239	.86912	.84703	.82604	.80607
4	.92928	.89597	.86497	.83604	.80899	.78363	.75982
5	.91594	.87583	.83909	.80530	.77413	.74528	.71851
6	.90287	.85647	.81461	.77665	.74207	.71044	.68139
7	.89004	.83784	.79142	.74989	.71248	.67864	.64786
8	.87746	.81991	.76944	.72482	.68510	.64950	.61742
9	.86512	.80263	.74856	.70131	.65967	.62270	.58966
10	.85302	.78598	.72870	.67921	.63601	.59798	.56424
11	.84115	.76991	.70980	.65839	.61393	.57509	.54088
12	.82950	.75441	.69178	.63876	.59328	.55385	.51933
13	.81807	.73943	.67459	.62020	.57393	.53408	.49941
14	.80686	.72497	.65817	.60264	.55575	.51563	.48092
15	.79586	.71099	.64247	.58600	.53865	.49838	.46371
16	.78507	.69746	.62744	.57020	.52253	.48221	.44767
17	.77448	.68437	.61305	.55519	.50731	.46703	.43268
18	.76408	.67170	.59925	.54090	.49291	.45274	.41863
19	.75388	.65943	.58601	.52730	.47928	.43928	.40544
20	.74387	.64754	.57329	.51432	.46635	.42656	.39303
21	.73405	.63601	.56107	.50193	.45407	.41454	.38134
22	.72441	.62483	.54932	.49009	.44239	.40315	.37031
23	.71494	.61398	.53800	.47876	.43127	.39235	.35988
24	.70565	.60345	.52711	.46792	.42067	.38210	.35000
25	.69653	.59323	.51661	.45752	.41056	.37234	.34063
26	.68757	.58330	.50648	.44755	.40090	.36306	.33174
27	.67878	.57365	.49671	.43798	.39166	.35420	.32329
28	.67015	.56427	.48728	.42878	.38282	.34576	.31524
29	.66167	.55515	.47817	.41993	.37435	.33769	.30757
30	.65335	.54628	.46936	.41142	.36622	.32997	.30025
31	.64518	.53764	.46084	.40323	.35843	.32258	.29326
32	.63715	.52924	.45259	.39534	.35094	.31551	.28657
33	.62927	.52106	.44461	.38772	.34374	.30872	.28018
34	.62152	.51310	.43688	.38038	.33682	.30221	.27405
35	.61392	.50534	.42939	.37329	.33016	.29596	.26818
36	.60645	.49778	.42213	.36644	.32374	.28994	.26254
37	.59911	.49041	.41509	.35982	.31755	.28416	.25713
38	.59191	.48322	.40825	.35342	.31158	.27859	.25192
39	.58483	.47621	.40162	.34723	.30582	.27323	.24692
40	.57787	.46937	.39518	.34124	.30026	.26806	.24210
41	.57103	.46270	.38892	.33543	.29488	.26307	.23746
42	.56432	.45619	.38284	.32981	.28968	.25826	.23299
43	.55772	.44984	.37693	.32436	.28466	.25361	.22867
44	.55123	.44363	.37118	.31907	.27979	.24912	.22451
45	.54486	.43757	.36559	.31394	.27508	.24478	.22049
46	.53860	.43165	.36014	.30896	.27051	.24058	.21661
47	.53244	.42587	.35484	.30412	.26609	.23651	.21285
48	.52639	.42022	.34968	.29943	.26180	.23257	.20922
49	.52044	.41469	.34466	.29486	.25764	.22876	.20570
50	.51460	.40929	.33976	.29042	.25360	.22506	.20230

TABLE 8

Present value of each $1 of total income receivable as a uniform annuity for n years. Redemption of capital at 3% with interest to the purchaser at the following rates percent.

Years	10%	11%	12%	15%	18%	20%	25%
1	.90909	.90090	.89286	.86957	.84746	.83333	.80000
2	.84372	.82972	.81618	.77808	.74337	.72191	.67330
3	.78704	.76888	.75155	.70393	.66199	.63670	.58120
4	.73740	.71628	.69633	.64263	.59662	.56944	.51122
5	.69359	.67034	.64860	.59110	.54296	.51499	.45625
6	.65463	.62989	.60695	.54717	.49811	.47002	.41193
7	.61975	.59398	.57027	.50928	.46008	.43224	.37544
8	.58836	.56191	.53774	.47627	.42741	.40006	.34487
9	.55994	.53308	.50867	.44725	.39906	.37231	.31889
10	.53410	.50702	.48255	.42153	.37421	.34815	.29653
11	.51050	.48336	.45896	.39859	.35226	.32692	.27710
12	.48877	.46178	.43753	.37799	.33272	.30811	.26004
13	.46896	.44201	.41799	.35940	.31522	.29134	.24495
14	.45058	.42384	.40010	.34254	.29946	.27629	.23152
15	.43356	.40708	.38366	.32717	.28518	.26271	.21947
16	.41775	.39158	.36849	.31311	.27220	.25039	.20860
17	.40303	.37719	.35446	.30019	.26034	.23917	.19876
18	.38929	.36380	.34144	.28829	.24945	.22890	.18980
19	.37644	.35131	.32933	.27728	.23944	.21947	.18160
20	.36439	.33964	.31803	.26707	.23019	.21078	.17409
21	.35307	.32870	.30747	.25758	.22162	.20274	.16716
22	.34241	.31843	.29758	.24873	.21365	.19530	.16076
23	.33237	.30876	.28829	.24046	.20624	.18837	.15483
24	.32288	.29966	.27955	.23271	.19932	.18191	.14932
25	.31390	.29106	.27132	.22544	.19284	.17588	.14418
26	.30540	.28293	.26355	.21861	.18676	.17023	.13938
27	.29733	.27524	.25620	.21217	.18105	.16493	.13489
28	.28967	.26794	.24924	.20609	.17568	.15994	.13068
29	.28238	.26101	.24264	.20035	.17061	.15525	.12672
30	.27544	.25442	.23637	.19491	.16582	.15082	.12299
31	.26882	.24814	.23042	.18975	.16129	.14663	.11947
32	.26250	.24216	.22474	.18486	.15700	.14266	.11615
33	.25647	.23645	.21934	.18021	.15293	.13891	.11301
34	.25069	.23100	.21418	.17578	.14905	.13534	.11002
35	.24517	.22579	.20925	.17156	.14537	.13195	.10719
36	.23987	.22080	.20454	.16753	.14187	.12872	.10450
37	.23479	.21602	.20003	.16369	.13852	.12564	.10195
38	.22991	.21144	.19572	.16001	.13533	.12271	.09951
39	.22523	.20704	.19157	.15650	.13228	.11991	.09718
40	.22073	.20282	.18760	.15313	.12936	.11723	.09496
41	.21639	.19876	.18378	.14990	.12656	.11466	.09284
42	.21222	.19485	.18011	.14680	.12338	.11221	.09081
43	.20820	.19109	.17658	.14382	.12131	.10985	.08887
44	.20433	.18747	.17319	.14096	.11885	.10759	.08700
45	.20059	.18398	.16991	.13821	.11648	.10543	.08521
46	.19698	.18061	.16676	.13556	.11420	.10334	.08350
47	.19349	.17736	.16372	.13301	.11201	.10134	.08185
48	.19012	.17422	.16078	.13055	.10989	.09941	.08026
49	.18687	.17119	.15794	.12818	.10786	.09755	.07873
50	.18371	.16826	.15520	.12589	.10590	.09576	.07726

TABLE 8

Present value of each $1 of total income receivable as a uniform annuity for n years. Redemption of capital at 4% with interest to the purchaser at the following rates percent.

Years	4%	5%	6%	7%	8%	9%	10%
1	.96154	.95238	.94340	.93458	.92593	.91743	.90909
2	.94305	.92559	.90877	.89254	.87689	.86178	.84718
3	.92503	.90005	.87639	.85394	.83261	.81232	.79299
4	.90747	.87569	.84605	.81836	.79242	.76807	.74518
5	.89036	.85242	.81757	.78546	.75578	.72826	.70267
6	.87369	.83017	.79078	.75496	.72225	.69225	.66464
7	.85744	.80889	.76554	.72660	.69144	.65951	.63041
8	.84159	.78851	.74172	.70017	.66303	.62963	.59944
9	.82615	.76897	.71920	.67548	.63677	.60225	.57129
10	.81109	.75024	.69788	.65235	.61240	.57706	.54558
11	.79641	.73226	.67767	.63066	.58975	.55382	.52202
12	.78209	.71499	.65849	.61027	.56863	.53230	.50034
13	.76813	.69839	.64026	.59106	.54889	.51233	.48034
14	.75451	.68242	.62291	.57295	.53040	.49374	.46182
15	.74123	.66706	.60639	.55583	.51305	.47639	.44462
16	.72827	.65226	.59063	.53963	.49674	.46017	.42861
17	.71563	.63801	.57558	.52428	.48138	.44496	.41367
18	.70329	.62427	.56121	.50972	.46688	.43069	.39970
19	.69126	.61101	.54746	.49588	.45318	.41725	.38660
20	.67952	.59822	.53429	.48271	.44021	.40459	.37430
21	.66806	.58586	.52168	.47017	.42792	.39264	.36273
22	.65687	.57393	.50959	.45822	.41625	.38133	.35182
23	.64595	.56240	.49798	.44681	.40517	.37063	.34152
24	.63529	.55124	.48684	.43590	.39462	.36048	.33178
25	.62488	.54045	.47612	.42548	.38457	.35084	.32255
26	.61472	.53001	.46582	.41550	.37499	.34168	.31380
27	.60480	.51990	.45590	.40594	.36584	.33295	.30549
28	.59511	.51011	.44636	.39677	.35710	.32464	.29759
29	.58565	.50062	.43716	.38797	.34873	.31670	.29006
30	.57640	.49142	.42828	.37952	.34073	.30913	.28289
31	.56737	.48251	.41972	.37140	.33305	.30189	.27605
32	.55855	.47385	.41146	.36359	.32570	.29495	.26952
33	.54993	.46546	.40348	.35607	.31863	.28832	.26327
34	.54151	.45731	.39577	.34883	.31185	.28195	.25729
35	.53327	.44940	.38832	.34186	.30532	.27585	.25156
36	.52523	.44171	.38111	.33513	.29905	.26998	.24607
37	.51737	.43424	.37413	.32864	.29301	.26435	.24080
38	.50968	.42698	.36738	.32237	.28719	.25893	.23574
39	.50217	.41993	.36083	.31632	.28158	.25372	.23087
40	.49482	.41306	.35449	.31047	.27617	.24870	.22620
41	.48764	.40639	.34835	.30481	.27095	.24386	.22169
42	.48061	.39989	.34239	.29934	.26591	.23920	.21736
43	.47374	.39357	.33660	.29404	.26104	.23469	.21318
44	.46702	.38741	.33099	.28891	.25633	.23035	.20915
45	.46045	.38142	.32554	.28394	.25177	.22615	.20526
46	.45401	.37558	.32025	.27913	.24737	.22210	.20151
47	.44772	.36989	.31511	.27446	.24310	.21817	.19788
48	.44157	.36434	.31011	.26993	.23897	.21438	.19438
49	.43554	.35894	.30525	.26553	.23496	.21070	.19099
50	.42964	.35367	.30053	.26127	.23108	.20715	.18770

TABLE 8

Present value of each $1 of total income receivable as a uniform annuity for n years. Redemption of capital at 4% with interest to the purchaser at the following rates percent.

Years	11%	12%	15%	18%	20%	25%
1	.90090	.89286	.86957	.84746	.83333	.80000
2	.83306	.81941	.78101	.74605	.72443	.67550
3	.77457	.75698	.70869	.66620	.64060	.58444
4	.72361	.70325	.64853	.60170	.57407	.51494
5	.67882	.65654	.59768	.54851	.51998	.46016
6	.63915	.61555	.55415	.50389	.47516	.41587
7	.60377	.57928	.51646	.46593	.43739	.37932
8	.57201	.54698	.48351	.43323	.40515	.34865
9	.54335	.51802	.45446	.40479	.37730	.32254
10	.51735	.49191	.42865	.37981	.35299	.30004
11	.49367	.46824	.40557	.35770	.33160	.28045
12	.47200	.44670	.38482	.33799	.31263	.26325
13	.45211	.42701	.36605	.32032	.29569	.24802
14	.43377	.40894	.34900	.30438	.28048	.23445
15	.41682	.39229	.33343	.28993	.26673	.22227
16	.40110	.37691	.31917	.27677	.25425	.21128
17	.38649	.36266	.30606	.26473	.24287	.20131
18	.37287	.34942	.29396	.25369	.23246	.19224
19	.36015	.33708	.28275	.24351	.22288	.18394
20	.34823	.32556	.27236	.23410	.21406	.17632
21	.33705	.31477	.26268	.22538	.20589	.16929
22	.32654	.30466	.25365	.21728	.19832	.16280
23	.31665	.29515	.24521	.20973	.19127	.15679
24	.30731	.28620	.23730	.20267	.18470	.15119
25	.29848	.27775	.22987	.19607	.17856	.14598
26	.29013	.26978	.22288	.18987	.17281	.14111
27	.28221	.26223	.21629	.18405	.16741	.13655
28	.27470	.25508	.21007	.17856	.16233	.13227
29	.26756	.24829	.20419	.17338	.15754	.12825
30	.26076	.24184	.19861	.16849	.15302	.12446
31	.25429	.23571	.19333	.16387	.14875	.12088
32	.24812	.22987	.18831	.15948	.14471	.11750
33	.24222	.22429	.18354	.15532	.14088	.11431
34	.23659	.21898	.17900	.15136	.13724	.11128
35	.23120	.21389	.17467	.14760	.13378	.10840
36	.22604	.20903	.17053	.14401	.13048	.10566
37	.22110	.20438	.16659	.14059	.12734	.10306
38	.21636	.19992	.16281	.13732	.12435	.10058
39	.21180	.19564	.15920	.13420	.12149	.09822
40	.20743	.19154	.15574	.13122	.11875	.09596
41	.20322	.18759	.15242	.12836	.11613	.09380
42	.19918	.18380	.14924	.12562	.11363	.09174
43	.19528	.18015	.14618	.12299	.11122	.08976
44	.19153	.17664	.14324	.12046	.10892	.08786
45	.18791	.17326	.14041	.11804	.10670	.08605
46	.18441	.16999	.13769	.11571	.10457	.08430
47	.18104	.16685	.13507	.11346	.10253	.08262
48	.17779	.16381	.13254	.11130	.10056	.08101
49	.17464	.16088	.13011	.10922	.09866	.07945
50	.17160	.15804	.12775	.10721	.09683	.07796

TABLE 8

Present value of each \$1 of total income receivable as a uniform annuity for n years. Redemption of capital at 5% with interest to the purchaser at the following rates percent.

Years	5%	6%	7%	8%	9%	10%	11%
1	.95238	.94339	.93457	.92592	.91743	.90909	.90090
2	.92970	.91273	.89637	.88058	.86534	.85062	.83639
3	.90775	.88366	.86086	.83918	.81858	.79896	.78026
4	.88649	.85612	.82778	.80125	.77637	.75298	.73097
5	.86590	.82996	.79689	.76636	.73808	.71181	.68734
6	.84595	.80508	.76798	.73415	.70318	.67471	.64846
7	.82662	.78141	.74088	.70435	.67126	.64113	.61359
8	.80790	.75885	.71542	.67669	.64194	.61058	.58214
9	.78976	.73735	.69146	.65095	.61493	.58268	.55364
10	.77217	.71682	.66888	.62694	.58995	.55709	.52769
11	.75513	.69721	.64755	.60449	.56680	.53354	.50396
12	.73860	.67847	.62739	.58346	.54528	.51180	.48218
13	.72258	.66053	.60830	.56372	.52523	.49166	.46212
14	.70705	.64336	.59020	.54516	.50650	.47296	.44359
15	.69198	.62691	.57302	.52767	.48897	.45555	.42641
16	.67736	.61113	.55669	.51116	.47252	.43931	.41046
17	.66398	.59599	.54116	.49557	.45706	.42411	.39563
18	.64942	.58145	.52636	.48081	.44251	.40986	.38170
19	.63607	.56749	.51225	.46682	.42878	.39649	.36871
20	.62311	.55406	.49879	.45355	.41582	.38390	.35652
21	.61053	.54115	.48592	.44093	.40356	.37204	.34507
22	.59832	.52872	.47363	.42893	.39194	.36083	.33429
23	.58646	.51675	.46186	.41751	.38093	.35024	.32413
24	.57494	.50523	.45059	.40662	.37047	.34022	.31453
25	.56376	.49412	.43979	.39623	.36051	.33071	.30545
26	.55289	.48340	.42943	.38630	.35104	.32168	.29685
27	.54233	.47306	.41948	.37681	.34201	.31310	.28869
28	.53208	.46308	.40993	.36772	.33340	.30493	.28094
29	.52211	.45345	.40075	.35902	.32517	.29714	.27357
30	.51242	.44414	.39191	.35068	.31730	.28972	.26656
31	.50299	.43514	.38342	.34269	.30978	.28263	.25987
32	.49383	.42644	.37523	.33501	.30257	.27586	.25349
33	.48493	.41803	.36735	.32763	.29566	.26938	.24739
34	.47626	.40989	.35975	.32054	.28904	.26318	.24156
35	.46783	.40201	.35242	.31372	.28268	.25723	.23599
36	.45963	.39438	.34534	.30715	.27657	.25153	.23065
37	.45166	.38699	.33851	.30084	.27070	.24606	.22553
38	.44389	.37982	.33192	.29474	.26505	.24080	.22061
39	.43633	.37288	.32554	.28887	.25962	.23575	.21590
40	.42898	.36615	.31937	.28320	.25438	.23089	.21137
41	.42181	.35962	.31341	.27772	.24933	.22621	.20701
42	.41484	.35328	.30764	.27244	.24446	.22170	.20281
43	.40804	.34714	.30205	.26733	.23977	.21736	.19877
44	.40143	.34117	.29663	.26239	.23523	.21317	.19489
45	.39498	.33537	.29139	.25761	.23085	.20913	.19114
46	.38870	.32974	.28631	.25299	.22662	.20523	.18752
47	.38257	.32427	.28138	.24852	.22253	.20146	.18403
48	.37661	.31895	.27660	.24418	.21856	.19781	.18066
49	.37079	.31378	.27196	.23998	.21473	.19429	.17740
50	.36512	.30875	.26746	.23591	.21102	.19088	.17425

TABLE 8

Present value of each $1 of total income receivable as a uniform annuity for n years. Redemption of capital at 5% with interest to the purchaser at the following rates percent.

Years	12%	15%	18%	20%	25%
1	.89285	.86956	.84745	.83333	.80000
2	.82263	.78394	.74872	.72695	.67769
3	.76241	.71346	.67041	.64449	.58767
4	.71020	.65443	.60678	.57869	.51866
5	.66451	.60427	.55406	.52497	.46406
6	.62418	.56113	.50966	.48028	.41980
7	.58832	.52363	.47176	.44253	.38318
8	.55624	.49073	.43903	.41021	.35239
9	.52737	.46164	.41047	.38223	.32614
10	.50124	.43572	.38535	.35778	.30349
11	.47749	.41249	.36307	.33622	.28375
12	.45581	.39156	.34318	.31707	.26639
13	.43593	.37259	.32532	.29995	.25101
14	.41765	.35532	.30918	.28455	.23729
15	.40078	.33954	.29454	.27063	.22497
16	.38516	.32506	.28119	.25798	.21384
17	.37066	.31173	.26897	.24643	.20375
18	.35716	.29941	.25774	.23586	.19456
19	.34457	.28801	.24739	.22613	.18615
20	.33280	.27740	.23782	.21716	.17842
21	.32175	.26752	.22894	.20886	.17129
22	.31139	.25830	.22068	.20115	.16471
23	.30164	.24967	.21289	.19398	.15860
24	.29245	.24158	.20579	.18720	.15292
25	.28378	.23398	.19905	.18103	.14763
26	.27558	.22682	.19273	.17517	.14268
27	.26782	.22007	.18678	.16967	.13805
28	.26046	.21370	.18118	.16449	.13370
29	.25346	.20767	.17589	.15961	.12961
30	.24682	.20196	.17090	.15500	.12576
31	.24049	.19654	.16617	.15065	.12213
32	.23447	.19139	.16168	.14652	.11869
33	.22872	.18649	.15743	.14261	.11544
34	.22323	.18183	.15338	.13889	.11236
35	.21798	.17738	.14953	.13536	.10944
36	.21296	.17314	.14587	.13200	.10666
37	.20816	.16909	.14237	.12880	.10401
38	.20355	.16521	.13903	.12574	.10149
39	.19913	.16150	.13584	.12282	.09909
40	.19489	.15794	.13278	.12003	.09679
41	.19081	.15454	.12986	.11736	.09460
42	.18690	.15127	.12706	.11480	.09250
43	.18313	.14813	.12437	.11235	.09049
44	.17950	.14511	.12179	.11000	.08857
45	.17600	.14221	.11931	.10774	.08672
46	.17263	.13941	.11692	.10557	.08494
47	.16938	.13672	.11463	.10348	.08324
48	.16624	.13413	.11242	.10147	.08160
49	.16321	.13163	.11029	.09953	.08002
50	.16029	.12921	.10824	.09767	.07850

TABLE 8

Present value of each $1 of total income receivable as a uniform annuity for n years. Redemption of capital at 6% with interest to the purchaser at the following rates percent.

Years	6%	7%	8%	9%	10%	11%	12%
1	.94340	.93458	.92593	.91743	.90909	.90090	.89286
2	.91670	.90019	.88427	.86891	.85406	.83972	.82585
3	.89100	.86781	.84579	.82486	.80494	.78595	.76785
4	.86628	.83726	.81013	.78470	.76082	.73835	.71717
5	.84247	.80842	.77701	.74795	.72099	.69590	.67250
6	.81955	.78114	.74617	.71420	.68485	.65782	.63284
7	.79748	.75532	.71739	.68309	.65191	.62346	.59739
8	.77622	.73084	.69047	.65433	.62178	.59232	.56552
9	.75574	.70761	.66525	.62767	.59411	.56395	.53671
10	.73601	.68555	.64157	.60289	.56861	.53802	.51055
11	.71699	.66457	.61930	.57980	.54504	.51421	.48668
12	.69865	.64461	.59833	.55825	.52320	.49229	.46483
13	.68097	.62559	.57854	.53807	.50290	.47204	.44474
14	.66393	.60746	.55985	.51916	.48398	.45327	.42622
15	.64748	.59016	.54217	.50139	.46632	.43584	.40909
16	.63162	.57365	.52542	.48468	.44980	.41960	.39320
17	.61631	.55786	.50954	.46892	.43429	.40444	.37842
18	.60153	.54277	.49446	.45405	.41974	.39026	.36464
19	.58727	.52832	.48012	.43999	.40604	.37696	.35177
20	.57350	.51449	.46649	.42668	.39313	.36447	.33971
21	.56019	.50123	.45350	.41406	.38094	.35272	.32840
22	.54734	.48852	.44111	.40209	.36941	.34165	.31776
23	.53493	.47633	.42929	.39072	.35850	.33119	.30775
24	.52293	.46462	.41801	.37990	.34815	.32131	.29830
25	.51133	.45338	.40722	.36959	.33833	.31195	.28938
26	.50012	.44257	.39690	.35978	.32900	.30308	.28094
27	.48928	.43218	.38702	.35041	.32012	.29465	.27294
28	.47879	.42219	.37756	.34146	.31166	.28665	.26535
29	.46865	.41257	.36849	.33291	.30360	.27903	.25814
30	.45883	.40331	.35978	.32473	.29590	.27178	.25129
31	.44933	.39439	.35142	.31690	.28855	.26486	.24476
32	.44013	.38579	.34340	.30940	.28153	.25826	.23855
33	.43122	.37750	.33568	.30221	.27480	.25195	.23261
34	.42259	.36950	.32826	.29530	.26836	.24592	.22695
35	.41424	.36178	.32112	.28868	.26219	.24015	.22153
36	.40614	.35433	.31425	.28231	.25626	.23462	.21635
37	.39829	.34713	.30762	.27619	.25058	.22932	.21138
38	.39068	.34018	.30124	.27030	.24512	.22423	.20663
39	.38331	.33346	.29508	.26463	.23987	.21935	.20207
40	.37616	.32696	.28915	.25917	.23483	.21466	.19769
41	.36922	.32068	.28341	.25391	.22997	.21015	.19348
42	.36249	.31459	.27788	.24884	.22529	.20582	.18944
43	.35596	.30871	.27253	.24394	.22078	.20164	.18555
44	.34962	.30301	.26736	.23922	.21644	.19762	.18181
45	.34346	.29748	.26236	.23466	.21225	.19374	.17820
46	.33749	.29213	.25753	.23025	.20820	.19000	.17473
47	.33168	.28695	.25285	.22599	.20429	.18640	.17138
48	.32604	.28192	.24832	.22187	.20052	.18291	.16815
49	.32056	.27705	.24393	.21789	.19687	.17955	.16503
50	.31524	.27232	.23968	.21403	.19334	.17630	.16202

TABLE 8

Present value of each $1 of total income receivable as a uniform annuity for n years. Redemption of capital at 6% with interest to the purchaser at the following rates percent.

Years	15%	18%	20%	25%
1	.86957	.84746	.83333	.80000
2	.78686	.75139	.72946	.67987
3	.71822	.67461	.64837	.59090
4	.66034	.61186	.58331	.52237
5	.61088	.55960	.52995	.46795
6	.56813	.51542	.48540	.42370
7	.53081	.47757	.44764	.38701
8	.49794	.44478	.41523	.35609
9	.46878	.41611	.38712	.32968
10	.44274	.39083	.36249	.30687
11	.41934	.36836	.34075	.28697
12	.39820	.34827	.32141	.26945
13	.37901	.33020	.30409	.25390
14	.36151	.31385	.28850	.24003
15	.34549	.29900	.27439	.22756
16	.33077	.28545	.26156	.21630
17	.31720	.27303	.24984	.20608
18	.30465	.26161	.23910	.19676
19	.29301	.25108	.22921	.18822
20	.28219	.24133	.22009	.18039
21	.27210	.23228	.21164	.17316
22	.26267	.22386	.20379	.16647
23	.25385	.21601	.19649	.16027
24	.24556	.20867	.18967	.15450
25	.23777	.20179	.18330	.14913
26	.23044	.19533	.17732	.14410
27	.22352	.18926	.17171	.13940
28	.21699	.18353	.16643	.13498
29	.21080	.17813	.16145	.13082
30	.20494	.17303	.15675	.12691
31	.19938	.16819	.15231	.12322
32	.19410	.16361	.14810	.11973
33	.18907	.15926	.14411	.11643
34	.18428	.15513	.14032	.11330
35	.17972	.15119	.13672	.11033
36	.17537	.14744	.13329	.10750
37	.17121	.14387	.13003	.10481
38	.16724	.14046	.12691	.10225
39	.16343	.13720	.12393	.09981
40	.15978	.13408	.12109	.09776
41	.15629	.13109	.11837	.09525
42	.15294	.12823	.11576	.09312
43	.14972	.12548	.11326	.09108
44	.14662	.12285	.11086	.08912
45	.14365	.12031	.10856	.08725
46	.14078	.11788	.10635	.08545
47	.13803	.11554	.10422	.08372
48	.13537	.11329	.10218	.08205
49	.13281	.11112	.10021	.08045
50	.13034	.10903	.09831	.07891

YEARS LIFE FOR DIVIDEND OVERPLUS TO REDEEM CAPITAL

TABLE 9

ANNUITY LIFE REQUIRED TO REDEEM CAPITAL
DIVIDENDS NECESSARY TO AMORTIZE INVESTMENT

The number of years of life required for a depleting reserve enterprise paying annual dividends at rates from 3 to 30 percent per annum to yield interest on invested capital at 2, 3, 4, 5, 6, 7, 8, 9, 10, and 12 percent per annum, and to provide further for redemption of capital at the expiration of the life of the annuity by annually investing the dividend overplus at the practicable rates of 2, 3, 4, 5, or 6 percent per annum.

Calculated to 3 significant figures for annual
dividend rates up to 30 percent.

The figures listed in this table are the number of years required for an annuity of X% per year to amount to 100% when improved at 'rates of 2 to 6 percent per annum. The annual redemption payment is referred to as X%. It represents the difference in percent between the actual dividend rate received and the expected speculative return (r′) on invested capital. It is, therefore, the dividend overplus expressed as a percentage of the capital invested. This annuity of X% per year is then invested annually at a practicable safe rate of interest (r) until the total amount so accumulated equals 100%, the time at which the invested capital has then been replaced. The figures given in the table represent values of

$$ n = \frac{\log\left(\dfrac{r}{X} + 1\right)}{\log R} $$

for various combinations of dividend rate, speculative rate, and redemption rate. For instance, the stock of a certain mining company is selling on the exchange for $20 per share and is paying dividends of $2.40 per year. How long will such dividends have to continue for an investor to redeem his capital at 4% and to receive 8% on his money besides?

In this case the dividend rate is $2.40 ÷ $20 = 12%

expected speculative return = 8%

and, from the tabulated values under redemption at 4%

$$n = 17.7 \text{ years.}$$

Or, from a different point of view, what dividend rate will a mine with an assured life of 15 years have to pay in order to net the investor an 8% speculative return over and above capital redemption at 4%?

$$d = 13\%.$$

These same examples may be solved graphically with reasonable accuracy from the chart shown on the page opposite the 4% redemption table, as follows:

Starting from the net expected return of 8% on the left side of the chart, thence horizontally to the right to the intersection of the 8% line with the 12% dividend curve, thence vertically downward to the years life at the bottom of the chart, where the value of

$$n = 17.7 \text{ (approximately),}$$

or, for the second instance:

Starting from 15 years at the bottom of the graph, thence vertically upward to the 8% net return horizontal line (scale shown on left of diagram), thence upward and to the right along (or parallel to) the curved dividend rate line to the right or top edge, where the percent dividend is found to be

$$d = 13\%.$$

TABLE 9

Number of years life required to yield r'% interest and to furnish overplus which, if reinvested at 2% compound interest, will return original investment at end of period.

Annual Dividend Rate

Net Return in Percent

%	2	3	4	5	6	7	8	9	10	12
3	55.5									
4	35.0	55.5								
5	25.8	35.0	55.5							
6	20.5	25.8	35.0	55.5						
7	17.0	20.5	25.8	35.0	55.5					
8	14.5	17.0	20.5	25.8	35.0	55.5				
9	12.6	14.5	17.0	20.5	25.8	35.0	55.5			
10	11.2	12.6	14.5	17.0	20.5	25.8	35.0	55.5		
11	10.1	11.2	12.6	14.5	17.0	20.5	25.8	35.0	55.5	
12	9.2	10.1	11.2	12.6	14.5	17.0	20.5	25.8	35.0	
13	8.4	9.2	10.1	11.2	12.6	14.5	17.0	20.5	25.8	55.5
14	7.8	8.4	9.2	10.1	11.2	12.6	14.5	17.0	20.5	35.0
15	7.2	7.8	8.4	9.2	10.1	11.2	12.6	14.5	17.0	25.8
16	6.7	7.2	7.8	8.4	9.2	10.1	11.2	12.6	14.5	20.5
17	6.3	6.7	7.2	7.8	8.4	9.2	10.1	11.2	12.6	17.0
18	6.0	6.3	6.7	7.2	7.8	8.4	9.2	10.1	11.2	14.5
19	5.6	6.0	6.3	6.7	7.2	7.8	8.4	9.2	10.1	12.6
20	5.3	5.6	6.0	6.3	6.7	7.2	7.8	8.4	9.2	11.2
21	5.0	5.3	5.6	6.0	6.3	6.7	7.2	7.8	8.4	10.1
22	4.8	5.0	5.3	5.6	6.0	6.3	6.7	7.2	7.8	9.2
23	4.6	4.8	5.0	5.3	5.6	6.0	6.3	6.7	7.2	8.4
24	4.4	4.6	4.8	5.0	5.3	5.6	6.0	6.3	6.7	7.8
25	4.2	4.4	4.6	4.8	5.0	5.3	5.6	6.0	6.3	7.2
26	4.0	4.2	4.4	4.6	4.8	5.0	5.3	5.6	6.0	6.7
27	3.9	4.0	4.2	4.4	4.6	4.8	5.0	5.3	5.6	6.3
28	3.7	3.9	4.0	4.2	4.4	4.6	4.8	5.0	5.3	6.0
29	3.6	3.7	3.9	4.0	4.2	4.4	4.6	4.8	5.0	5.6
30	3.5	3.6	3.7	3.9	4.0	4.2	4.4	4.6	4.8	5.3

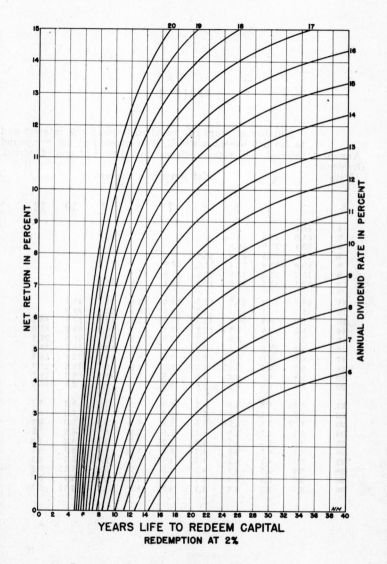

Fig. 49. Annuity life to redeem capital.

TABLE 9

Number of years life required to yield r'% interest and to furnish overplus which, if reinvested at 3% compound interest, will return original investment at end of period.

Annual Dividend Rate

Net Return in Percent

%	3	4	5	6	7	8	9	10	12
4	46.9								
5	31.0	46.9							
6	23.4	31.0	46.9						
7	18.9	23.4	31.0	46.9					
8	15.9	18.9	23.4	31.0	46.9				
9	13.7	15.9	18.9	23.4	31.0	46.9			
10	12.1	13.7	15.9	18.9	23.4	31.0	46.9		
11	10.8	12.1	13.7	15.9	18.9	23.4	31.0	46.9	
12	9.7	10.8	12.1	13.7	15.9	18.9	23.4	31.0	
13	8.9	9.7	10.8	12.1	13.7	15.9	18.9	23.4	46.9
14	8.2	8.9	9.7	10.8	12.1	13.7	15.9	18.9	31.0
15	7.5	8.2	8.9	9.7	10.8	12.1	13.7	15.9	23.4
16	7.0	7.5	8.2	8.9	9.7	10.8	12.1	13.7	18.9
17	6.6	7.0	7.5	8.2	8.9	9.7	10.8	12.1	15.9
18	6.2	6.6	7.0	7.5	8.2	8.9	9.7	10.8	13.7
19	5.8	6.2	6.6	7.0	7.5	8.2	8.9	9.7	12.1
20	5.5	5.8	6.2	6.6	7.0	7.5	8.2	8.9	10.8
21	5.25	5.5	5.8	6.2	6.6	7.0	7.5	8.2	9.7
22	5.0	5.25	5.5	5.8	6.2	6.6	7.0	7.5	8.9
23	4.75	5.0	5.25	5.5	5.8	6.2	6.6	7.0	8.2
24	4.5	4.75	5.0	5.25	5.5	5.8	6.2	6.6	7.5
25	4.3	4.5	4.75	5.0	5.25	5.5	5.8	6.2	7.0
26	4.1	4.3	4.5	4.75	5.0	5.25	5.5	5.8	6.6
27	3.9	4.1	4.3	4.5	4.75	5.0	5.25	5.5	6.2
28	3.8	3.9	4.1	4.3	4.5	4.75	5.0	5.25	5.8
29	3.7	3.8	3.9	4.1	4.3	4.5	4.75	5.0	5.5
30	3.6	3.7	3.8	3.9	4.1	4.3	4.5	4.75	5.25

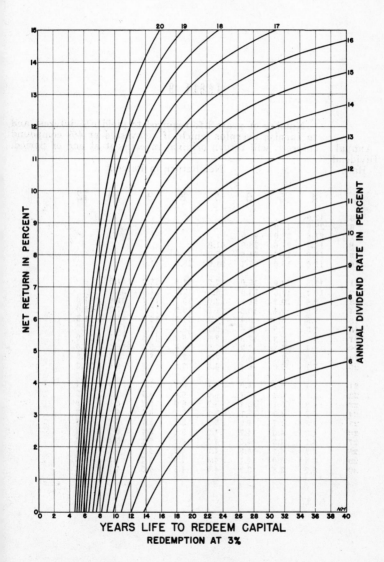

Fig. 50. Annuity life to redeem capital.

TABLE 9

Number of years life required to yield r′% interest and
to furnish overplus which, if reinvested at 4% compound
interest, will return original investment at end of period.

Annual
Dividend
Rate

Net Return in Percent

%	4	5	6	7	8	9	10	12
5	41.0							
6	28.0	41.0						
7	21.6	28.0	41.0					
8	17.7	21.6	28.0	41.0				
9	15.0	17.7	21.6	28.0	41.0			
10	13.0	15.0	17.7	21.6	28.0	41.0		
11	11.5	13.0	15.0	17.7	21.6	28.0	41.0	
12	10.3	11.5	13.0	15.0	17.7	21.6	28.0	
13	9.4	10.3	11.5	13.0	15.0	17.7	21.6	41.0
14	8.6	9.4	10.3	11.5	13.0	15.0	17.7	28.0
15	7.9	8.6	9.4	10.3	11.5	13.0	15.0	21.6
16	7.3	7.9	8.6	9.4	10.3	11.5	13.0	17.7
17	6.8	7.3	7.9	8.6	9.4	10.3	11.5	15.0
18	6.4	6.8	7.3	7.9	8.6	9.4	10.3	13.0
19	6.0	6.4	6.8	7.3	7.9	8.6	9.4	11.5
20	5.7	6.0	6.4	6.8	7.3	7.9	8.6	10.3
21	5.4	5.7	6.0	6.4	6.8	7.3	7.9	9.4
22	5.1	5.4	5.7	6.0	6.4	6.8	7.3	8.6
23	4.9	5.1	5.4	5.7	6.0	6.4	6.8	7.9
24	4.7	4.9	5.1	5.4	5.7	6.0	6.4	7.3
25	4.5	4.7	4.9	5.1	5.4	5.7	6.0	6.8
26	4.3	4.5	4.7	4.9	5.1	5.4	5.7	6.4
27	4.1	4.3	4.5	4.7	4.9	5.1	5.4	6.0
28	3.9	4.1	4.3	4.5	4.7	4.9	5.1	5.7
29	3.8	3.9	4.1	4.3	4.5	4.7	4.9	5.4
30	3.7	3.8	3.9	4.1	4.3	4.5	4.7	5.1

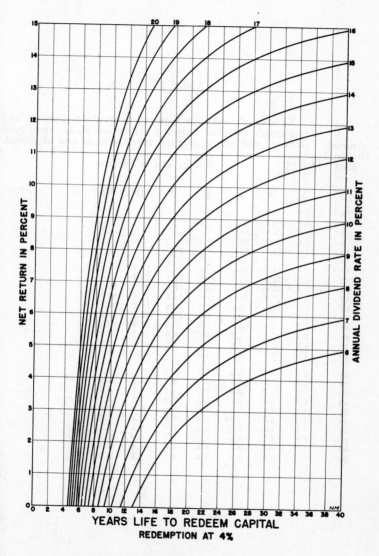

Fig. 51. Annuity life to redeem capital.

TABLE 9

Number of years life required to yield r´% interest and to furnish overplus which, if reinvested at 5% compound interest, will return original investment at end of period.

Annual Dividend Rate

Net Return in Percent

%	5	6	7	8	9	10	12
6	36.7						
7	25.7	36.7					
8	20.1	25.7	36.7				
9	16.6	20.1	25.7	36.7			
10	14.2	16.6	20.1	25.7	36.7		
11	12.4	14.2	16.6	20.1	25.7	36.7	
12	11.0	12.4	14.2	16.6	20.1	25.7	
13	9.9	11.0	12.4	14.2	16.6	20.1	36.7
14	9.0	9.9	11.0	12.4	14.2	16.6	25.7
15	8.3	9.0	9.9	11.0	12.4	14.2	20.1
16	7.7	8.3	9.0	9.9	11.0	12.4	16.6
17	7.2	7.7	8.3	9.0	9.9	11.0	14.2
18	6.7	7.2	7.7	8.3	9.0	9.9	12.4
19	6.3	6.7	7.2	7.7	8.3	9.0	11.0
20	5.9	6.3	6.7	7.2	7.7	8.3	9.9
21	5.6	5.9	6.3	6.7	7.2	7.7	9.0
22	5.3	5.6	5.9	6.3	6.7	7.2	8.3
23	5.0	5.3	5.6	5.9	6.3	6.7	7.7
24	4.8	5.0	5.3	5.6	5.9	6.3	7.2
25	4.6	4.8	5.0	5.3	5.6	5.9	6.7
26	4.4	4.6	4.8	5.0	5.3	5.6	6.3
27	4.2	4.4	4.6	4.8	5.0	5.3	5.9
28	4.0	4.2	4.4	4.6	4.8	5.0	5.6
29	3.9	4.0	4.2	4.4	4.6	4.8	5.3
30	3.7	3.9	4.0	4.2	4.4	4.6	5.0

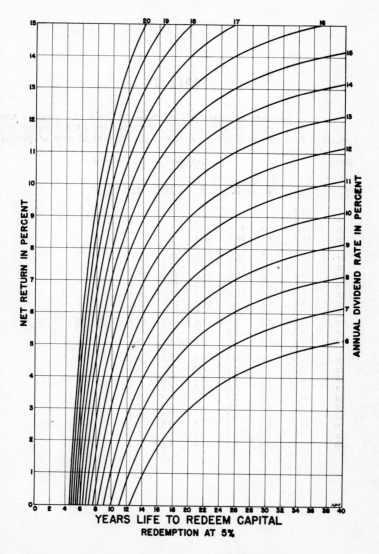

Fig. 52. Annuity life to redeem capital.

TABLE 9

Number of years life required to yield r'% interest and to furnish overplus which, if reinvested at 6% compound interest, will return original investment at end of period.

Annual
Dividend
Rate

Net Return in Percent

%	6	7	8	9	10	12
7	33.4					
8	23.8	33.4				
9	18.9	23.8	33.4			
10	15.7	18.9	23.8	33.4		
11	13.5	15.7	18.9	23.8	33.4	
12	11.9	13.5	15.7	18.9	23.8	
13	10.6	11.9	13.5	15.7	18.9	33.4
14	9.6	10.6	11.9	13.5	15.7	23.8
15	8.8	9.6	10.6	11.9	13.5	18.9
16	8.1	8.8	9.6	10.6	11.9	15.7
17	7.5	8.1	8.8	9.6	10.6	13.5
18	7.0	7.5	8.1	8.8	9.6	11.9
19	6.5	7.0	7.5	8.1	8.8	10.6
20	6.1	6.5	7.0	7.5	8.1	9.6
21	5.8	6.1	6.5	7.0	7.5	8.8
22	5.5	5.8	6.1	6.5	7.0	8.1
23	5.2	5.5	5.8	6.1	6.5	7.5
24	4.9	5.2	5.5	5.8	6.1	7.0
25	4.7	4.9	5.2	5.5	5.8	6.5
26	4.5	4.7	4.9	5.2	5.5	6.1
27	4.3	4.5	4.7	4.9	5.2	5.8
28	4.1	4.3	4.5	4.7	4.9	5.5
29	4.0	4.1	4.3	4.5	4.7	5.2
30	3.8	4.0	4.1	4.3	4.5	4.9

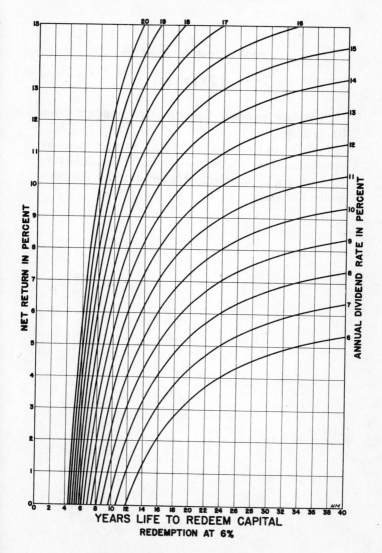

Fig. 53. Annuity life to redeem capital.

LOGARITHMS OF NUMBERS

TABLE 10

Five-place common logarithms of numbers from 100 to 1000.

Table 10 in its entirety (18 pp.) is reproduced by permission from *Macmillan Log and Trig. Tables* by E. R. Hedrick; copyright 1913 and 1920 by The Macmillan Company.

N.	0	1	2	3	4	5	6	7	8	9	Prop. Pts.
100	00 000	043	087	130	173	217	260	303	346	389	

101	432	475	518	561	604	647	689	732	775	817
102	860	903	945	988	*030	*072	*115	*157	*199	*242
103	01 284	326	368	410	452	494	536	578	620	662
104	703	745	787	828	870	912	953	995	*036	*078
105	02 119	160	202	243	284	325	366	407	449	490
106	531	572	612	653	694	735	776	816	857	898
107	938	979	*019	*060	*100	*141	*181	*222	*262	*302
108	03 342	383	423	463	503	543	583	623	663	703
109	743	782	822	862	902	941	981	*021	*060	*100
110	04 139	179	218	258	297	336	376	415	454	493
111	532	571	610	650	689	727	766	805	844	883
112	922	961	999	*038	*077	*115	*154	*192	*231	*269
113	05 308	346	385	423	461	500	538	576	614	652
114	690	729	767	805	843	881	918	956	994	*032
115	06 070	108	145	183	221	258	296	333	371	408
116	446	483	521	558	595	633	670	707	744	781
117	819	856	893	930	967	*004	*041	*078	*115	*151
118	07 188	225	262	298	335	372	408	445	482	518
119	555	591	628	664	700	737	773	809	846	882
120	918	954	990	*027	*063	*099	*135	*171	*207	*243
121	08 279	314	350	386	422	458	493	529	565	600
122	636	672	707	743	778	814	849	884	920	955
123	991	*026	*061	*096	*132	*167	*202	*237	*272	*307
124	09 342	377	412	447	482	517	552	587	621	656
125	691	726	760	795	830	864	899	934	968	*003
126	10 037	072	106	140	175	209	243	278	312	346
127	380	415	449	483	517	551	585	619	653	687
128	721	755	789	823	857	890	924	958	992	*025
129	11 059	093	126	160	193	227	261	294	327	361
130	394	428	461	494	528	561	594	628	661	694
131	727	760	793	826	860	893	926	959	992	*024
132	12 057	090	123	156	189	222	254	287	320	352
133	385	418	450	483	516	548	581	613	646	678
134	710	743	775	808	840	872	905	937	969	*001
135	13 033	066	098	130	162	194	226	258	290	322
136	354	386	418	450	481	513	545	577	609	640
137	672	704	735	767	799	830	862	893	925	956
138	988	*019	*051	*082	*114	*145	*176	*208	*239	*270
139	14 301	333	364	395	426	457	489	520	551	582
140	613	644	675	706	737	768	799	829	860	891
141	922	953	983	*014	*045	*076	*106	*137	*168	*198
142	15 229	259	290	320	351	381	412	442	473	503
143	534	564	594	625	655	685	715	746	776	806
144	836	866	897	927	957	987	*017	*047	*077	*107
145	16 137	167	197	227	256	286	316	346	376	406
146	435	465	495	524	554	584	613	643	673	702
147	732	761	791	820	850	879	909	938	967	997
148	17 026	056	085	114	143	173	202	231	260	289
149	319	348	377	406	435	464	493	522	551	580

N.	0	1	2	3	4	5	6	7	8	9	Prop. Pts.
150	609	638	667	696	725	754	782	811	840	869	

Prop. Pts.

	44	43	42
1	4.4	4.3	4.2
2	8.8	8.6	8.4
3	13.2	12.9	12.6
4	17.6	17.2	16.8
5	22.0	21.5	21.0
6	26.4	25.8	25.2
7	30.8	30.1	29.4
8	35.2	34.4	33.6
9	39.6	38.7	37.8

	41	40	39
1	4.1	4.0	3.9
2	8.2	8.0	7.8
3	12.3	12.0	11.7
4	16.4	16.0	15.6
5	20.5	20.0	19.5
6	24.6	24.0	23.4
7	28.7	28.0	27.3
8	32.8	32.0	31.2
9	36.9	36.0	35.1

	38	37	36
1	3.8	3.7	3.6
2	7.6	7.4	7.2
3	11.4	11.1	10.8
4	15.2	14.8	14.4
5	19.0	18.5	18.0
6	22.8	22.2	21.6
7	26.6	25.9	25.2
8	30.4	29.6	28.8
9	34.2	33.3	32.4

	35	34	33
1	3.5	3.4	3.3
2	7.0	6.8	6.6
3	10.5	10.2	9.9
4	14.0	13.6	13.2
5	17.5	17.0	16.5
6	21.0	20.4	19.8
7	24.5	23.8	23.1
8	28.0	27.2	26.4
9	31.5	30.6	29.7

	32	31	30
1	3.2	3.1	3.0
2	6.4	6.2	6.0
3	9.6	9.3	9.0
4	12.8	12.4	12.0
5	16.0	15.5	15.0
6	19.2	18.6	18.0
7	22.4	21.7	21.0
8	25.6	24.8	24.0
9	28.8	27.9	27.0

N.	0	1	2	3	4	5	6	7	8	9
150	17 609	638	667	696	725	754	782	811	840	869
151	898	926	955	984	*013	*041	*070	*099	*127	*156
152	18 184	213	241	270	298	327	355	384	412	441
153	469	498	526	554	583	611	639	667	696	724
154	752	780	808	837	865	893	921	949	977	*005
155	19 033	061	089	117	145	173	201	229	257	285
156	312	340	368	396	424	451	479	507	535	562
157	590	618	645	673	700	728	756	783	811	838
158	866	893	921	948	976	*003	*030	*058	*085	*112
159	20 140	167	194	222	249	276	303	330	358	385
160	412	439	466	493	520	548	575	602	629	656
161	683	710	737	763	790	817	844	871	898	925
162	952	978	*005	*032	*059	*085	*112	*139	*165	*192
163	21 219	245	272	299	325	352	378	405	431	458
164	484	511	537	564	590	617	643	669	696	722
165	748	775	801	827	854	880	906	932	958	985
166	22 011	037	063	089	115	141	167	194	220	246
167	272	298	324	350	376	401	427	453	479	505
168	531	557	583	608	634	660	686	712	737	763
169	789	814	840	866	891	917	943	968	994	*019
170	23 045	070	096	121	147	172	198	223	249	274
171	300	325	350	376	401	426	452	477	502	528
172	553	578	603	629	654	679	704	729	754	779
173	805	830	855	880	905	930	955	980	*005	*030
174	24 055	080	105	130	155	180	204	229	254	279
175	304	329	353	378	403	428	452	477	502	527
176	551	576	601	625	650	674	699	724	748	773
177	797	822	846	871	895	920	944	969	993	*018
178	25 042	066	091	115	139	164	188	212	237	261
179	285	310	334	358	382	406	431	455	479	503
180	527	551	575	600	624	648	672	696	720	744
181	768	792	816	840	864	888	912	935	959	983
182	26 007	031	055	079	102	126	150	174	198	221
183	245	269	293	316	340	364	387	411	435	458
184	·482	505	529	553	576	600	623	647	670	694
185	717	741	764	788	811	834	858	881	905	928
186	951	975	998	*021	*045	*068	*091	*114	*138	*161
187	27 184	207	231	254	277	300	323	346	370	393
188	416	439	462	485	508	531	554	577	600	623
189	646	669	692	715	738	761	784	807	830	852
190	875	898	921	944	967	989	*012	*035	*058	*081
191	28 103	126	149	171	194	217	240	262	285	307
192	330	353	375	398	421	443	466	488	511	533
193	556	578	601	623	646	668	691	713	735	758
194	780	803	825	847	870	892	914	937	959	981
195	29 003	026	048	070	092	115	137	159	181	203
196	226	248	270	292	314	336	358	380	403	425
197	447	469	491	513	535	557	579	601	623	645
198	667	688	710	732	754	776	798	820	842	863
199	885	907	929	951	973	994	*016	*038	*060	*081
200	30 103	125	146	168	190	211	233	255	276	298
N.	0	1	2	3	4	5	6	7	8	9

Prop. Pts.

	29	28
1	2.9	2.8
2	5.8	5.6
3	8.7	8.4
4	11.6	11.2
5	14.5	14.0
6	17.4	16.8
7	20.3	19.6
8	23.2	22.4
9	26.1	25.2

	27	26
1	2.7	2.6
2	5.4	5.2
3	8.1	7.8
4	10.8	10.4
5	13.5	13.0
6	16.2	15.6
7	18.9	18.2
8	21.6	20.8
9	24.3	23.4

	25	24
1	2.5	2.4
2	5.0	4.8
3	7.5	7.2
4	10.0	9.6
5	12.5	12.0
6	15.0	14.4
7	17.5	16.8
8	20.0	19.2
9	22.5	21.6

	23	22
1	2.3	2.2
2	4.6	4.4
3	6.9	6.6
4	9.2	8.8
5	11.5	11.0
6	13.8	13.2
7	16.1	15.4
8	18.4	17.6
9	20.7	19.8

	21
1	2.1
2	4.2
3	6.3
4	8.4
5	10.5
6	12.6
7	14.7
8	16.8
9	18.9

N.	0	1	2	3	4	5	6	7	8	9	Prop. Pts.
200	30 103	125	146	168	190	211	233	255	276	298	
201	320	341	363	384	406	428	449	471	492	514	
202	535	557	578	600	621	643	664	685	707	728	
203	750	771	792	814	835	856	878	899	920	942	
204	963	984	*006	*027	*048	*069	*091	*112	*133	*154	
205	31 175	197	218	239	260	281	302	323	345	366	
206	387	408	429	450	471	492	513	534	555	576	
207	597	618	639	660	681	702	723	744	765	785	
208	806	827	848	869	890	911	931	952	973	994	
209	32 015	035	056	077	098	118	139	160	181	201	
210	222	243	263	284	305	325	346	366	387	408	
211	428	449	469	490	510	531	552	572	593	613	
212	634	654	675	695	715	736	756	777	797	818	
213	838	858	879	899	919	940	960	980	*001	*021	
214	33 041	062	082	102	122	143	163	183	203	224	
215	244	264	284	304	325	345	365	385	405	425	
216	445	465	486	506	526	546	566	586	606	626	
217	646	666	686	706	726	746	766	786	806	826	
218	846	866	885	905	925	945	965	985	*005	*025	
219	34 044	064	084	104	124	143	163	183	203	223	
220	242	262	282	301	321	341	361	380	400	420	
221	439	459	479	498	518	537	557	577	596	616	
222	635	655	674	694	713	733	753	772	792	811	
223	830	850	869	889	908	928	947	967	986	*005	
224	35 025	044	064	083	102	122	141	160	180	199	
225	218	238	257	276	295	315	334	353	372	392	
226	411	430	449	468	488	507	526	545	564	583	
227	603	622	641	660	679	698	717	736	755	774	
228	793	813	832	851	870	889	908	927	946	965	
229	984	*003	*021	*040	*059	*078	*097	*116	*135	*154	
230	36 173	192	211	229	248	267	286	305	324	342	
231	361	380	399	418	436	455	474	493	511	530	
232	549	568	586	605	624	642	661	680	698	717	
233	736	754	773	791	810	829	847	866	884	903	
234	922	940	959	977	996	*014	*033	*051	*070	*088	
235	37 107	125	144	162	181	199	218	236	254	273	
236	291	310	328	346	365	383	401	420	438	457	
237	475	493	511	530	548	566	585	603	621	639	
238	658	676	694	712	731	749	767	785	803	822	
239	840	858	876	894	912	931	949	967	985	*003	
240	38 021	039	057	075	093	112	130	148	166	184	
241	202	220	238	256	274	292	310	328	346	364	
242	382	399	417	435	453	471	489	507	525	543	
243	561	578	596	614	632	650	668	686	703	721	
244	739	757	775	792	810	828	846	863	881	899	
245	917	934	952	970	987	*005	*023	*041	*058	*076	
246	39 094	111	129	146	164	182	199	217	235	252	
247	270	287	305	322	340	358	375	393	410	428	
248	445	463	480	498	515	533	550	568	585	602	
249	620	637	655	672	690	707	724	742	759	777	
250	794	811	829	846	863	881	898	915	933	950	
N.	0	1	2	3	4	5	6	7	8	9	Prop. Pts.

Prop. Pts.

log 2 = .30102 99957

	22	21
1	2.2	2.1
2	4.4	4.2
3	6.6	6.3
4	8.8	8.4
5	11.0	10.5
6	13.2	12.6
7	15.4	14.7
8	17.6	16.8
9	19.8	18.9

	20	19
1	2.0	1.9
2	4.0	3.8
3	6.0	5.7
4	8.0	7.6
5	10.0	9.5
6	12.0	11.4
7	14.0	13.3
8	16.0	15.2
9	18.0	17.1

	18	17
1	1.8	1.7
2	3.6	3.4
3	5.4	5.1
4	7.2	6.8
5	9.0	8.5
6	10.8	10.2
7	12.6	11.9
8	14.4	13.6
9	16.2	15.3

N.	0	1	2	3	4	5	6	7	8	9
250	39 794	811	829	846	863	881	898	915	933	950
251	967	985	*002	*019	*037	*054	*071	*088	*106	*123
252	40 140	157	175	192	209	226	243	261	278	295
253	312	329	346	364	381	398	415	432	449	466
254	483	500	518	535	552	569	586	603	620	637
255	654	671	688	705	722	739	756	773	790	807
256	824	841	858	875	892	909	926	943	960	976
257	993	*010	*027	*044	*061	*078	*095	*111	*128	*145
258	41 162	179	196	212	229	246	263	280	296	313
259	330	347	363	380	397	414	430	447	464	481
260	497	514	531	547	564	581	597	614	631	647
261	664	681	697	714	731	747	764	780	797	814
262	830	847	863	880	896	913	929	946	963	979
263	996	*012	*029	*045	*062	*078	*095	*111	*127	*144
264	42 160	177	193	210	226	243	259	275	292	308
265	325	341	357	374	390	406	423	439	455	472
266	488	504	521	537	553	570	586	602	619	635
267	651	667	684	700	716	732	749	765	781	797
268	813	830	846	862	878	894	911	927	943	959
269	975	991	*008	*024	*040	*056	*072	*088	*104	*120
270	43 136	152	169	185	201	217	233	249	265	281
271	297	313	329	345	361	377	393	409	425	441
272	457	473	489	505	521	537	553	569	584	600
273	616	632	648	664	680	696	712	727	743	759
274	775	791	807	823	838	854	870	886	902	917
275	933	949	965	981	996	*012	*028	*044	*059	*075
276	44 091	107	122	138	154	170	185	201	217	232
277	248	264	279	295	311	326	342	358	373	389
278	404	420	436	451	467	483	498	514	529	545
279	560	576	592	607	623	638	654	669	685	700
280	716	731	747	762	778	793	809	824	840	855
281	871	886	902	917	932	948	963	979	994	*010
282	45 025	040	056	071	086	102	117	133	148	163
283	179	194	209	225	240	255	271	286	301	317
284	332	347	362	378	393	408	423	439	454	469
285	484	500	515	530	545	561	576	591	606	621
286	637	652	667	682	697	712	728	743	758	773
287	788	803	818	834	849	864	879	894	909	924
288	939	954	969	984	*000	*015	*030	*045	*060	*075
289	46 090	105	120	135	150	165	180	195	210	225
290	240	255	270	285	300	315	330	345	359	374
291	389	404	419	434	449	464	479	494	509	523
292	538	553	568	583	598	613	627	642	657	672
293	687	702	716	731	746	761	776	790	805	820
294	835	850	864	879	894	909	923	938	953	967
295	982	997	*012	*026	*041	*056	*070	*085	*100	*114
296	47 129	144	159	173	188	202	217	232	246	261
297	276	290	305	319	334	349	363	378	392	407
298	422	436	451	465	480	494	509	524	538	553
299	567	582	596	611	625	640	654	669	683	698
300	712	727	741	756	770	784	799	813	828	842
N.	0	1	2	3	4	5	6	7	8	9

Prop. Pts.

	18	17
1	1.8	1.7
2	3.6	3.4
3	5.4	5.1
4	7.2	6.8
5	9.0	8.5
6	10.8	10.2
7	12.6	11.9
8	14.4	13.6
9	16.2	15.3

M
$= \log_{10} e$
$= \log_{10} 2.718 \cdots$
$= .43429\ 44819$

	16	15
1	1.6	1.5
2	3.2	3.0
3	4.8	4.5
4	6.4	6.0
5	8.0	7.5
6	9.6	9.0
7	11.2	10.5
8	12.8	12.0
9	14.4	13.5

	14
1	1.4
2	2.8
3	4.2
4	5.6
5	7.0
6	8.4
7	9.8
8	11.2
9	12.6

N.	0	1	2	3	4	5	6	7	8	9
300	47 712	727	741	756	770	784	799	813	828	842
301	857	871	885	900	914	929	943	958	972	986
302	48 001	015	029	044	058	073	087	101	116	130
303	144	159	173	187	202	216	230	244	259	273
304	287	302	316	330	344	359	373	387	401	416
305	430	444	458	473	487	501	515	530	544	558
306	572	586	601	615	629	643	657	671	686	700
307	714	728	742	756	770	785	799	813	827	841
308	855	869	883	897	911	926	940	954	968	982
309	996	*010	*024	*038	*052	*066	*080	*094	*108	*122
310	49 136	150	164	178	192	206	220	234	248	262
311	276	290	304	318	332	346	360	374	388	402
312	415	429	443	457	471	485	499	513	527	541
313	554	568	582	596	610	624	638	651	665	679
314	693	707	721	734	748	762	776	790	803	817
315	831	845	859	872	886	900	914	927	941	955
316	969	982	996	*010	*024	*037	*051	*065	*079	*092
317	50 106	120	133	147	161	174	188	202	215	229
318	243	256	270	284	297	311	325	338	352	365
319	379	393	406	420	433	447	461	474	488	501
320	515	529	542	556	569	583	596	610	623	637
321	651	664	678	691	705	718	732	745	759	772
322	786	799	813	826	840	853	866	880	893	907
323	920	934	947	961	974	987	*001	*014	*028	*041
324	51 055	068	081	095	108	121	135	148	162	175
325	188	202	215	228	242	255	268	282	295	308
326	322	335	348	362	375	388	402	415	428	441
327	455	468	481	495	508	521	534	548	561	574
328	587	601	614	627	640	654	667	680	693	706
329	720	733	746	759	772	786	799	812	825	838
330	851	865	878	891	904	917	930	943	957	970
331	983	996	*009	*022	*035	*048	*061	*075	*088	*101
332	52 114	127	140	153	166	179	192	205	218	231
333	244	257	270	284	297	310	323	336	349	362
334	375	388	401	414	427	440	453	466	479	492
335	504	517	530	543	556	569	582	595	608	621
336	634	647	660	673	686	699	711	724	737	750
337	763	776	789	802	815	827	840	853	866	879
338	892	905	917	930	943	956	969	982	994	*007
339	53 020	033	046	058	071	084	097	110	122	135
340	148	161	173	186	199	212	224	237	250	263
341	275	288	301	314	326	339	352	364	377	390
342	403	415	428	441	453	466	479	491	504	517
343	529	542	555	567	580	593	605	618	631	643
344	656	668	681	694	706	719	732	744	757	769
345	782	794	807	820	832	845	857	870	882	895
346	908	920	933	945	958	970	983	995	*008	*020
347	54 033	045	058	070	083	095	108	120	133	145
348	158	170	183	195	208	220	233	245	258	270
349	283	295	307	320	332	345	357	370	382	394
350	407	419	432	444	456	469	481	494	506	518
N.	0	1	2	3	4	5	6	7	8	9

Prop. Pts.

log 3 = .47712 12547

log π = .49714 98727

	15	14
1	1.5	1.4
2	3.0	2.8
3	4.5	4.2
4	6.0	5.6
5	7.5	7.0
6	9.0	8.4
7	10.5	9.8
8	12.0	11.2
9	13.5	12.6

	13	12
1	1.3	1.2
2	2.6	2.4
3	3.9	3.6
4	5.2	4.8
5	6.5	6.0
6	7.8	7.2
7	9.1	8.4
8	10.4	9.6
9	11.7	10.8

N.	0	1	2	3	4	5	6	7	8	9	Prop. Pts.	
350	54 407	419	432	444	456	469	481	494	506	518		
351	531	543	555	568	580	593	605	617	630	642		
352	654	667	679	691	704	716	728	741	753	765		
353	777	790	802	814	827	839	851	864	876	888		
354	900	913	925	937	949	962	974	986	998	*011		
355	55 023	035	047	060	072	084	096	108	121	133		
356	145	157	169	182	194	206	218	230	242	255		
357	267	279	291	303	315	328	340	352	364	376		
358	388	400	413	425	437	449	461	473	485	497		
359	509	522	534	546	558	570	582	594	606	618		
360	630	642	654	666	678	691	703	715	727	739		
361	751	763	775	787	799	811	823	835	847	859	**13**	**12**
362	871	883	895	907	919	931	943	955	967	979	1 1.3	1.2
363	991	*003	*015	*027	*038	*050	*062	*074	*086	*098	2 2.6	2.4
364	56 110	122	134	146	158	170	182	194	205	217	3 3.9	3.6
365	229	241	253	265	277	289	301	312	324	336	4 5.2	4.8
366	348	360	372	384	396	407	419	431	443	455	5 6.5	6.0
											6 7.8	7.2
367	467	478	490	502	514	526	538	549	561	573	7 9.1	8.4
368	585	597	608	620	632	644	656	667	679	691	8 10.4	9.6
369	703	714	726	738	750	761	773	785	797	808	9 11.7	10.8
370	820	832	844	855	867	879	891	902	914	926		
371	937	949	961	972	984	996	*008	*019	*031	*043		
372	57 054	066	078	089	101	113	124	136	148	159		
373	171	183	194	206	217	229	241	252	264	276		
374	287	299	310	322	334	345	357	368	380	392		
375	403	415	426	438	449	461	473	484	496	507		
376	519	530	542	553	565	576	588	600	611	623		
377	634	646	657	669	680	692	703	715	726	738		
378	749	761	772	784	795	807	818	830	841	852		
379	864	875	887	898	910	921	933	944	955	967		
380	978	990	*001	*013	*024	*035	*047	*058	*070	*081		
381	58 092	104	115	127	138	149	161	172	184	195	**11**	**10**
382	206	218	229	240	252	263	274	286	297	309	1 1.1	1.0
383	320	331	343	354	365	377	388	399	410	422	2 2.2	2.0
384	433	444	456	467	478	490	501	512	524	535	3 3.3	3.0
385	546	557	569	580	591	602	614	625	636	647	4 4.4	4.0
386	659	670	681	692	704	715	726	737	749	760	5 5.5	5.0
											6 6.6	6.0
387	771	782	794	805	816	827	838	850	861	872	7 7.7	7.0
388	883	894	906	917	928	939	950	961	973	984	8 8.8	8.0
389	995	*006	*017	*028	*040	*051	*062	*073	*084	*095	9 9.9	9.0
390	59 106	118	129	140	151	162	173	184	195	207		
391	218	229	240	251	262	273	284	295	306	318		
392	329	340	351	362	373	384	395	406	417	428		
393	439	450	461	472	483	494	506	517	528	539		
394	550	561	572	583	594	605	616	627	638	649		
395	660	671	682	693	704	715	726	737	748	759		
396	770	780	791	802	813	824	835	846	857	868		
397	879	890	901	912	923	934	945	956	966	977		
398	988	999	*010	*021	*032	*043	*054	*065	*076	*086		
399	60 097	108	119	130	141	152	163	173	184	195		
400	206	217	228	239	249	260	271	282	293	304		
N.	0	1	2	3	4	5	6	7	8	9	Prop. Pts.	

N.	0	1	2	3	4	5	6	7	8	9
400	60 206	217	228	239	249	260	271	282	293	304
401	314	325	336	347	358	369	379	390	401	412
402	423	433	444	455	466	477	487	498	509	520
403	531	541	552	563	574	584	595	606	617	627
404	638	649	660	670	681	692	703	713	724	735
405	746	756	767	778	788	799	810	821	831	842
406	853	863	874	885	895	906	917	927	938	949
407	959	970	981	991	*002	*013	*023	*034	*045	*055
408	61 066	077	087	098	109	119	130	140	151	162
409	172	183	194	204	215	225	236	247	257	268
410	278	289	300	310	321	331	342	352	363	374
411	384	395	405	416	426	437	448	458	469	479
412	490	500	511	521	532	542	553	563	574	584
413	595	606	616	627	637	648	658	669	679	690
414	700	711	721	731	742	752	763	773	784	794
415	805	815	826	836	847	857	868	878	888	899
416	909	920	930	941	951	962	972	982	993	*003
417	62 014	024	034	045	055	066	076	086	097	107
418	118	128	138	149	159	170	180	190	201	211
419	221	232	242	252	263	273	284	294	304	315
420	325	335	346	356	366	377	387	397	408	418
421	428	439	449	459	469	480	490	500	511	521
422	531	542	552	562	572	583	593	603	613	624
423	634	644	655	665	675	685	696	706	716	726
424	737	747	757	767	778	788	798	808	818	829
425	839	849	859	870	880	890	900	910	921	931
426	941	951	961	972	982	992	*002	*012	*022	*033
427	63 043	053	063	073	083	094	104	114	124	134
428	144	155	165	175	185	195	205	215	225	236
429	246	256	266	276	286	296	306	317	327	337
430	347	357	367	377	387	397	407	417	428	438
431	448	458	468	478	488	498	508	518	528	538
432	548	558	568	579	589	599	609	619	629	639
433	649	659	669	679	689	699	709	719	729	739
434	749	759	769	779	789	799	809	819	829	839
435	849	859	869	879	889	899	909	919	929	939
436	949	959	969	979	988	998	*008	*018	*028	*038
437	64 048	058	068	078	088	098	108	118	128	137
438	147	157	167	177	187	197	207	217	227	237
439	246	256	266	276	286	296	306	316	326	335
440	345	355	365	375	385	395	404	414	424	434
441	444	454	464	473	483	493	503	513	523	532
442	542	552	562	572	582	591	601	611	621	631
443	640	650	660	670	680	689	699	709	719	729
444	738	748	758	768	777	787	797	807	816	826
445	836	846	856	865	875	885	895	904	914	924
446	933	943	953	963	972	982	992	*002	*011	*021
447	65 031	040	050	060	070	079	089	099	108	118
448	128	137	147	157	167	176	186	196	205	215
449	225	234	244	254	263	273	283	292	302	312
450	321	331	341	350	360	369	379	389	398	408
N.	0	1	2	3	4	5	6	7	8	9

Prop. Pts.

	11	10
1	1.1	1.0
2	2.2	2.0
3	3.3	3.0
4	4.4	4.0
5	5.5	5.0
6	6.6	6.0
7	7.7	7.0
8	8.8	8.0
9	9.9	9.0

$$\log M = \log [\log e] = 9.63778\ 431 - 10$$

	9
1	0.9
2	1.8
3	2.7
4	3.6
5	4.5
6	5.4
7	6.3
8	7.2
9	8.1

N.	0	1	2	3	4	5	6	7	8	9
450	65 321	331	341	350	360	369	379	389	398	408
451	418	427	437	447	456	466	475	485	495	504
452	514	523	533	543	552	562	571	581	591	600
453	610	619	629	639	648	658	667	677	686	696
454	706	715	725	734	744	753	763	772	782	792
455	801	811	820	830	839	849	858	868	877	887
456	896	906	916	925	935	944	954	963	973	982
457	992	*001	*011	*020	*030	*039	*049	*058	*068	*077
458	66 087	096	106	115	124	134	143	153	162	172
459	181	191	200	210	219	229	238	247	257	266
460	276	285	295	304	314	323	332	342	351	361
461	370	380	389	398	408	417	427	436	445	455
462	464	474	483	492	502	511	521	530	539	549
463	558	567	577	586	596	605	614	624	633	642
464	652	661	671	680	689	699	708	717	727	736
465	745	755	764	773	783	792	801	811	820	829
466	839	848	857	867	876	885	894	904	913	922
467	932	941	950	960	969	978	987	997	*006	*015
468	67 025	034	043	052	062	071	080	089	099	108
469	117	127	136	145	154	164	173	182	191	201
470	210	219	228	237	247	256	265	274	284	293
471	302	311	321	330	339	348	357	367	376	385
472	394	403	413	422	431	440	449	459	468	477
473	486	495	504	514	523	532	541	550	560	569
474	578	587	596	605	614	624	633	642	651	660
475	669	679	688	697	706	715	724	733	742	752
476	761	770	779	788	797	806	815	825	834	843
477	852	861	870	879	888	897	906	916	925	934
478	943	952	961	970	979	988	997	*006	*015	*024
479	68 034	043	052	061	070	079	088	097	106	115
480	124	133	142	151	160	169	178	187	196	205
481	215	224	233	242	251	260	269	278	287	296
482	305	314	323	332	341	350	359	368	377	386
483	395	404	413	422	431	440	449	458	467	476
484	485	494	502	511	520	529	538	547	556	565
485	574	583	592	601	610	619	628	637	646	655
486	664	673	681	690	699	708	717	726	735	744
487	753	762	771	780	789	797	806	815	824	833
488	842	851	860	869	878	886	895	904	913	922
489	931	940	949	958	966	975	984	993	*002	*011
490	69 020	028	037	046	055	064	073	082	090	099
491	108	117	126	135	144	152	161	170	179	188
492	197	205	214	223	232	241	249	258	267	276
493	285	294	302	311	320	329	338	346	355	364
494	373	381	390	399	408	417	425	434	443	452
495	461	469	478	487	496	504	513	522	531	539
496	548	557	566	574	583	592	601	609	618	627
497	636	644	653	662	671	679	688	697	705	714
498	723	732	740	749	758	767	775	784	793	801
499	810	819	827	836	845	854	862	871	880	888
500	897	906	914	923	932	940	949	958	966	975
N.	**0**	**1**	**2**	**3**	**4**	**5**	**6**	**7**	**8**	**9**

Prop. Pts.

	10	9
1	1.0	0.9
2	2.0	1.8
3	3.0	2.7
4	4.0	3.6
5	5.0	4.5
6	6.0	5.4
7	7.0	6.3
8	8.0	7.2
9	9.0	8.1

	8
1	0.8
2	1.6
3	2.4
4	3.2
5	4.0
6	4.8
7	5.6
8	6.4
9	7.2

N.	0	1	2	3	4	5	6	7	8	9	Prop. Pts.
500	69 897	906	914	923	932	940	949	958	966	975	
501	984	992	*001	*010	*018	*027	*036	*044	*053	*062	
502	70 070	079	088	096	105	114	122	131	140	148	
503	157	165	174	183	191	200	209	217	226	234	
504	243	252	260	269	278	286	295	303	312	321	
505	329	338	346	355	364	372	381	389	398	406	log 5
506	415	424	432	441	449	458	467	475	484	492	=.69897 00043
507	501	509	518	526	535	544	552	561	569	578	
508	586	595	603	612	621	629	638	646	655	663	
509	672	680	689	697	706	714	723	731	740	749	
510	757	766	774	783	791	800	808	817	825	834	
511	842	851	859	868	876	885	893	902	910	919	
512	927	935	944	952	961	969	978	986	995	*003	
513	71 012	020	029	037	046	054	063	071	079	088	

		9	8
1		0.9	0.8
2		1.8	1.6
3		2.7	2.4
4		3.6	3.2
5		4.5	4.0
6		5.4	4.8
7		6.3	5.6
8		7.2	6.4
9		8.1	7.2

N.	0	1	2	3	4	5	6	7	8	9
514	096	105	113	122	130	139	147	155	164	172
515	181	189	198	206	214	223	231	240	248	257
516	265	273	282	290	299	307	315	324	332	341
517	349	357	366	374	383	391	399	408	416	425
518	433	441	450	458	466	475	483	492	500	508
519	517	525	533	542	550	559	567	575	584	592
520	600	609	617	625	634	642	650	659	667	675
521	684	692	700	709	717	725	734	742	750	759
522	767	775	784	792	800	809	817	825	834	842
523	850	858	867	875	883	892	900	908	917	925
524	933	941	950	958	966	975	983	991	999	*008
525	72 016	024	032	041	049	057	066	074	082	090
526	099	107	115	123	132	140	148	156	165	173
527	181	189	198	206	214	222	230	239	247	255
528	263	272	280	288	296	304	313	321	329	337
529	346	354	362	370	378	387	395	403	411	419
530	428	436	444	452	460	469	477	485	493	501
531	509	518	526	534	542	550	558	567	575	583
532	591	599	607	616	624	632	640	648	656	665
533	673	681	689	697	705	713	722	730	738	746

		7
1		0.7
2		1.4
3		2.1
4		2.8
5		3.5
6		4.2
7		4.9
8		5.6
9		6.3

N.	0	1	2	3	4	5	6	7	8	9
534	754	762	770	779	787	795	803	811	819	827
535	835	843	852	860	868	876	884	892	900	908
536	916	925	933	941	949	957	965	973	981	989
537	997	*006	*014	*022	*030	*038	*046	*054	*062	*070
538	73 078	086	094	102	111	119	127	135	143	151
539	159	167	175	183	191	199	207	215	223	231
540	239	247	255	263	272	280	288	296	304	312
541	320	328	336	344	352	360	368	376	384	392
542	400	408	416	424	432	440	448	456	464	472
543	480	488	496	504	512	520	528	536	544	552
544	560	568	576	584	592	600	608	616	624	632
545	640	648	656	664	672	679	687	695	703	711
546	719	727	735	743	751	759	767	775	783	791
547	799	807	815	823	830	838	846	854	862	870
548	878	886	894	902	910	918	926	933	941	949
549	957	965	973	981	989	997	*005	*013	*020	*028
550	74 036	044	052	060	068	076	084	092	099	107
N.	0	1	2	3	4	5	6	7	8	9	Prop. Pts.

N.	0	1	2	3	4	5	6	7	8	9
550	74 036	044	052	060	068	076	084	092	099	107
551	115	123	131	139	147	155	162	170	178	186
552	194	202	210	218	225	233	241	249	257	265
553	.273	280	288	296	304	312	320	327	335	343
554	351	359	367	374	382	390	398	406	414	421
555	429	437	445	453	461	468	476	484	492	500
556	507	515	523	531	539	547	554	562	570	578
557	586	593	601	609	617	624	632	640	648	656
558	663	671	679	687	695	702	710	718	726	733
559	741	749	757	764	772	780	788	796	803	811
560	819	827	834	842	850	858	865	873	881	889
561	896	904	912	920	927	935	943	950	958	966
562	974	981	989	997	*005	*012	*020	*028	*035	*043
563	75 051	059	066	074	082	089	097	105	113	120
564	128	136	143	151	159	166	174	182	189	197
565	205	213	220	228	236	243	251	259	266	274
566	282	289	297	305	312	320	328	335	343	351
567	358	366	374	381	389	397	404	412	420	427
568	435	442	450	458	465	473	481	488	496	504
569	511	519	526	534	542	549	557	565	572	580
570	587	595	603	610	618	626	633	641	648	656
571	664	671	679	686	694	702	709	717	724	732
572	740	747	755	762	770	778	785	793	800	808
573	815	823	831	838	846	853	861	868	876	884
574	891	899	906	914	921	929	937	944	952	959
575	967	974	982	989	997	*005	*012	*020	*027	*035
576	76 042	050	057	065	072	080	087	095	103	110
577	118	125	133	140	148	155	163	170	178	185
578	193	200	208	215	223	230	238	245	253	260
579	268	275	283	290	298	305	313	320	328	335
580	343	350	358	365	373	380	388	395	403	410
581	418	425	433	440	448	455	462	470	477	485
582	492	500	507	515	522	530	537	545	552	559
583	567	574	582	589	597	604	612	619	626	634
584	641	649	656	664	671	678	686	693	701	708
585	716	723	730	738	745	753	760	768	775	782
586	790	797	805	812	819	827	834	842	849	856
587	864	871	879	886	893	901	908	916	923	930
588	938	945	953	960	967	975	982	989	997	*004
589	77 012	019	026	034	041	048	056	063	070	078
590	085	093	100	107	115	122	129	137	144	151
591	159	166	173	181	188	195	203	210	217	225
592	232	240	247	254	262	269	276	283	291	298
593	305	313	320	327	335	342	349	357	364	371
594	379	386	393	401	408	415	422	430	437	444
595	452	459	466	474	481	488	495	503	510	517
596	525	532	539	546	554	561	568	576	583	590
597	597	605	612	619	627	634	641	648	656	663
598	670	677	685	692	699	706	714	721	728	735
599	743	750	757	764	772	779	786	793	801	808
600	815	822	830	837	844	851	859	866	873	880
N.	0	1	2	3	4	5	6	7	8	9

Prop. Pts.

	8	7
1	0.8	0.7
2	1.6	1.4
3	2.4	2.1
4	3.2	2.8
5	4.0	3.5
6	4.8	4.2
7	5.6	4.9
8	6.4	5.6
9	7.2	6.3

N.	0	1	2	3	4	5	6	7	8	9
600	77 815	822	830	837	844	851	859	866	873	880
601	887	895	902	909	916	924	931	938	945	952
602	960	967	974	981	988	996	*003	*010	*017	*025
603	78 032	039	046	053	061	068	075	082	089	097
604	104	111	118	125	132	140	147	154	161	168
605	176	183	190	197	204	211	219	226	233	240
606	247	254	262	269	276	283	290	297	305	312
607	319	326	333	340	347	355	362	369	376	383
608	390	398	405	412	419	426	433	440	447	455
609	462	469	476	483	490	497	504	512	519	526
610	533	540	547	554	561	569	576	583	590	597
611	604	611	618	625	633	640	647	654	661	668
612	675	682	689	696	704	711	718	725	732	739
613	746	753	760	767	774	781	789	796	803	810
614	817	824	831	838	845	852	859	866	873	880
615	888	895	902	909	916	923	930	937	944	951
616	958	965	972	979	986	993	*000	*007	*014	*021
617	79 029	036	043	050	057	064	071	078	085	092
618	099	106	113	120	127	134	141	148	155	162
619	169	176	183	190	197	204	211	218	225	232
620	239	246	253	260	267	274	281	288	295	302
621	309	316	323	330	337	344	351	358	365	372
622	379	386	393	400	407	414	421	428	435	442
623	449	456	463	470	477	484	491	498	505	511
624	518	525	532	539	546	553	560	567	574	581
625	588	595	602	609	616	623	630	637	644	650
626	657	664	671	678	685	692	699	706	713	720
627	727	734	741	748	754	761	768	775	782	789
628	796	803	810	817	824	831	837	844	851	858
629	865	872	879	886	893	900	906	913	920	927
630	934	941	948	955	962	969	975	982	989	996
631	80 003	010	017	024	030	037	044	051	058	065
632	072	079	085	092	099	106	113	120	127	134
633	140	147	154	161	168	175	182	188	195	202
634	209	216	223	229	236	243	250	257	264	271
635	277	284	291	298	305	312	318	325	332	339
636	346	353	359	366	373	380	387	393	400	407
637	414	421	428	434	441	448	455	462	468	475
638	482	489	496	502	509	516	523	530	536	543
639	550	557	564	570	577	584	591	598	604	611
640	618	625	632	638	645	652	659	665	672	679
641	686	693	699	706	713	720	726	733	740	747
642	754	760	767	774	781	787	794	801	808	814
643	821	828	835	841	848	855	862	868	875	882
644	889	895	902	909	916	922	929	936	943	949
645	956	963	969	976	983	990	996	*003	*010	*017
646	81 023	030	037	043	050	057	064	070	077	084
647	090	097	104	111	117	124	131	137	144	151
648	158	164	171	178	184	191	198	204	211	218
649	224	231	238	245	251	258	265	271	278	285
650	291	298	305	311	318	325	331	338	345	351
N.	0	1	2	3	4	5	6	7	8	9

Prop. Pts.

	8	7
1	0.8	0.7
2	1.6	1.4
3	2.4	2.1
4	3.2	2.8
5	4.0	3.5
6	4.8	4.2
7	5.6	4.9
8	6.4	5.6
9	7.2	6.3

	6
1	0.6
2	1.2
3	1.8
4	2.4
5	3.0
6	3.6
7	4.2
8	4.8
9	5.4

N.	0	1	2	3	4	5	6	7	8	9	Prop. Pts.
650	81 291	298	305	311	318	325	331	338	345	351	
651	358	365	371	378	385	391	398	405	411	418	
652	425	431	438	445	451	458	465	471	478	485	
653	491	498	505	511	518	525	531	538	544	551	
654	558	564	571	578	584	591	598	604	611	617	
655	624	631	637	644	651	657	664	671	677	684	
656	690	697	704	710	717	723	730	737	743	750	
657	757	763	770	776	783	790	796	803	809	816	
658	823	829	836	842	849	856	862	869	875	882	
659	889	895	902	908	915	921	928	935	941	948	
660	954	961	968	974	981	987	994	*000	*007	*014	
661	82 020	027	033	040	046	053	060	066	073	079	
662	086	092	099	105	112	119	125	132	138	145	
663	151	158	164	171	178	184	191	197	204	210	
664	217	223	230	236	243	249	256	263	269	276	
665	282	289	295	302	308	315	321	328	334	341	
666	347	354	360	367	373	380	387	393	400	406	
667	413	419	426	432	439	445	452	458	465	471	
668	478	484	491	497	504	510	517	523	530	536	
669	543	549	556	562	569	575	582	588	595	601	
670	607	614	620	627	633	640	646	653	659	666	
671	672	679	685	692	698	705	711	718	724	730	
672	737	743	750	756	763	769	776	782	789	795	
673	802	808	814	821	827	834	840	847	853	860	
674	866	872	879	885	892	898	905	911	918	924	
675	930	937	943	950	956	963	969	975	982	988	
676	995	*001	*008	*014	*020	*027	*033	*040	*046	*052	
677	83 059	065	072	078	085	091	097	104	110	117	
678	123	129	136	142	149	155	161	168	174	181	
679	187	193	200	206	213	219	225	232	238	245	
680	251	257	264	270	276	283	289	296	302	308	
681	315	321	327	334	340	347	353	359	366	372	
682	378	385	391	398	404	410	417	423	429	436	
683	442	448	455	461	467	474	480	487	493	499	
684	506	512	518	525	531	537	544	550	556	563	
685	569	575	582	588	594	601	607	613	620	626	
686	632	639	645	651	658	664	670	677	683	689	
687	696	702	708	715	721	727	734	740	746	753	
688	759	765	771	778	784	790	797	803	809	816	
689	822	828	835	841	847	853	860	866	872	879	
690	885	891	897	904	910	916	923	929	935	942	
691	948	954	960	967	973	979	985	992	998	*004	
692	84 011	017	023	029	036	042	048	055	061	067	
693	073	080	086	092	098	105	111	117	123	130	
694	136	142	148	155	161	167	173	180	186	192	
695	198	205	211	217	223	230	236	242	248	255	
696	261	267	273	280	286	292	298	305	311	317	
697	323	330	336	342	348	354	361	367	373	379	
698	386	392	398	404	410	417	423	429	435	442	
699	448	454	460	466	473	479	485	491	497	504	
700	510	516	522	528	535	541	547	553	559	566	
N.	0	1	2	3	4	5	6	7	8	9	Prop. Pts.

Prop. Pts.

	7	6
1	0.7	0.6
2	1.4	1.2
3	2.1	1.8
4	2.8	2.4
5	3.5	3.0
6	4.2	3.6
7	4.9	4.2
8	5.6	4.8
9	6.3	5.4

N.	0	1	2	3	4	5	6	7	8	9
700	84 510	516	522	528	535	541	547	553	559	566
701	572	578	584	590	597	603	609	615	621	628
702	634	640	646	652	658	665	671	677	683	689
703	696	702	708	714	720	726	733	739	745	751
704	757	763	770	776	782	788	794	800	807	813
705	819	825	831	837	844	850	856	862	868	874
706	880	887	893	899	905	911	917	924	930	936
707	942	948	954	960	967	973	979	985	991	997
708	85 003	009	016	022	028	034	040	046	052	058
709	065	071	077	083	089	095	101	107	114	120
710	126	132	138	144	150	156	163	169	175	181
711	187	193	199	205	211	217	224	230	236	242
712	248	254	260	266	272	278	285	291	297	303
713	309	315	321	327	333	339	345	352	358	364
714	370	376	382	388	394	400	406	412	418	425
715	431	437	443	449	455	461	467	473	479	485
716	491	497	503	509	516	522	528	534	540	546
717	552	558	564	570	576	582	588	594	600	606
718	612	618	625	631	637	643	649	655	661	667
719	673	679	685	691	697	703	709	715	721	727
720	733	739	745	751	757	763	769	775	781	788
721	794	800	806	812	818	824	830	836	842	848
722	854	860	866	872	878	884	890	896	902	908
723	914	920	926	932	938	944	950	956	962	968
724	974	980	986	992	998	*004	*010	*016	*022	*028
725	86 034	040	046	052	058	064	070	076	082	088
726	094	100	106	112	118	124	130	136	141	147
727	153	159	165	171	177	183	189	195	201	207
728	213	219	225	231	237	243	249	255	261	267
729	273	279	285	291	297	303	308	314	320	326
730	332	338	344	350	356	362	368	374	380	386
731	392	398	404	410	415	421	427	433	439	445
732	451	457	463	469	475	481	487	493	499	504
733	510	516	522	528	534	540	546	552	558	564
734	570	576	581	587	593	599	605	611	617	623
735	629	635	641	646	652	658	664	670	676	682
736	688	694	700	705	711	717	723	729	735	741
737	747	753	759	764	770	776	782	788	794	800
738	806	812	817	823	829	835	841	847	853	859
739	864	870	876	882	888	894	900	906	911	917
740	923	929	935	941	947	953	958	964	970	976
741	982	988	994	999	*005	*011	*017	*023	*029	*035
742	87 040	046	052	058	064	070	075	081	087	093
743	099	105	111	116	122	128	134	140	146	151
744	157	163	169	175	181	186	192	198	204	210
745	216	221	227	233	239	245	251	256	262	268
746	274	280	286	291	297	303	309	315	320	326
747	332	338	344	349	355	361	367	373	379	384
748	390	396	402	408	413	419	425	431	437	442
749	448	454	460	466	471	477	483	489	495	500
750	506	512	518	523	529	535	541	547	552	558
N.	0	1	2	3	4	5	6	7	8	9

Prop. Pts.

log 7
= .84509 80400

	7	6
1	0.7	0.6
2	1.4	1.2
3	2.1	1.8
4	2.8	2.4
5	3.5	3.0
6	4.2	3.6
7	4.9	4.2
8	5.6	4.8
9	6.3	5.4

	5
1	0.5
2	1.0
3	1.5
4	2.0
5	2.5
6	3.0
7	3.5
8	4.0
9	4.5

N.	0	1	2	3	4	5	6	7	8	9	Prop. Pts.		
750	87 506	512	518	523	529	535	541	547	552	558			
751	564	570	576	581	587	593	599	604	610	616			
752	622	628	633	639	645	651	656	662	668	674			
753	679	685	691	697	703	708	714	720	726	731			
754	737	743	749	754	760	766	772	777	783	789			
755	795	800	806	812	818	823	829	835	841	846			
756	852	858	864	869	875	881	887	892	898	904			
757	910	915	921	927	933	938	944	950	955	961			
758	967	973	978	984	990	996	*001	*007	*013	*018			
759	88 024	030	036	041	047	053	058	064	070	076			
760	081	087	093	098	104	110	116	121	127	133			
761	138	144	150	156	161	167	173	178	184	190			
762	195	201	207	213	218	224	230	235	241	247			
763	252	258	264	270	275	281	287	292	298	304			
764	309	315	321	326	332	338	343	349	355	360			
765	366	372	377	383	389	395	400	406	412	417			
766	423	429	434	440	446	451	457	463	468	474			
767	480	485	491	497	502	508	513	519	525	530			
768	536	542	547	553	559	564	570	576	581	587			
769	593	598	604	610	615	621	627	632	638	643			
770	649	655	660	666	672	677	683	689	694	700		**.6**	**5**
771	705	711	717	722	728	734	739	745	750	756			
772	762	767	773	779	784	790	795	801	807	812	1	0.6	0.5
773	818	824	829	835	840	846	852	857	863	868	2	1.2	1.0
774	874	880	885	891	897	902	908	913	919	925	3	1.8	1.5
775	930	936	941	947	953	958	964	969	975	981	4	2.4	2.0
776	986	992	997	*003	*009	*014	*020	*025	*031	*037	5	3.0	2.5
777	89 042	048	053	059	064	070	076	081	087	092	6	3.6	3.0
778	098	104	109	115	120	126	131	137	143	148	7	4.2	3.5
779	154	159	165	170	176	182	187	193	198	204	8	4.8	4.0
780	209	215	221	226	232	237	243	248	254	260	9	5.4	4.5
781	265	271	276	282	287	293	298	304	310	315			
782	321	326	332	337	343	348	354	360	365	371			
783	376	382	387	393	398	404	409	415	421	426			
784	432	437	443	448	454	459	465	470	476	481			
785	487	492	498	504	509	515	520	526	531	537			
786	542	548	553	559	564	570	575	581	586	592			
787	597	603	609	614	620	625	631	636	642	647			
788	653	658	664	669	675	680	686	691	697	702			
789	708	713	719	724	730	735	741	746	752	757			
790	763	768	774	779	785	790	796	801	807	812			
791	818	823	829	834	840	845	851	856	862	867			
792	873	878	883	889	894	900	905	911	916	922			
793	927	933	938	944	949	955	960	966	971	977			
794	982	988	993	998	*004	*009	*015	*020	*026	*031			
795	90 037	042	048	053	059	064	069	075	080	086			
796	091	097	102	108	113	119	124	129	135	140			
797	146	151	157	162	168	173	179	184	189	195			
798	200	206	211	217	222	227	233	238	244	249			
799	255	260	266	271	276	282	287	293	298	304			
800	309	314	320	325	331	336	342	347	352	358			
N.	0	1	2	3	4	5	6	7	8	9	Prop. Pts.		

N.	0	1	2	3	4	5	6	7	8	9	Prop. Pts.
800	90 309	314	320	325	331	336	342	347	352	358	
801	363	369	374	380	385	390	396	401	407	412	
802	417	423	428	434	439	445	450	455	461	466	
803	472	477	482	488	493	499	504	509	515	520	
804	526	531	536	542	547	553	558	563	569	574	
805	580	585	590	596	601	607	612	617	623	628	
806	634	639	644	650	655	660	666	671	677	682	
807	687	693	698	703	709	714	720	725	730	736	
808	741	747	752	757	763	768	773	779	784	789	
809	795	800	806	811	816	822	827	832	838	843	
810	849	854	859	865	870	875	881	886	891	897	
811	902	907	913	918	924	929	934	940	945	950	
812	956	961	966	972	977	982	988	993	998	*004	
813	91 009	014	020	025	030	036	041	046	052	057	
814	062	068	073	078	084	089	094	100	105	110	
815	116	121	126	132	137	142	148	153	158	164	
816	169	174	180	185	190	196	201	206	212	217	
817	222	228	233	238	243	249	254	259	265	270	
818	275	281	286	291	297	302	307	312	318	323	
819	328	334	339	344	350	355	360	365	371	376	
820	381	387	392	397	403	408	413	418	424	429	
821	434	440	445	450	455	461	466	471	477	482	
822	487	492	498	503	508	514	519	524	529	535	
823	540	545	551	556	561	566	572	577	582	587	
824	593	598	603	609	614	619	624	630	635	640	
825	645	651	656	661	666	672	677	682	687	693	
826	698	703	709	714	719	724	730	735	740	745	
827	751	756	761	766	772	777	782	787	793	798	
828	803	808	814	819	824	829	834	840	845	850	
829	855	861	866	871	876	882	887	892	897	903	
830	908	913	918	924	929	934	939	944	950	955	
831	960	965	971	976	981	986	991	997	*002	*007	
832	92 012	018	023	028	033	038	044	049	054	059	
833	065	070	075	080	085	091	096	101	106	111	
834	117	122	127	132	137	143	148	153	158	163	
835	169	174	179	184	189	195	200	205	210	215	
836	221	226	231	236	241	247	252	257	262	267	
837	273	278	283	288	293	298	304	309	314	319	
838	324	330	335	340	345	350	355	361	366	371	
839	376	381	387	392	397	402	407	412	418	423	
840	428	433	438	443	449	454	459	464	469	474	
841	480	485	490	495	500	505	511	516	521	526	
842	531	536	542	547	552	557	562	567	572	578	
843	583	588	593	598	603	609	614	619	624	629	
844	634	639	645	650	655	660	665	670	675	681	
845	686	691	696	701	706	711	716	722	727	732	
846	737	742	747	752	758	763	768	773	778	783	
847	788	793	799	804	809	814	819	824	829	834	
848	840	845	850	855	860	865	870	875	881	886	
849	891	896	901	906	911	916	921	927	932	937	
850	942	947	952	957	962	967	973	978	983	988	
N.	0	1	2	3	4	5	6	7	8	9	Prop. Pts.

Prop. Pts.

	6	5
1	0.6	0.5
2	1.2	1.0
3	1.8	1.5
4	2.4	2.0
5	3.0	2.5
6	3.6	3.0
7	4.2	3.5
8	4.8	4.0
9	5.4	4.5

N.	0	1	2	3	4	5	6	7	8	9
850	92 942	947	952	957	962	967	973	978	983	988
851	993	998	*003	*008	*013	*018	*024	*029	*034	*039
852	93 044	049	054	059	064	069	075	080	085	090
853	095	100	105	110	115	120	125	131	136	141
854	146	151	156	161	166	171	176	181	186	192
855	197	202	207	212	217	222	227	232	237	242
856	247	252	258	263	268	273	278	283	288	293
857	298	303	308	313	318	323	328	334	339	344
858	349	354	359	364	369	374	379	384	389	394
859	399	404	409	414	420	425	430	435	440	445
860	450	455	460	465	470	475	480	485	490	495
861	500	505	510	515	520	526	531	536	541	546
862	551	556	561	566	571	576	581	586	591	596
863	601	606	611	616	621	626	631	636	641	646
864	651	656	661	666	671	676	682	687	692	697
865	702	707	712	717	722	727	732	737	742	747
866	752	757	762	767	772	777	782	787	792	797
867	802	807	812	817	822	827	832	837	842	847
868	852	857	862	867	872	877	882	887	892	897
869	902	907	912	917	922	927	932	937	942	947
870	952	957	962	967	972	977	982	987	992	997
871	94 002	007	012	017	022	027	032	037	042	047
872	052	057	062	067	072	077	082	086	091	096
873	101	106	111	116	121	126	131	136	141	146
874	151	156	161	166	171	176	181	186	191	196
875	201	206	211	216	221	226	231	236	240	245
876	250	255	260	265	270	275	280	285	290	295
877	300	305	310	315	320	325	330	335	340	345
878	349	354	359	364	369	374	379	384	389	394
879	399	404	409	414	419	424	429	433	438	443
880	448	453	458	463	468	473	478	483	488	493
881	498	503	507	512	517	522	527	532	537	542
882	547	552	557	562	567	571	576	581	586	591
883	596	601	606	611	616	621	626	630	635	640
884	645	650	655	660	665	670	675	680	685	689
885	694	699	704	709	714	719	724	729	734	738
886	743	748	753	758	763	768	773	778	783	787
887	792	797	802	807	812	817	822	827	832	836
888	841	846	851	856	861	866	871	876	880	885
889	890	895	900	905	910	915	919	924	929	934
890	939	944	949	954	959	963	968	973	978	983
891	988	993	998	*002	*007	*012	*017	*022	*027	*032
892	95 036	041	046	051	056	061	066	071	075	080
893	085	090	095	100	105	109	114	119	124	129
894	134	139	143	148	153	158	163	168	173	177
895	182	187	192	197	202	207	211	216	221	226
896	231	236	240	245	250	255	260	265	270	274
897	279	284	289	294	299	303	308	313	318	323
898	328	332	337	342	347	352	357	361	366	371
899	376	381	386	390	395	400	405	410	415	419
900	424	429	434	439	444	448	453	458	463	468
N.	0	1	2	3	4	5	6	7	8	9

Prop. Pts.

	6	5
1	0.6	0.5
2	1.2	1.0
3	1.8	1.5
4	2.4	2.0
5	3.0	2.5
6	3.6	3.0
7	4.2	3.5
8	4.8	4.0
9	5.4	4.5

	4
1	0.4
2	0.8
3	1.2
4	1.6
5	2.0
6	2.4
7	2.8
8	3.2
9	3.6

N.	0	1	2	3	4	5	6	7	8	9	Prop. Pts.
900	95 424	429	434	439	444	448	453	458	463	468	
901	472	477	482	487	492	497	501	506	511	516	
902	521	525	530	535	540	545	550	554	559	564	
903	569	574	578	583	588	593	598	602	607	612	
904	617	622	626	631	636	641	646	650	655	660	
905	665	670	674	679	684	689	694	698	703	708	
906	713	718	722	727	732	737	742	746	751	756	
907	761	766	770	775	780	785	789	794	799	804	
908	809	813	818	823	828	832	837	842	847	852	
909	856	861	866	871	875	880	885	890	895	899	
910	904	909	914	918	923	928	933	938	942	947	
911	952	957	961	966	971	976	980	985	990	*995	
912	999	*004	*009	*014	*019	*023	*028	*033	*038	*042	
913	96 047	052	057	061	066	071	076	080	085	090	
914	095	099	104	109	114	118	123	128	133	137	
915	142	147	152	156	161	166	171	175	180	185	
916	190	194	199	204	209	213	218	223	227	232	
917	237	242	246	251	256	261	265	270	275	280	
918	284	289	294	298	303	308	313	317	322	327	
919	332	336	341	346	350	355	360	365	369	374	
920	379	384	388	393	398	402	407	412	417	421	
921	426	431	435	440	445	450	454	459	464	468	
922	473	478	483	487	492	497	501	506	511	515	
923	520	525	530	534	539	544	548	553	558	562	
924	567	572	577	581	586	591	595	600	605	609	
925	614	619	624	628	633	638	642	647	652	656	
926	661	666	670	675	680	685	689	694	699	703	
927	708	713	717	722	727	731	736	741	745	750	
928	755	759	764	769	774	778	783	788	792	797	
929	802	806	811	816	820	825	830	834	839	844	
930	848	853	858	862	867	872	876	881	886	890	
931	895	900	904	909	914	918	923	928	932	937	
932	942	946	951	956	960	965	970	974	979	984	
933	988	993	997	*002	*007	*011	*016	*021	*025	*030	
934	97 035	039	044	049	053	058	063	067	072	077	
935	081	086	090	095	100	104	109	114	118	123	
936	128	132	137	142	146	151	155	160	165	169	
937	174	179	183	188	192	197	202	206	211	216	
938	220	225	230	234	239	243	248	253	257	262	
939	267	271	276	280	285	290	294	299	304	308	
940	313	317	322	327	331	336	340	345	350	354	
941	359	364	368	373	377	382	387	391	396	400	
942	405	410	414	419	424	428	433	437	442	447	
943	451	456	460	465	470	474	479	483	488	493	
944	497	502	506	511	516	520	525	529	534	539	
945	543	548	552	557	562	566	571	575	580	585	
946	589	594	598	603	607	612	617	621	626	630	
947	635	640	644	649	653	658	663	667	672	676	
948	681	685	690	695	699	704	708	713	717	722	
949	727	731	736	740	745	749	754	759	763	768	
950	772	777	782	786	791	795	800	804	809	813	
N.	0	1	2	3	4	5	6	7	8	9	Prop. Pts.

Prop. Pts.

	5	4
1	0.5	0.4
2	1.0	0.8
3	1.5	1.2
4	2.0	1.6
5	2.5	2.0
6	3.0	2.4
7	3.5	2.8
8	4.0	3.2
9	4.5	3.6

N.	0	1	2	3	4	5	6	7	8	9	Prop. Pts.
950	97 772	777	782	786	791	795	800	804	809	813	
951	818	823	827	832	836	841	845	850	855	859	
952	864	868	873	877	882	886	891	896	900	905	
953	909	914	918	923	928	932	937	941	946	950	
954	955	959	964	968	973	978	982	987	991	996	
955	98 000	005	009	014	019	023	028	032	037	041	
956	046	050	055	059	064	068	073	078	082	087	
957	091	096	100	105	109	114	118	123	127	132	
958	137	141	146	150	155	159	164	168	173	177	
959	182	186	191	195	200	204	209	214	218	223	
960	227	232	236	241	245	250	254	259	263	268	
961	272	277	281	286	290	295	299	304	308	313	
962	318	322	327	331	336	340	345	349	354	358	
963	363	367	372	376	381	385	390	394	399	403	
964	408	412	417	421	426	430	435	439	444	448	
965	453	457	462	466	471	475	480	484	489	493	
966	498	502	507	511	516	520	525	529	534	538	
967	543	547	552	556	561	565	570	574	579	583	
968	588	592	597	601	605	610	614	619	623	628	
969	632	637	641	646	650	655	659	664	668	673	
970	677	682	686	691	695	700	704	709	713	717	
971	722	726	731	735	740	744	749	753	758	762	
972	767	771	776	780	784	789	793	798	802	807	
973	811	816	820	825	829	834	838	843	847	851	
974	856	860	865	869	874	878	883	887	892	896	
975	900	905	909	914	918	923	927	932	936	941	
976	945	949	954	958	963	967	972	976	981	985	
977	989	994	998	*003	*007	*012	*016	*021	*025	*029	
978	99 034	038	043	047	052	056	061	065	069	074	
979	078	083	087	092	096	100	105	109	114	118	
980	123	127	131	136	140	145	149	154	158	162	
981	167	171	176	180	185	189	193	198	202	207	
982	211	216	220	224	229	233	238	242	247	251	
983	255	260	264	269	273	277	282	286	291	295	
984	300	304	308	313	317	322	326	330	335	339	
985	344	348	352	357	361	366	370	374	379	383	
986	388	392	396	401	405	410	414	419	423	427	
987	432	436	441	445	449	454	458	463	467	471	
988	476	480	484	489	493	498	502	506	511	515	
989	520	524	528	533	537	542	546	550	555	559	
990	564	568	572	577	581	585	590	594	599	603	
991	607	612	616	621	625	629	634	638	642	647	
992	651	656	660	664	669	673	677	682	686	691	
993	695	699	704	708	712	717	721	726	730	734	
994	739	743	747	752	756	760	765	769	774	778	
995	782	787	791	795	800	804	808	813	817	822	
996	826	830	835	839	843	848	852	856	861	865	
997	870	874	878	883	887	891	896	900	904	909	
998	913	917	922	926	930	935	939	944	948	952	
999	957	961	965	970	974	978	983	987	991	996	
1000	00 000	004	009	013	017	022	026	030	035	039	
N.	0	1	2	3	4	5	6	7	8	9	Prop. Pts.

Prop. Pts.

	5	4
1	0.5	0.4
2	1.0	0.8
3	1.5	1.2
4	2.0	1.6
5	2.5	2.0
6	3.0	2.4
7	3.5	2.8
8	4.0	3.2
9	4.5	3.6

APPENDIX A

A brief summary of the history, functions, and operation of the system used by the State of Michigan for the appraisal of mines for taxation purposes.

THE MICHIGAN MINE APPRAISAL SYSTEM

By

FRANKLIN G. PARDEE

Mining Engineer and Appraiser of Mines
Michigan Geological Survey.

The appraisal of mines in Michigan for the purpose of determining values upon which real estate taxes are to be levied has been going on for over thirty-five years. The iron mines have been assessed each year since 1911 by the State Tax Commission. The copper mines were assessed in 1911, 1919, and each year since 1924. The coal mines and quarries were assessed in 1911 and have been reassessed only upon petition of the owner or local assessor since that date.

The methods used and the results obtained by the appraisal of mines by the Michigan State Tax Commission have been tested in the courts, the valuations have been compared with commercial transactions, and constant scrutiny has been maintained over the relationship of the assessments of the mines to the assessments of other properties. Changes have taken place at all the mines; new ones opened up, old mines worked out, and non-profitable mines closed. The industrial and economic conditions under which the mines have operated have changed time and again during the past quarter of a century, but throughout all this period the fundamental principles used in the valuation of mines in Michigan for tax purposes have not been altered. This would indicate that these principles are sound, and for that reason they are of interest to anyone studying the appraisal of mines. The following description of procedure is given, not as an argument either for or against the application of this method of mine valuation for tax purposes, but as a practical illustration of the valuation of a group of mines for a particular purpose.

A brief review of the background and history of mine taxation in Michigan is essential to an understanding of the situation in this State. Under Article Ten of the Michigan constitution is the provision that ''all assessments hereafter authorized shall be on property at its cash value.'' The legislature interpreted this provision by defining ''cash value'' in the general tax law as the ''usual selling price at the place where the property to which the term is applied shall be at the time of the assessment, being the price which could be obtained at private sale and not at forced or auction sale.'' Prior to 1911 the local assessing offices were obliged to place a value on each mine in their assessing district each year. The size of the mines, their influence on the local communities, the technical questions involved, and the fact that few sales of mines were made which could be used as a guide, presented annual problems that were beyond the experience of most of the local tax officials. Neither was the situation satisfactory from the standpoint of the mining companies, since there were inequalities in assessments between mining companies and between mining districts. From the viewpoint of the State, two questions were continually raised: (1) as to the tax burden in the mining districts compared with that in the agricultural and manufacturing areas, and (2) as to the ratio of the contributions made by the mines to those made by other property in the same assessing district.

The Legislature studied the problem and, in order to get facts, authorized the State Tax Commission to appraise all mines and quarries. Mr. J. R. Finlay was the mining engineer selected to make the appraisal. As the time allowed for this large undertaking was short, Mr. Finlay secured the assistance of Dr. C. K. Leith to aid with the iron mines, of Mr. Wm. Hague for the copper districts, and of Dr. H. M. Chance for the coal mines, salt wells, and quarries.

The first appraisal brought to light many inequalities in the mine assessments as these had been determined by the local tax officers, and indicated that some uniform system of mine valuation would be more equitable to all concerned. Mr. Finlay's work brought to the State Tax Commission a realization of the technical nature of mine valuation and showed them also that in order to keep abreast of the changing conditions at the mines, it would be necessary to make a yearly assessment. The State Geologist was accordingly delegated to report on the value of the mines and mineral property in the State each year.

This arrangement has been in effect, for iron mines, since 1912. The copper mines were not appraised regularly by the State Tax Commission from 1911 until 1924. During this period a formula using stock market quotations seemed a fair basis for valuing the copper properties. Quarries, because of the small yearly change in their physical conditions, have been valued only when necessary. The size of the coal mines has favored assessment by local officials, with occasional checks by the Tax Commission on the work of these assessors. The iron mines, being the only ones which have been revalued each year since 1912, offer the best example of the Michigan method of mine appraisal. Consequently this discussion will be limited to them.

The method used for appraising the Michigan mines is often referred to as the Hoover or Finlay method. Hoover and Finlay were the first American mining engineers to advocate the principles underlying the method used in Michigan. The adaptation of the theory proposed by these men to the particular purpose of mine taxation has become known as the "Michigan System of Mine Appraisal."

In valuing mines for commercial purposes, the engineer must adjust his factors to meet the physical and economic conditions in evidence at the time the examination is made. This flexibility and freedom from definite laws and rules is an essential feature of the Michigan System, and has been largely responsible for the continuance of this work for thirty-five years.

The ultimate value of a mine depends on the profit that can be obtained by the extraction and sale of the ore over and above the return of the capital invested in the property. This value can be obtained only after the mine has been completely worked out and abandoned. The ultimate value of a mine, however, is of no use except for historical purposes. In order to approximate this final figure at any time during the life of the mine, future profits must be estimated. It is evident that these profits can be realized only by an orderly extraction of the orebody over a period of time and that they must be translated into their actual worth at the time the calculation is made by discounting them to present value at a predetermined rate of interest. A mine is a wasting asset: each dividend represents not only the interest on the money put into the mine, but also a partial return of this invested capital. By the time the mine is exhausted, the investor should have had returned to him the money he contributed to the venture together with the interest on that money while it was in use. It is necessary, therefore, to set aside such a portion of each dividend that, at a given rate of interest, the annuity thus created will, when the mine is worked out, equal the capital invested. This practical viewpoint is used by every prudent investor in a mining enterprise and would be considered in any exchange of property that met the requirements of a normal sale under the Michigan tax law.

The value of a mining property depends to some extent on its equipment and supplies. As the Michigan tax law makes no distinction between real and personal property in the matter of tax rates, it is possible in this State to value a mine as a unit. This means that it is not necessary to value separately the real estate from the movable machinery, mine cars, supplies, and so forth, which are part of the mine plant and contribute to the value of the complete enterprise.

The profit from any mine includes any rent, royalty, or bonus paid for the use of the land. These items are considered as a cost to the operator of the mine; but since, for tax purposes, the State does not recognize any division in the ownership of land, these charges are included under the heading of profit and become part of the income that is capitalized to determine the valuation of the mine.

The generally accepted figure for interest on capital in a nonspeculative industry is six percent. This rate, used by the Michigan Tax Commission in the computation of taxes for other industries in the State, was adopted for the mines. The first report, by Mr. Finlay, recommended a five percent interest rate on capital and a four percent rate for the return of the investment. The Tax Commission adopted the six percent rate for both the interest on the investment and the return of the capital.

These interest rates as set by the Commission have always caused a great deal of argument. It was thought by many that, because mining is a speculative enterprise, the return for the risk involved should be proportionately greater than that allowed for a nonspeculative venture. Back of the requests for lower interest rates on the sinking fund was the theory that this fund should be set up on a conservative basis and that securities paying six percent would not meet this requirement.

The Tax Commission supported the use of the six percent rate on both capital and sinking fund by following the lead suggested in Mr. Finlay's report, which was the elimination, as far as possible, of the speculative features of the valuations before the interest rate entered the computations. In other words, the plan was to consider separately all the speculative features of the particular mine in direct proportion to their bearing on the valuation. Under this method, the Tax Commission felt, the use of the six percent interest rate would be fair to the mine owner. As the return of capital invested in mining is usually reinvested in the same type of business and is not put into ultraconservative bonds, the Commission felt that the use of six percent was justified for the interest rate on the sinking fund.

One of the first things to determine in computing the valuation of a property is the amount of ore reserves. The grade and sales price of the ore, together with the cost of mining, have an important bearing on the limits of mining. Many other factors have some influence on the size of the orebody that can be mined at a profit. In mines that are active and where past experience can be used as a guide, these various influences can be estimated by a study of the past results. For new mines and drilled reserves, the history of adjoining or similar properties offers the best source of information.

It is logical to expect that past records of production, cost of mining, and profits will give some clue to future production, cost of mining, and profits. In the Michigan appraisal, all this background is gone over carefully, especially for the five years preceding the appraisal. This is a long enough period so that the average result usually gives a representative picture of the condition of the mine. A longer average would often cover phases of the history that are not representative of what may be expected in the future.

The first step in the Michigan appraisal is to estimate the reserves at each mine. This is done by studying the maps, reports, and tonnage reserves as submitted by the company engineers. The geology of each property is examined to assist in the understanding of the relationship of the orebody to the structural and geological features of the particular area. As these reports and estimates are received every year and filed, there is soon built up a history of each mine that is invaluable in working out the future possibilities of the deposit being examined.

In an operating mine the orebody is divided naturally into two parts—the ore wholly or partly developed, and the ore probably present but not definitely proven by the drill holes and openings already completed. Ore which is blocked out for mining purposes and that which is nearly ready for mining can be estimated with accuracy. This is particularly true after some record has been built up showing how successfully the mining system operates, what the percentages for loss, dilution, and barren areas will average, and what is the correct cubic-foot-per-ton factor. The past results also show the relation of the orebodies to the geological features and give important data for determining the expected ore boundaries.

The estimate of probable ore tonnage, as contrasted with the tonnage in sight or developed, involves the same factors that govern the estimates of developed ore except that the question of geological possibilities becomes more important and the future operating conditions must be visualized as completely as possible. The estimate of the amount of probable ore expresses the judgment of the engineer regarding the life and expectations of the mine beyond the time needed to extract the ore blocked out. It should include something of the speculative possibilities that everyone looks for in any mining operation. It is evident that a new mine located in a district where ore has been found to depths around 5000 feet has more chance for a long life than a similar mine started in a district where mineralization usually plays out at 1000 feet. In a comparison of two such mines, the one situated in the district of deep ore bodies would be the more valuable because of the better chances for a larger tonnage. This speculative feature is of utmost importance in the valuation of a mine. Since the future possibilities are essentially a matter of tonnage, they are logically represented by adding to the developed and probable tonnages a certain amount of "possible" ore beyond that which can be accurately measured or reasonably expected. In considering orebody extensions, the appraiser must take account of possible changes in analysis of the ore. In the same way he always keeps in mind the practical aspects of mining the ore, as mineral that cannot be mined at a profit under normal conditions should not be considered in the valuation of the mine.

Deposits that have not been opened up except by drilling or whose existence is anticipated only from work on adjoining properties are estimated in a manner similar to that used for probable ore. For determining the ore limits of these undeveloped properties, the factors that control in comparable properties in the same district are used as a guide.

No rules may be laid down for making ore estimates. The correct procedure in one case would not be the right thing in another. Orebodies which, in one mine, can be safely counted on to continue for 500 feet cannot, in another, be projected more than 50 feet with any degree of assurance. All the evidence available is considered for each mine, and in this way every mine is treated as an individual problem.

After the ore reserve estimates have been made, the next step is to obtain the average profit that may be expected from mining and selling the ore. The profit is considered on a unit basis—per ton—and represents the difference between the expected cost and the expected selling price per ton. The amount of money spent to mine and prepare a unit of the ore in the past is accurately known, and the peculiar conditions that surround the individual mine have all had their effect on this cost figure. In the same manner, the analyses, structure, and other physical characteristics of the ore already produced have had their influence on the demand and selling price of this ore. It is safe to assume that many of these factors governing cost and selling price in the past will continue to have a bearing on these items, and study of them is important.

There is another way of looking at this matter of future profit per ton. The probable costs for the mine can be estimated and the future sales price of the product predicted. However, it is extremely difficult to estimate with any degree of accuracy the cost of mining at some particular mine for an extended period. It is still more difficult to predict the economic changes that will influence the price of the product of the mine over any appreciable number of years. The longer the time involved in both instances, the more difficult the problem.

It has been found, however, from a study of mining records, that for most mines the cost of mining and the selling price of the ore move up and down together, and that over a number of years this spread or profit will tend to remain fairly constant. In any case, the "profit spread" fluctuates over a narrower range than either cost of mining or selling price; and projecting this spread into the future will decrease appreciably the chance of error. To carry the history back too far in the life of the property would introduce considerations that have no bearing on the future of the mine; for that reason a limited period is selected for this historical review. In Michigan a five-year period was decided upon as a fair measure of past performance. The experience in this State shows that five years is not too long and only infrequently too short. In making valuations for tax purposes (and for other purposes as well) the use of the five-year period or any set number of years cannot be arbitrary: conditions which can be foreseen though they have not yet had any effect on the mine accounts to date must be used to temper the average figures obtained from the past record.

A copy, reduced in size, of the cost sheets submitted each year by the companies operating iron mines in Michigan is shown in Plate 1 (in pocket in rear cover). One of these forms is filled out for each mine or for each group of mines operated as a unit. Though largely self-explanatory, these forms contain a few items peculiar to the iron-mining industry and to the appraisal of mines for tax purposes. Such items are discussed below.

The questions asked on the first page of the cost sheet are general and are common to most forms of this nature. The labor statistics are used in conjunction with the labor costs. At the bottom of the first page a space is provided in which the tonnage of ore in stock is to be reported. The question of hoisting capacity is of importance only in considering the possible production of the mine. On the back page is found a table in which are to be listed the tonnage of ore in reserve in the mine, both developed and prospective, and the shipments for the previous five years. Space is provided for analyses of the various grades of ore, since the chemical composition practically determines the sales price. The ''dried'' analysis of the ore is made after the water has been removed from the sample by drying at 212°F until the weight is constant.

The answers to the questions on the inside of the cost sheet provide the data for determining the average cost per ton over the five-year period covered by the report. The sales for the same years are recorded, and the average price received per ton is computed. For tax purposes, only certain costs are allowed in determining the profits; these costs are separated from those that are not considered in the appraisal of the Michigan mines.

The charges for labor and supplies need no comment, being common to all mining operations. The amounts listed under deferred mining costs are those which have been expended— for example, the cost of shafts or development not charged directly to operations, etc.—but which must be charged off as the ore is produced. The tax bracket covers those taxes that apply directly against the mine. The general overhead expenses are the usual accounts found in nearly every set of mine account books.

Depreciation, under general overhead expenses, is hardly an item of cost in the computation of future expected profits. The purchaser of a mine is not greatly interested in the amounts being charged off on the buildings, machinery, and equipment. But he is very much concerned about the amount of money that will have to be spent in the future on new construction and machinery. In the early years of the Michigan mine appraisal, the charge for construction and installation of machinery was included as a cost. This item, however, was found to fluctuate over wide limits from year to year and from one mine to another. For all the mines the average cost of construction and installation very closely approximated the average charge for depreciation. As it is better for the mining companies and the communities in which the mines are located to keep valuations and taxes on a fairly uniform basis, the item of depreciation was substituted for the cost of construction and installation of machinery and equipment, and is used except in those few instances where this charge does not give a true picture of conditions.

One important factor in the valuation of an iron mine is its location in respect to the blast furnace, as this governs the cost of transporting the ore to the furnace. For many years the published price for iron ore has been known as the Lake Erie Price; it is determined largely by the grade and analysis of the ore as delivered f.o.b. the docks at Lake Erie ports. From these docks the ore is shipped to the various blast furnaces. In order to permit the use of this published price as a basis of ore value, the cost of transportation by rail from mine to dock and by boat from upper lake (Lakes Superior and Michigan) to Lake Erie ports is included in the total allowable ore cost. Mines which have lower freight charges show correspondingly greater profits than mines which are located farther away from the blast furnaces, and consequently are more valuable.

For tax purposes no separation of interest is allowed in valuing the Michigan mines, even though in most cases the land is leased to the operating company and a rental charge or royalty is paid for the privilege of mining. This royalty or rent is actually a profit on the ore mined, and as such is not considered an allowable cost in computing the valuation of the mine. The item of cost adjustment, an item seldom used, is a book charge including such various items as inventory changes, etc. For State purposes, federal income and excess profits taxes are not a cost of operation. The same is true of interest on bonds and other indebtedness. The charge for depletion is accounted for in the final computation of the value of the mine and should not be duplicated by using it as a cost here.

The lower half of the inside of the cost sheet is used to list the shipments and receipts from the sale of the ore. Both actual receipts and Lake Erie prices are asked for, as these usually differ. Most iron ores are sold under long-term contracts at a discount from published prices. Ores that do not measure up to the average because of their structure, moisture, or some other quality are also sold below the market, and, frequently, other considerations may control the actual receipts.

Many of the steel manufacturing companies are self-contained, and own the mines as well as the plants devoted to the production of steel. In such cases the ore sales represent nothing more than book charges between the mine organizations and the blast furnace department. This type of transaction has become more common in recent years. For ores transferred in this manner, no real sales price is available for use in determining the actual market value of the ore. But since practically all the open market ore is sold below published Lake Erie prices and since the assessment of mines for tax purposes is to a great extent a matter of equalization, the use of this published price seems fair to all concerned. On it the assessment of Michigan mines is based.

The reports of tons mined and shipped not only give an indication of the amount of ore each mine can produce but also furnish some measure of the capacity of the market to absorb the particular class of ore produced by the mine under consideration. Usually the average shipment for the previous five years is used to measure the life of the mines when computing the valuations for tax purposes.

After the determination of the estimated future profit per ton, the probable length of life, and the expected yearly production over this length of life, the valuation of the mine is computed by multiplying the expected yearly shipments by the profit per ton and the present-worth factor for the life of the property. Either Table 4 or Table 7 gives the present-value factors used in the valuation of Michigan mines, since the six percent rate is used for both interest and sinking fund. This is the procedure under ideal conditions; but in nearly every valuation one or more factors have to be adjusted in view of such expected future conditions as probably will differ from the past five-year record.

The innumerable possibilities that must be considered at this point can be illustrated best by a few examples. For instance, a higher cost for the future may be anticipated if a large volume of water is encountered in developing the lower levels. This would point to higher pumping charges due both to increased volume and to greater depth. Again, changes in metallurgical practice may make it difficult and expensive to use an ore which sold readily for a good price in the five-year period preceding the appraisal. The possibility that the ore may be cut off below the present workings by a fault and the possibility that ore concentration may be limited by changes in geological conditions are items that must not be overlooked. For a mine just opened up, the first five-year record cannot be accepted as a measure of the performance in the future. A similar situation occurs during the last years of the life of the mine. Finally, a new shaft may afford economies which will warrant an increase in the profit factor, and the discovery of a new orebody may favorably influence both mining costs and sales.

These examples represent only a few of the considerations that must be investigated before determining the final factors to be used. No set rule is laid down by the Michigan appraisers for the consideration of these expected changes in conditions. As far as possible, the probability that the tonnage reserve may be altered by future developments is adjusted in arriving at the final reserve tonnage that is to be used in the valuation of the mine. The profit factor is moved up or down as the evidence indicates, and the probable life—which determines the expected annual production—is varied to meet what is judged to represent a fair future rate of extraction and probable sales.

It is evident from the preceding discussion that the appraisal of the Michigan iron mines depends on no set of rules or regulations. Essentially the previous five-year performance is taken as a standard and is used where normal conditions have obtained in the past and are expected in the future. For those mines where there is a past or expected deviation from the average of the past five years, the appraiser must alter the necessary factors until the final result expresses the summarization of all the pertinent data available at the time of the appraisal.

It has been previously stated that the Michigan Tax Commission has always held to a six percent rate both for interest on investment and for return of capital. Just how this interest rate is used in the final calculation can be shown by the illustration of a mine having a million tons of ore in reserve, an expected life of seven years, and a profit of $1.10 a ton as shown by the past five-year record. If market conditions are such that a smaller shipment may be expected in the future and if mining conditions, together with curtailed profit due to lower production, will reduce the profit per ton about ten cents for the remaining ore, the adjusted figures might be as follows:

Estimated reserve — 1,000,000 tons
Estimated life — 10 years
Estimated future production — 100,000 tons per year
Estimated future profit — $1.00 per ton
Present worth factor — 6% interest and 6% sinking fund — 7.3601 (See table 7)
$100,000 \times 1.00 \times 7.3601 = \$736,000$, the value of the mine.

The value of the reserves of Michigan are determined as of January 1st each year but because of the time needed to make this appraisal, the valuations are not reported to the local tax officials until the middle of May. This gives a little over three months for the examination of the mines, review of the estimates and financial statements, and the computation of the valuations. On an average, this means the determination of the valuation of about 50 active mines and explorations and the review of the valuation of nearly 100 idle properties.

For about thirty years, it was customary for the appraiser of mines to report his recommended valuations of the mines and explorations to the State Tax Commission, which would hold public reviews to give the taxpayers and other interested parties an opportunity to be heard on these valuations before they are entered on the tax rolls. Under the present law, the appraiser reports his recommended valuations to the local tax officials, who place them on the tax rolls in the same manner as other property is entered by the local assessor. Protests are heard by the State Tax Commission upon appeal in the same manner that is provided for all other taxable property in the state.

Tables I and II, following, of average costs are computed from the reports submitted to the appraiser of mines by the iron mining companies.

Table III is a similar report published annually for the iron mines of Minnesota.

TABLE I
SUMMARY OF FACTS OF IRON ORE PRODUCTION
MICHIGAN
Underground and Open Pit Mines*

	1938	1939	1940	1941
Tons Mined	5,908,108	9,116,938	12,293,376	14,591,643
Tons Shipped	4,107,549	11,239,895	13,771,279	15,201,321
Number of Active Mines	35	35	40	41
Av. number days worked	157	206	213	248
Av. no. men employed	5,633	5,818	6,743	7,553
Average daily wage	$ 7.594	$ 7.073	$ 7.483	$ 7.604
Average yearly wage	$ 1,192.29	$ 1,457.12	$ 1,593.82	$ 1,885.79
Tons/man/day	5.32	6.63	5.10	7.15
Tons/miner/day (underground only)	7.32	9.63	7.36	8.96
State & Local Taxes paid	$1,822,774.28	$1,791,897.99	$1,767,214.89	$1,922,310.87
State & Local Taxes paid per ton mined	$.3085	$.1965	$.1438	$.1317

	1942	1943	1944	1945
Tons Mined	15,690,987	15,482,611	12,699,055	11,760,250
Tons Shipped	16,163,104	14,576,819	13,734,266	11,834,652
Number of Active Mines	43	45	43	40
Av. number days worked	273	277	256	242
Av. no. men employed	8,242	8,188	7,191	6,405
Average daily wage	$7.595	$8.72	$8.68	$9.41
Average yearly wage	$2,073.53			
Tons/man/day	6.75	6.82	6.37	6.43
Tons/miner/day (underground only)	8.52	8.76	8.41	8.83
State & Local Taxes paid	$1,743,961.70	$1,756,064.00	$1,963,910.22	$1,864,292.17
State & Local Taxes paid per ton mined	$.1112	$.1134	$.1547	$.1585

	1946	1947
Tons Mined	8,637,051	12,434,198
Tons Shipped	8,481,480	12,919,529
Number of Active Mines	38	36
Av. number days worked	191	245
Av. no. men employed	5,455	6,227
Average daily wage	$10.51	$12.18
Tons/man/day	6.49	7.32
Tons/miner/day (underground only)	8.50	9.35
State & Local Taxes paid	$1,885,999.71	$1,924,532.00
State & Local Taxes paid per ton mined	$.2184	$.1548

*Note: Includes only mines active in respective years. Does not include idle mine tax or maintenance costs.

TABLE II
TOTAL STATE UNDERGROUND MINES
MICHIGAN

Average per-ton Costs

Cost of Mining	1933-37 Incl. 5-year average		1938-42 Incl. 5-year average	
Labor	.9434		1.0783	
Supplies	.6254		.5635	
		1.5688		1.6418
Deferred Costs		.1437		.1408
Taxes				
General Property	.2462		.1597	
State Corporation	.0171		.0107	
Social Security & Old Age	—		.0425	
Federal (except Income)	.0128		.0066	
General Overhead		.2761		.2195
General Office	.0750		.0665	
General Superintendence	.0496		.0308	
Fire Insurance	.0051		.0037	
Contingent	.0101		.0118	
Depreciation	.1026		.0906	
Transportation		.2424		.2034
Rail Freight	.7999		.8052	
Boat Freight	.7911		.8203	
Cargo Insurance	.0024		.0025	
Marketing		1.5934		1.6280
Selling	.0672		.0750	
Analysis	.0049		.0054	
		.0721		.0804
Total Ore Cost		3.8965		3.9139
Lake Erie Value Per Ton		4.9143		4.7873
Gross Ore Profit*		1.0178		.8734
Other Costs				
Royalty	.2967		.2823	
Interest on borrowed money	.0179		.0215	
Fed. Inc. & Exc. Profits Tax	—		.1321	

*Not true profit; much ore is sold at a discount.

TABLE II (Continued)

	1945		1946		1947		1943-47 Incl. 5-year average
1.4367		1.6781		1.7181		1.4550	
.6460		.7128		.7034		.6356	
	2.0827		2.3909		2.4215		2.0906
	.1366		.1197		.1416		.1413
.1527		.2135		.1546		.1558	
.0153		.0126		.0075		.0091	
.0333		.0411		.0391		.0337	
.0006		.0001		—		.0020	
	.2019		.2673		.2012		.2006
.0661		.0743		.0620		.0644	
.0327		.0469		.0301		.0326	
.0051		.0080		.0082		.0064	
.0014		.0020		.0070		.0027	
.0931		.0752		.0789		.0769	
	.1984		.2064		.1862		.1930
.8550		.8762		.8390		.8575	
.8534		.9572		1.0677		.9139	
.0030		.0024		.0024		.0024	
	1.7114		1.8358		1.9091		1.7738
.0769		.0480		.0457		.0655	
.0059		.0057		.0059		.0058	
	.0828		.0537		.0516		.0713
4.4138		4.8738		4.9112		4.4706	
4.7849		5.3123		5.7559		4.9989	
	.3711		.4385		.8447		.5283
.2388		.2701		.2754		.2681	
.0152		.0130		.0078		.0116	
.1174		.1616		.2345		.1441	

TABLE III
AVERAGE PRODUCTION COSTS OF OPEN-PIT AND UNDERGROUND ORE
PRODUCED IN MINNESOTA

Year	Total Tonnage Mined	Total Cost of Development, Royalty, and Mining	Average Cost Per Ton of Development	Average Cost per Ton of Mining and Beneficiation					Average Cost Per Ton of Royalty Paid	Average Cost Per Ton of All Preceding Items
				Labor	Supplies	Total Labor and Supplies	Other Items	Total		
OPEN PIT OPERATIONS										
1936	28,316,112	$31,333,496	$.230	$.149	$.134	$.283	$.197	$.480	$.396	$1.106
1937	43,751,264	47,198,257	.242	.169	.142	.311	.151	.462	.375	1.079
1938	11,535,101	15,967,137	.225	.238	.174	.412	.358	.770	.389	1.384
1939	28,033,250	32,953,986	.238	.141	.125	.266	.231	.497	.440	1.175
1940	44,008,093	44,640,364	.217	.108	.109	.217	.184	.401	.397	1.015
1941	58,771,355	60,547,192	.218	.138	.109	.247	.149	.396	.418	1.032
1942	64,951,827	72,290,635	.202	.154	.131	.285	.232	.517	.394	1.113
1943	63,761,539	75,491,717	.221	.195	.152	.347	.267	.614	.352	1.187
1944	61,177,038	75,309,811	.246	.185	.170	.355	.279	.634	.351	1.231
1945	59,012,981	72,960,183	.217	.183	.175	.358	.320	.678	.341	1.236
UNDERGROUND OPERATIONS										
1936	4,185,617	8,369,116	.048	.774	.456	1.230	.275	1.505	.446	1.999
1937	5,868,666	13,127,843	.055	.973	.517	1.490	.283	1.773	.410	2.238
1938	3,193,455	8,230,438	.048	1.027	.544	1.571	.585	2.156	.374	2.578
1939	3,756,400	8,817,523	.042	.997	.494	1.491	.466	1.957	.378	2.377
1940	4,296,565	10,140,522	.040	.947	.487	1.434	.507	1.941	.381	2.362
1941	4,964,992	11,466,023	.060	1.033	.501	1.534	.335	1.869	.380	2.309
1942	5,096,889	12,877,388	.054	1.238	.543	1.781	.347	2.128	.344	2.526
1943	5,242,922	13,655,699	.064	1.353	.550	1.903	.293	2.196	.343	2.603
1944	3,896,438	10,847,052	.043	1.321	.628	1.949	.425	2.374	.367	2.784
1945	3,469,065	10,139,631	.050	1.403	.637	2.040	.392	2.432	.441	2.923

* Tonnage of all ore mined in Minnesota in years 1936-1945, inclusive; comparison of total costs and costs per ton for development and other costs incurred in mining, as between open pit, and underground operations.
Authority: Minnesota Department of Taxation—Biennial Report 1945-1946.
Source: Mining Directory of Minnesota, 1947; Table 24, p. 238.

APPENDIX B

REFERENCE BIBLIOGRAPHY

The following list of references is intended primarily as a guide for selective readings on subjects relating to Examination and Valuation of Mineral Property. No claim is made for the completeness of the list.

LEGEND.

A.I.M.E.—American Institute of Mining and Metallurgical Engineers Transactions.
L.S.M.I.—Lake Superior Mining Institute Proceedings.
E.&M.J.—Engineering and Mining Journal.
C.I.M.M.—Canadian Institute of Mining and Metallurgy.
I.M.M.—Institution of Mining and Metallurgy.
U.S.B.M.—United States Bureau of Mines.
U.S.G.S.—United States Geological Survey.
Min. & Met.—Mining and Metallurgy (A.I.M.E.).
Min. Mag.—Mining Magazine, London.
T.P.—Technical Publication (A.I.M.E.).
Pet. Tech.—Petroleum Technology (A.I.M.E.).
Min. Tech.—Mining Technology (A.I.M.E.).

MINE EXAMINATION.

"Mining Engineers' Handbook"—R. Peele, 1918, 1927. R. Peele & J. A. Church, 3rd Ed., 1941,
John Wiley & Sons, Inc.

"The Principles of Coal Property Valuation"—A. W. Hesse.
John Wiley & Sons, Inc., 1930.

"Examination, Boring & Valuation of Alluvial and Kindred Ore Deposits"—H. L. H. Harrison. Mining Publications, Ltd., London, 1946.

"The Examination of Prospects"—G. C. Gunther, 1912,
　　Revised by R. C. Fleming, 1932,
　　　McGraw-Hill Book Co., Inc.
"Principles of Mining"—H. C. Hoover.
　　McGraw-Hill Book Co., Inc., 1909.
"The Sampling and Estimating of Ore in a Mine"—T. A. Rickard.
　　Hill Publishing Company, 1903, 1907.
"Prospectuses"—F. D. Power.
　　Australasian Inst. of Min. Engrs. Trans., Vol. 10, 1905, p. 1.
"Elements of Mining"—G. J. Young. 4th Ed., Chap. 19,
　　McGraw-Hill Book Co., Inc., 1946.
"The Mine Examiner and Prospector's Companion"—G. W. Miller.
　　Hall & Williams, 1908.
"Elements of Mining"—R. S. Lewis. 2nd Ed., Chap. 14, John Wiley &
　　Sons, Inc., 1941.
"Examination of Abandoned Mines"—W. W. Varvill.
　　I.M.M., Bulletins 371, 372, Aug., 1935, and 374, Nov., 1935.
"Essentials for a Preliminary Report on a Small Lode-Gold Mine or
　　Prospect, with Notes on Sampling"—C. W. Wright.
　　U. S. B. M., I.C. 6748, 1933.
"The Professional Examination of Undeveloped Mineral Deposits"—
　　C. Catlett. A.I.M.E. Trans., Vol. 39, 1908, p. 774.
"Professional Ethics"—R. W. Raymond.
　　A.I.M.E. Trans., Vol. 41, 1910, p. 541.
"Professional Ethics"—J. H. Hammond.
　　A.I.M.E. Trans., Vol. 39, 1908, p. 620.
"Professional Ethics for the Mining Engineer"—J. H. Hammond.
　　Eng. News, Vol. 60, No. 17, p. 443.
"Professional Ethics"—V. G. Hills.
　　A.I.M.E. Trans., Vol. 41, 1910, p. 549.
"Prospecting, Locating & Valuing Mines"—R. H. Stretch.
　　E.&M.J., N. Y., 1904, 4th Ed.
"Valuation of Mines"—A. McLaren.
　　Min. & Sci. Press, Vol. 105, 1912, p. 634.
"Valuing Partly Exhausted Mines"—M. Webber.
　　Min. & Sci. Press, Vol. 123, 1921, p. 385, 489, 524,
　　See also p. 667, 703 for discussion.
"Saving Time in a Mine Examination"—I. B. Joralemon.
　　E.&M.J., Vol. 125, 1928, p. 536.
"Geophysical Methods of Prospecting"—A. S. Eve.
　　U. S. B. M., Tech. Pub. 420, 1927.

"A Handbook of Prospecting"—W. L. Goodwin.
    Ind. & Ed. Pub. Co., Gardenvale, Que., 2nd Ed., 1929.
"Experiences in Mine Examination"—V. V. Clark.
    Min. Jour. (Phoenix), Vol. 19, No. 5, July, August, 1935.

    GEOLOGY.

"Ore Deposits of the Western United States"—Lindgren Memorial
    Vol. A.I.M.E., 1933.
"Ore Deposits as Related to Structural Features"—W. H. Newhouse,
    editor.
    Princeton Univ. Press, 1942.
"Geological Factors in the Valuation of Mines"—D. H. McLaughlin.
    Econ. Geol., Vol. 34, 1939, pp. 581-621.
"Geological Theory in Mine Examinations"—N. Clark.
    Pan-American Geologist, Vol. 63, No. 1, Feb., 1935, pp. 33-40.
"Structural Geology"—M. P. Billings.
    Prentice-Hall, Inc., 1942.
"Field Geology"—F. H. Lahee.
    McGraw-Hill Book Co., Inc., 4th Ed., 1941.
"Principles of Field and Mining Geology"—J. D. Forrester.
    John Wiley & Sons, Inc., 1946. (Bibliography.).
"Mining Geology"—H. E. McKinstry.
    Prentice-Hall, Inc., 1948.
"Geology of Coal"—O. Stutzer & A. C. Noe.
    University of Chicago Press, 1940.
"Geology of Petroleum and Natural Gas"—E. R. Lilley.
    D. Van Nostrand Co., 1928.
"Geology of Petroleum"—W. H. Emmons.
    McGraw-Hill Book Co., Inc., 2nd ed., 1931.
"Oil Fields in United States"—W. A. Ver Wiebe.
    McGraw-Hill Book Co., Inc., 1930.
"Reservoir Analysis and Geologic Structure"—J. M. Bugbee.
    A.I.M.E., Pet. Tech., Nov., 1942.
"Methods of Study of Sediments"—W. H. Twenhofel & S. A. Tyler.
    McGraw-Hill Book Co., Inc., 1941.
"A Study of Geologic Structure at Climax in Relation to Mining and
    Block Carving"—R. U. King. A.I.M.E. Trans., Vol. 163, 1945.
"Laboratory Manual for Structural Geology and Map Reading Prob-
    lems"—F. J. Pettijohn. Univ. of Chicago, 3rd Ed., 1940. (Bibliog-
    raphy.)

SAMPLING.

"Mining Engineers' Handbook"—R. Peele.
    John Wiley & Sons, Inc., 1918, 1927. R. Peele and J. A. Church,
    3rd Ed., 1941,

"Sampling and Estimation of Ore Deposits".—C. F. Jackson & J. B.
    Knaebel.
        U.S.B.M. Bull. 356, 1932.

"Examination, Boring & Valuation of Alluvial and Kindred Ore De-
    posits"—H. L. H. Harrison. Mining Publications, Ltd., London,
    1946.

"Mine Economics"—S. J. Truscott.
    Mining Publications, Ltd., London, 1947.

"Probabilities in Estimating the Grade of Gold Deposits"—C. O.
    Swanson. C.I.M.M. Bul. 397, Trans., Vol. 48, 1945, pp. 323-50.

"The Valuation of Ore Reserves"—Review of S. J. Truscott paper.
    Mining Magazine, London, Vol. 42, 1930, pp. 313-18.

"Prospecting for Gold and Silver"—E. M. Savage.
    McGraw-Hill Book Co., Inc., 1934.

"Handbook for Prospectors"—M. W. Bernewitz.
    McGraw-Hill Book Co., Inc., 2nd Ed., 1931.

"Essentials for a Preliminary Report on a Small Lode-Gold Mine or
    Prospect, with Notes on Sampling"—C. W. Wright.
        U.S.B.M., I.C. 6748, 1933.

"Recovering and Interpreting Diamond Drill Samples"—R. D. Long-
    year. Min. & Met., May, 1937, p. 238.

"Estimation of Average Value of Gold Ore"—W. A. Jones.
    C.I.M.M. Trans., Vol. 46, 1943, pp. 209-25.

"New Technique of Boring Overcomes Sampling Problems"—O. G.
    Parker, Jr. E.&M.J., July, 1939, p. 32.

"Improved Barrel and Bit Increases Core Recovery"—L. J. Barrows.
    E.&M.J., Nov., 1946, p. 80.

"Calculations from Diamond-Drill Sampling—a Comparison of
    Methods"—C. W. Greenhalgh. A.I.M.E. Trans., Vol. 163, 1945 (T.
    P. 1842).

"Some Problems Involved with Interpretations of Diamond-Drill-Hole
    Sampling and Surveying"—J. J. Collins. A.I.M.E. Trans., Vol. 163,
    1945 (T. P. 1842).

"Sampling and Testing a Gold-Scheelite Placer Deposit in Califor-
    nia"—H. W. C. Prommel. U.S.B.M., I.C. 6960, 1937.

"Core Control in Alluvial Drilling"—V. V. Clark. E. & M. J., July,
    1934.

"Theory of Sampling"—T. T. Read.
    E.&M.J., Vol., 125, 1928, p. 574.
"Mine Sampling and Valuing"—C. S. Herzig. Mine. & Sci. Press, San
    Francisco, 1914.
"The Sampling and Estimating of Ore in a Mine"—T. A. Rickard.
    Hill Publishing Company, 1903, 1907.
"The Mine Examiner and Prospector's Companion"—G. W. Miller.
    Hall & Williams, 1908.
"Lake Superior Iron Ores"—The Lake Superior Iron Ore Assoc.,
    Cleveland, Ohio, 1938.
"The Iron Ores of Lake Superior"—Crowell & Murray (yearly).
    Crowell & Murray, Inc., Cleveland, Ohio.
"Methods of the Chemists of the U. S. Steel Corp., Sampling &
    Analysis"—J. M. Camp. Carnegie Steel Co., 1908, 1914, 1926.
"Sampling and Estimating Ore Deposits"—Committee Report.
    A.I.M.E. Trans., Vol. 72, 1925, p. 591.
"Sampling and Estimating Disseminated Copper Deposits"—I. B.
    Joralemon. A.I.M.E. Trans., Vol. 72, 1925, p. 607.
"Sampling and Estimating Cordilleran Lead-Silver Limestone Replace-
    ment Deposits"—B. Prescott. A.I.M.E. Trans., Vol. 72, 1925, p.
    666.
"Sampling and Estimating Orebodies in the Warren District, Ari-
    zona"—R. H. Dickson. A.I.M.E. Trans., Vol. 72, 1925, p. 621.
"Sampling and Estimating Zinc and Lead Orebodies in the Mississippi
    Valley"—W. F. Boericke. A.I.M.E. Trans., Vol. 68, 1923, p. 417.
"Methods of Sampling and Estimating Ore in Underground and
    Steam Shovel Mines of Copper Queen Branch, Phelps Dodge Corpo-
    ration"—R. W. Prouty, R. T. Green. A.I.M.E. Trans., Vol. 72, p.
    628.
"Sampling and Estimating Lake Superior Iron Ores"—J. W. Wolff,
    E. L. Derby, W. A. Cole. A.I.M.E. Trans., Vol. 72, 1925, p. 641.
"Methods of Sampling Ores on the Marquette Range"—R. W. Bowen.
    A.I.M.E. Trans., Vol. 72, 1925, p. 657.
"Organization of Mine Sampling at Anaconda"—W. B. Daly, F. A.
    Linforth. A.I.M.E. Trans., Vol. 68, 1923, p. 134.
"Sampling Replacement Deposits"—B. Prescott.
    Min. & Met., Sept., 1924, p. 445.
"Churn-Drilling of Disseminated Copper Deposits"—R. Rice.
    E.&M.J., 1921, Vol. 111, p. 1063, Vol. 112, p. 14.
"Diamond Drill Sampling Methods"—R. D. Longyear.
    A.I.M.E. Trans., Vol. 68, 1923, p. 423.

"Sampling Churn-Drill Sludge at Utah Copper"—L. S. Breckon.
E.&M.J., Vol. 126, 1928, p. 491.

"Deep-hole Prospecting at the Chief Consolidated Mines"—C. A. Dobbel. A.I.M.E. Trans., Vol. 72, 1925, p. 677.

"Bibliography of Literature on Sampling to July 1921"—W. J. Sharwood & M. von Bernewitz. Gov't Printing Office, Wash., 1922.
U. S. B. M. Reports of Investigations, No. 2336.

"The Theory and Practice of Ore Sampling"—D. W. Brunton.
A.I.M.E. Trans., Vol. 25, 1895, p. 826.

"Modern Practice of Ore-Sampling"—D. W. Brunton.
A.I.M.E. Trans., Vol. 40, 1909, p. 567.

"Witwatersrand Banket and Mining Practice"—S. J. Truscott.
Macmillan & Co., Ltd., London, 1907.

"The Deep-Level Mines of the Rand"—G. A. Denny.
Crosby Lockwood & Son, London, 1902.

"Prospectors' Field Book and Guide"—M. W. von Bernewitz.
H. C. Baird & Co., New York, 1920.

"The Sampling and Measurement of Ore Bodies in Mine Examinations"—E. B. Kirby. Proc. Colo. Sci. Society, Dec. 3, 1894.

"Mine Sampling and the Commercial Value of Ores"—R. W. Lewis.
Bulletin No. 10, Utah Engineering Exp. Station.

"Mine Sampling and Valuation"—H. S. Munroe.
Mining & Met. Soc. of America. Bulletin 1912, Vol. 118.

"Notes on Sampling"—A. C. Thomas.
Australasian Inst. of Min. Engrs. Trans., Vol. 10, 1905, p. 276.

"Methods of Sampling at Lake Superior Iron Mines"—B. Crowell.
L.S.M.I. Proceedings, Vol. 17, 1912, p. 76.

"The Sampling of Iron Ores"—L. S. Austin.
L.S.M.I. Proceedings, Vol. 13, 1908, p. 225.

"Methods of Sampling Iron Ore"—C. T. Mixer.
L.S.M.I. Proceedings, Vol. 4, 1896, p. 27.

"Standard Method for Sampling Cargoes of Iron Ore at Lower Lake Ports"—O. Textor. L.S.M.I. Proceedings, Vol. 13, 1908, p. 231.

"Unloading and Sampling Ore at Lower Lake Ports"—P. C. McCormack, C. C. Walsh. L.S.M.I. Proceedings, Vol. 23, 1923, p. 147.

"Cargo Sampling of Iron Ore Received at Lower Lake Ports"—W. J. Rattle & Son. L.S.M.I. Proceedings, Vol. 11, 1905, p. 173.

"Development Sampling and Ore-Valuation of Gold Mines"—C. B. Horwood, M. Park. A.I.M.E. Trans., Vol. 39, 1908, p. 685.

"Primary Gold in Colorado Granite"—J. B. Hastings.
A.I.M.E. Trans., Vol. 39, 1908, p. 97.

"Surveying and Sampling Diamond-Drill Holes"—E. E. White.
        A.I.M.E. Trans., Vol. 44, 1912, p. 69.
"Relative Value of Quartz and Placer Gold"—W. Lindgren.
        Min. & Sci. Press, Vol. 103, 1911, p. 615.
"Sampling and Estimating Gold in a Placer Deposit"—Geo. R.
        Fausett. Ariz. Bureau of Mines Bull. 51, Tucson, 1917.
"Sampling Mineralized Veins"—Geo. R. Fausett.
        Ariz. Bur of Mines, 1917, Bull. 66, Samp. Ser. 3.
"Sampling Dumps and Tailings"—Geo. R. Fausett.
        Ariz. Bur. of Mines, 1917, Bull. 63, Samp. Ser. 2.
"Principles & Practice of Sampling Metallic Metallurgical Materials
        with Special reference to Sampling of Copper Bullion"—Edward
        Keller. Gov't. Printing Office, Wash., D. C., 1916.
"Mechanical Ore Sampling in Montana"—H. B. Pulsifer.
        Mont. Bureau of Mines & Geol., Butte, 1920, Bulletin No. 3.
"Ore-Sampling Conditions in the West"—T. R. Woodbridge.
        Gov't. Printing Office, Wash., 1916, Tech. Paper No. 86.
"Mill & Smelter Methods of Sampling"—H. J. Stander.
        Ariz. Bur. of Mines, Tucson, Bull. 26, Met. Series 1, 1916.
"How to Sample Coal and Coke"—Ervin G. Bailey.
        Fuel Testing Co., Boston, 1910, Bulletin No. 4.
"The Sampling of Coal in the Mine"—J. A. Holmes.
        Gov't. Print. Off., Wash., D. C., 1911, Revised Ed. 1918.
        (U. S. B. M. Tech. Paper No. 1.)
"Standard Method for Sampling of Coal"—Am. Society for Testing
        Materials, Philadelphia, 1916.
"Standard Methods for Laboratory Sampling & Analysis of Coal &
        Coke"—Am. Soc. for Testing Materials, Philadelphia, 1916.
"The Sampling of Small Coal"—E. S. Grumell and A. C. Dunningham.
        Colliery Guardian, Vol. 142, 1931, p. 127.
"Sampling Operations in the Pench Valley Coal-field"—
        (India Geol. Survey Record Vol. 59, No. 2, p. 165-190.) Calcutta,
        1926.
"The Commercial Value of Coal-Mine Sampling"—M. R. Campbell.
        A.I.M.E. Trans., Vol. 36, 1906, p. 341.

SALTING.

"Salting"—T. A. Rickard.
        E.&M.J., 1941, Mar., p. 42; May, p. 52; June, p. 50.
"Dangers of Careless Sampling and Assaying"—B. W. Hill.
        E.&M.J., Oct., 1940, p. 38.

"Mine Reports and Mine Salting"—Walter McDermott.
   Trans. I.M.M., London, Vol. 3, 1894-5, pp. 108-49.

ECONOMICS.

"Mineral Valuations of the Future"—C. K. Leith.
   A.I.M.E., 1938.
"The Economics of Mining"—T. J. Hoover.
   Stanford Univ. Press, Calif., 1948.
"Economics of the Petroleum Industry"—J. E. Pogue.
   The Chase National Bank, New York, 1939.
"Factors Affecting Investment in South American Mines"—N. B. Knox. Min. & Met., 1945-6; Vol. 24: 589-92; Vol. 26: 173-4; 292-4; 340-1; 432-3; 479-80; Vol. 27: 178.
"Minerals Yearbook", Annual—U.S.B.M.
   Gov't. Printing Office, Wash., D. C.
"World Minerals and World Peace"—C. K. Leith, J. W. Furness, C. Lewis. Brookings Inst., Wash., D. C., 1943.
"Raw Materials in Peace and War"—E. Staley.
   Council on Foreign Relations, 1937.
"Marketing of Metals and Minerals"—J. E. Spurr & F. E. Wormser.
   McGraw-Hill Book Co., Inc., 1925.
"Capital Employed in the Petroleum Industry"—J. E. Pogue & F. G. Coqueron. Min. & Met., Nov., 1944, pp. 537-42.
"Development of the Mineral Industry in Peace and War"—J. R. Finlay. Min. & Met., Mar., 1944, pp. 156-62.
"International Control of the Non-Ferrous Metals"—Elliott, May, Rowe, Skelton, and Wallace. MacMillan, N. Y., 1937.
"Mineral Raw Materials"—Staff of the Foreign Minerals Div. of U.S.B.M. McGraw-Hill Book Co., Inc., 1937.
"The Economics of Mining"—T. A. Rickard.
   Hill Publishing Co., 1905, 1907.
"Cost of Mining"—J. R. Finlay.
   McGraw-Hill Book Co., Inc., 1909, 1910, 1920.
"Principles of Mining"—H. C. Hoover.
   McGraw-Hill Book Co., Inc., 1909.
"World Minerals and World Politics"—C. K. Leith.
   McGraw-Hill Book Co., Inc., 1931.
"Elements of a National Mineral Policy"—C. K. Leith, H. F. Bain and S. M. Marshall. A.I.M.E., New York, 1933.
"World Minerals"—C. K. Leith.
   A.I.M.E. Trans., Vol. 75, 1927, p. 346.

"Geography and the Mining Industry"—L. F. Thomas.
    Min. & Met., Dec., 1941, pp. 579-81.
"Money & Mines"—Hugh F. Marriott.
    MacMillan, N. Y., 1925.
"Our Oil Resources"—L. M. Fanning.
    McGraw-Hill Book Co., Inc., 1945.
"American Oil Operations Abroad"—L. M. Fanning.
    McGraw-Hill Book Co., Inc., 1947.
"Competitive Fuel Prices"—A. J. McIntosh.
    Min. & Met., Sept., 1947, pp. 447-50.
"Economics of Proration"—J. E. Pogue.
    Chap. II, Petroleum Dev. & Tech., 1932, A.I.M.E.
"The Petroleum Products Situation"—A. J. McIntosh.
    Petroleum Dev. & Tech., 1932, A.I.M.E., pp. 100-8.
"Mining Engineers' Handbook"—R. Peele, 1918, 1927. R. Peele and
    J. A. Church. 3rd Ed., 1941,
    John Wiley & Sons, Inc.
"The Future of the Mining Industry from an Economic Standpoint"
    —A. G. Charleston. I.M.M. Trans., Vol. 20, 1910-11, p. 466.
"Petroleum"—Albert Lidgett.
    Sir Isaac Pitman & Sons, New York, 1928.
"Business Cycles" (The Problem and Its Setting)—Wesley C. Mit-
    chell. Nat'l. Bur. Econ. Research, Inc., New York, 1928.
"Cycles in Metal Production"—D. F. Hewett.
    A.I.M.E. Trans., Vol. Metal Mining, 1929, p. 65.
"Long Term Graphical Metal Prices"—P. E. Barbour.
    Reprinted from Mineral Industry, Vol. 39,
    McGraw-Hill Book Co., Inc., New York, 1931.
"Some Political Aspects of the World Manganese Situation"—C. K.
    Leith. A.I.M.E. Trans., Vol. 75, 1927, p. 260.
"Manganese Resources in Relation to Domestic Consumption"—J. V.
    W. Reynders. A.I.M.E. Trans., Vol. 75, 1927, p. 272.
"Economics of the Current Revival in Adirondack Iron Ore Mining"
    —D. B. Gillies. Min. & Met., Nov., 1943, pp. 478-9.
"Lake Superior Iron Ores"—The Lake Superior Iron Ore Assoc.,
    Cleveland, Ohio, 1938.
"Reserves of Lake Superior Manganiferous Iron Ores"—C. Zapffe.
    A.I.M.E. Trans., Vol. 75, 1927, p. 346.
"Production and Reserves of the Pittsburgh Coal Bed"—G. H. Ashley.
    Trans., Coal Div., A.I.M.E., Vol. 130, 1938, pp. 56-64.
"Economics in Preparing Coal for Steam Generation"—H. F. Hebley.
    Trans. Coal Div., A.I.M.E., Vol. 130, 1938, pp. 79-106.

"Economic Factors in the Phosphate Industry"—B. L. Johnson.
Min. & Met., Oct., 1944, pp. 455-64.
"What for Copper after the War?"—W. R. Ingalls.
Min. & Met., Sept., 1944, pp. 427-9.
"The Annual Production of Copper and the Average Yearly Price of Copper"—E. Koepel. L.S.M.I. Proceedings, Vol. 28, 1930, p. 220.
"The Annual Production of Copper and the Average Yearly Price of Copper from 1880 to 1928"—E. Koepel.
L.S.M.I. Proceedings, Vol. 27, 1929, p. 147.
"Some Economic Aspects of the Copper Industry"—L. C. Graton.
Min. & Met. Soc. of America Bull., Vol. 23, No. 1, Jan., 1930.
"Copper Production and Consumption"—P. E. Barbour.
E.&M.J., Vol. 129, 1930, p. 303.
"The Price of Copper"—P. E. Barbour.
E.&M.J., Vol. 129, 1930, p. 402.
"World Copper-Ore Reserve"—P. E. Barbour.
E.&M.J., Vol. 131, 1931, p. 178.
"The Price of Copper"—R. E. Tally.
Min. Cong. Jour., Vol. 16, No. 4, April, 1930.
"Oil Fields in U. S."—Walter A. VerWiebe.
McGraw-Hill Book Co., Inc., New York, 1930.
"Engineering and Mining Journal—Metal Quotations."
"The Federal Reserve Bulletin," Fed. Res. Bd., Wash., D. C.
"Alexander Hamilton Institute Bulletin No. 19, Index Numbers & Prices."
"Quarterly Index of British Cycles"—Dr. Dorothy S. Thomas.
"U. S. Dept. of Commerce, Bureau of Labor Statistics Bulletins."
"Mineral Industry"—G. A. Roush, Ed.
"The Miners' Handbook and Copper Handbook"—Weed.
"The Copper Handbook"—Stevens.
"Mines Register,"Vol. 22, 1946.
"State of Mich., Statistical Summary Reports."
Dept. of Conservation, Lansing, Mich.
"Minnesota Dep't. of Taxation, Biennial Report," St. Paul, Minn.

ESTIMATION OF ORE.

"Sampling and Estimating of Ore Deposits"—C. F. Jackson & J. B. Knaebel. U.S.B.M. Bull. 356, 1932.
"Metal Mining Practice"—C. F. Jackson & J. H. Hedges.
U.S.B.M. Bull. 419, 1939.
"Examination, Boring & Valuation of Alluvial and Kindred Ore Deposits"—H. L. H. Harrison, Mining Pub., Ltd., London, 1946.

"The Appraisal of Ore Expectancies"—E. F. Fitzhugh, Jr., A.I.M.E.,
     T.P. 2090, Min. Tech., Jan., 1947.

"The Sampling and Estimating of Ore in a Mine"—T. A. Rickard.
     Hill Publishing Company, 1903, 1907.

"Mining Engineers' Handbook"—R. Peele, 1918, 1927. R. Peele and
     J. A. Church, 3rd Ed., 1941,
     John Wiley & Sons, Inc.

"Principles of Mining"—H. C. Hoover.
     McGraw-Hill Book Co., Inc., 1909.

"Cost of Mining"—J. R. Finlay.
     McGraw-Hill Book Co., Inc., 1909, 1910, 1920.

"The Economics of Mining"—T. A. Rickard.
     Hill Publishing Company, 1905, 1907.

"The Search for Concealed Deposits—A Reorientation of Philosophy"
     —S. G. Lasky. A.I.M.E., Mining Tech., May, 1947.

"The Concept of Ore Reserves"—S. G. Lasky.
     Min. & Met., Oct., 1945, pp. 471-4.

"Some Observations in Ore Search"—Symposium.
     A.I.M.E., T.P. 1209, 1940.

"Mine Sampling & Valuing"—C. S. Herzig.
     Min. & Sci. Press, San Francisco, 1914.

"Computations of Probable Value of Ore Reserves from Assay Re-
     sults"—S. J. Truscott.
     I.M.M. Bulls. 313, 314, 315.
     I.M.M. Trans. Vol. 39, p 482

"Notes on the Estimation of Tonnage and Grade of Some Chromite
     Dumps"—W. N. Wilson. I.M.M. Bull. 480, Sept., 1946.

"How to Calculate Tonnage and Grade of an Orebody"—J. E.
     Harding. E.&M.J., Vol. 116, 1923, p. 445.

"Correction Factor for Specific Gravity and Volume Differences in
     Fragment Analysis"—F. Chayes.
     Econ. Geol., Vol. 41, 1946, pp. 749-60.

"Estimating Ore by the Polygon Method"—T. T. Read.
     E.&M.J., Aug., 1943, pp. 84-5.

"On Mapping Underground Geology"—Harrison Schmitt.
     E.&M.J., Vol. 137, 1936, p. 557.

"Cartography for Mining Geology"—Harrison Schmitt.
     Econ. Geol., Vol. 27, 1932, pp. 716-36.

"Extension of Ore Shoots with Comments on the Art of Ore Finding"
     —Harrison Schmitt. A.I.M.E., T.P. 164, 1929.

"The Porphyry Coppers"—A. B. Parsons.
  Chap. 17, Prospecting and Estimating Ore, A.I.M.E., 1933, pp. 335-68.
"Estimating & Valuing the Future of Mines"—M. Webber.
  Min. & Sci. Press, Vol. 103, 1911, p. 353.
"Alluvial Prospecting; the Technical Investigation of Economic Alluvial Minerals"—C. Raeburn & H. B. Milner.
  London, Murby, 1927. (Has glossary & bibliography.)
"Testing & Estimating Alluvials for Gold, Platinum, Diamonds, or Tin"—Wm. E. Thorne. Mining Publications, Ltd., London, 1926.
"Sampling and Estimating Gold in a Placer Deposit"—G. R. Fausett.
  Ariz. Bureau of Mines Bull. No. 51, 1917.
"The Iron Ores of Lake Superior"—Crowell & Murray.
  Cleveland, Ohio, Annually.
"Calculation of Ore Tonnage and Grade from Drill-hole Samples"—J. E. Harding. A.I.M.E. Trans., Vol. 66, 1921, p. 117.
"Sampling & Estimating Zinc and Lead Orebodies in Mississippi Valley"—W. F. Boericke. A.I.M.E. Trans., Vol. 68, 1923, p. 417.
"Estimating on the Gogebic Range"—J. W. Wolff.
  A.I.M.E. Trans., Vol. 72, 1925, p. 653.
"Estimating in the Cuyuna Iron Ore District, Minnesota"—C. Zapffe.
  A.I.M.E. Trans., Vol. 72, 1925, p. 661.
"Sampling and Estimating Ore Deposits"—Committee Report.
  A.I.M.E. Trans., Vol. 72, 1925, p. 591.
"Sampling and Estimating Disseminated Copper Deposits"—L. B. Joralemon.
  A.I.M.E. Trans., Vol. 72, 1925, p. 607.
"Sampling and Estimating Orebodies in the Warren District, Arizona"—R. H. Dickson. A.I.M.E. Trans., Vol. 72, 1925, p. 621.
"Methods of Sampling and Estimating Ore in Underground and Steam Shovel Mines of Copper Queen Branch, Phelps Dodge Corp."—R. W. Prouty, R. T. Green. A.I.M.E. Trans., Vol. 72, 1925, p. 628.
"Determining Cut-off Grades with Triangular Coordinates, for Ores Containing Three Valuable Components"—H. I. Altschuler.
  E.&M.J., Vol. 139, 1938, p. 35.
"Sampling and Estimating Lake Superior Iron Ores"—J. W. Wolff, E. L. Derby, W. A. Cole. A.I.M.E. Trans., Vol. 72, 1925, p. 641.
"Sampling and Estimating Cordilleran Lead-Silver Limestone Replacement Deposits"—B. Prescott. A.I.M.E. Trans., Vol. 72, 1925, p. 666.
"Drill Sampling & Interpretation of Sampling Results in Copper Fields of Northern Rhodesia"—H. T. Matson & C. A. Wallis.
  A.I.M.E. Tech. Pub. No. 373. (Class A Metal Min. No. 42.)

"Coal Evaluation & Preparation"—T. F. Downing, Jr.
    A.I.M.E. Trans., Vol. 101, 1932, p. 47.
"The Technical Examination of Crude Petroleum"—Wm. A. Hamor
    & F. W. Padgett. (Evaluation of Oil Shale.)
    McGraw-Hill Book Co., Inc., 1920.
"Deep Borehole Surveys & Problems"—M. H. Haddock.
    McGraw-Hill Book Co., Inc., 1931. (Has bibliography.)
"Valuing Dredging Ground"—L. A. Decoto.
    Min. & Sci. Press, Vol. 108, 1914, p. 773.
"Valuing Dredging Ground"—H. N. Herrick.
    Min. & Sci. Press, Vol. 108, 1914, p. 1061.
"Valuation of Dredging Ground"—E. B. Thornhill.
    Min. & Sci. Press, Vol. 109, 1914, p. 105.
"Valuation of Dredging Ground"—L. J. Hohl.
    Min. & Sci. Press, Vol. 109, 1914, p. 493.
"Valuing Placer Ground"—R. C. Jennings.
    Min. & Sci. Press, Vol. 109, 1914, p. 527.
"Valuation of Dredging Ground"—C. S. Herzig.
    Min. & Sci. Press, Vol. 109, 1914, p. 563.
"Valuation of Dredging Ground"—H. N. Herrick.
    Min. & Sci. Press, Vol. 109, 1914, p. 692.
"Valuing Placer Ground"—D. Steel.
    Min. & Sci. Press, Vol. 109, 1914, p. 845.
"Valuation of Dredging Ground"—J. T. Nixon.
    Min. & Sci. Press, Vol. 109, 1914, p. 962.
"Valuation of Dredging Ground"—E. Bonella.
    Min. & Sci. Press, Vol. 110, 1915, pp. 111, 585.
"Valuation of Dredging Ground"—E. J. Valentine.
    Min. & Sci. Press, Vol. 110, 1915, p. 262.
"Valuation of Dredging Ground"—R. T. Hancock.
    Min. & Sci. Press, Vol. 110, 1915, p. 585.
"Valuation of Dredging Ground"—J. J. Bristol.
    Min. & Sci. Press, Vol. 110, 1915, p. 825.
"Method of Calculating Average Value of Placer Ground"—J. Sen.
    Min. & Sci. Press, Vol. 122, 1921, p. 704.
"Valuation of Placer Deposits"—G. H. Hutton.
    Min. & Sci. Press, Vol. 123, 1921, p. 365.
"Valuation of Ore"—W. Crocker.
    Min. & Sci. Press, Vol. 123, 1921, p. 531.
"Valuation of Placers"—W. Crocker.
    Min. & Sci. Press, Vol. 123, 1921, p. 567.

"Valuation of Placer Deposits"—J. W. Neill.
Min. & Sci. Press, Vol. 123, 1921, p. 529.
"Valuing Partly Exhausted Mines"—L. O. Howard.
Min. & Sci. Press, Vol. 123, 1921, p. 568.

VALUATION.

"The Engineer's Valuing Assistant"—H. D. Hoskold.
Longmans, Green & Co., 1877, 1905.
"Principles of Valuation"—Grimes & Craigue.
Prentice-Hall, Inc., 1928.
"Valuation of Mineral Property"—T. A. O'Donahue.
Crosby Lockwood & Sons, London, 1910.
"Mineral Valuations of the Future"—C. K. Leith.
A.I.M.E., 1938.
"Engineering Valuation"—Marston & Agg.
McGraw-Hill Book Co., Inc., 1936.
"Mineral Valuation in South Africa"—L. W. Luttrell-West.
South African Min. & Eng. Jour., Feb. 28, Mar. 6, Mar. 13, 1948.
"Examination, Boring and Valuation of Alluvial and Kindred Ore
Deposits"—H. L. H. Harrison.
Mining Publications, Ltd., London, 1946.
"Mine Economics"—S. J. Truscott.
Mining Publications, Ltd., London, 1947.
"Risks of Mining Ventures Should be Evaluated"—A. S. Lewis.
E.&M.J., Sept., 1946, pp. 61-3.
"Problem of Deferment in Valuation of Mineral Properties"—F. B.
Clark. Trans., I.M.M., Vol. 95, Pt. 4, July, 1938.
"Natural Resource Assets; Their Treatment in Accounts and Valua-
tion"—M. E. Peloubet.
Harvard Business Review, Vol. 16, No. 1, 1937, p. 74.
"The Fundamentals of Mineral Property Valuation"—G. C. Riddell.
E.&M.J., Nov., 1940, pp. 37-40.
"Valuation of Property"—J. C. Bonbright.
McGraw-Hill Book Co., Inc., 1937.
"Cost of Mining"—J. R. Finlay.
McGraw-Hill Book Co., Inc., 1909, 1910, 1920.
"Principles of Mining"—H. C. Hoover.
McGraw-Hill Book Co., Inc., 1909.
"Modern Mine Valuation"—M. H. Burnham.
London, 1912.
"Economics of Mining"—T. A. Rickard.
Hill Publishing Co., 1905, 1907.

"Mathematical Principles of Finance"—F. C. Kent.
   McGraw-Hill Book Co., Inc., 1927.

"Compound Interest and Annuity Tables"—F. C. & M. E. Kent.
   McGraw-Hill Book Co., Inc., 1926.

"Inwood's Tables of Interest and Mortality"—Sir Wm. Schooling.
   Tech. Press, Ltd., London, 33rd Ed., 1930.

"Mathematical Theory of Investments"—E. B. Skinner.
   Ginn & Company, 1924.

"Application, Use and Construction of Valuation Tables"—R. Parry.
   Estates Gazette, 1936.

"Valuation Tables for Mineral Rents, Royalties and Terminable Annuities"—R. F. Percey.
   Trans. I.M.M., London, Vol. 86, Pt. 3, Dec., 1933.

"Valuation of Future Profits with Variable Annual Income"—C. E. Mills. E.&M.J., Vol. 142, No. 12, 1941, pp. 47-8.

"Mining Engineers' Handbook"—R. Peele, 1918, 1927.
   R. Peele and J. A. Church, 3rd Ed., 1941,
      John Wiley & Sons, Inc.

"Mineral Valuation"—H. Louis.
   Charles Griffin & Co., Ltd., 1923.

"Interest Rates, Bond Yields & Stock Prices"—F. R. Macauley.
   Nat'l. Bureau of Economic Research, New York, 1938.

"The Rate of Interest"—Irving Fisher.
   (Rate of extractions in mining, p. 185, rate of interest in mining communities, pp. 306-08.)
      New York, 1907.

"Principles of Mine Valuation"—J. R. Finlay.
   School of Mines Quarterly. Vol. 34, 1913, p. 87, or
   Min. & Sci. Press, Vol. 106, 1913, p. 302.

"Valuation of Mines and Prospects Under Present-day Conditions"—
   H. Schmitt. E.&M.J., Vol. 139, 1938, p. 43.

"Valuation of Mines"—J. D. Kendall.
   Bulletin Can. Min. Inst., July, 1914.

"The Principles of Coal Property Valuation"—A. W. Hesse.
   John Wiley & Sons, Inc., 1930.

"Methods of Valuing Coal Properties"—Committee Report.
   Trans. A.I.M.E., Vol. 108, p. 400.

"Coal Evaluation and Preparation"—T. F. Downing.
   Trans., Coal Div., A.I.M.E., Vol. 101, 1932, pp. 47-54.

"Valuation of Coal Land"—G. H. Ashley.
   A.I.M.E. Bull. 83, Nov., 1913.

"Appraisal of Coal Land for Valuation"—H. M. Chance.
    A.I.M.E. Bull. 81, July, 1914.
"The Valuation of Public Coal Lands"—G. H. Ashley.
    Bull. 424, U.S.G.S., 1910.
"Method for Mine Valuation in the Philippines"—H. Foster Bain.
    Min. & Met., Vol. 18, 1937, p. 255.
"A Study of Methods of Mine Valuation and Assessment with Special
    Reference to the Zinc Mines of Southwestern Wisconsin"—W. L.
    Uglow. Wis. Geol. & Nat. Hist. Survey, 1914; Bull. 41, Econ, Ser. 18.
"The Valuation of Mines of Definite Average Income"—H. D. Hos-
    kold. A.I.M.E. Trans., Vol. 33, 1903, p. 777.
"The Valuation of Mineral Properties"—T. A. O'Donahue.
    Inst. of Min. Engrs. Trans., Vol. 32, p. 399.
"Notes on the Valuation of Mineral Properties"—T. A. O'Donahue.
    Inst. of Min. Engrs. Trans., Vol. 43, pp. 19, 391, 540 and Vol. 45,
    p. 182.
"New Interest Tables for the Valuation of Mineral Properties"—
    T. A. O'Donahue. Inst. of Min. Engrs. Trans., Vol. 47, p. 100.
"Valuation of Iron Mines"—J. R. Finlay.
    E.&M.J., Vol. 95, 1913, p. 477.
"Mine Valuation"—J. R. Finlay.
    (Bull. Min. & Met. Soc. of Amer., May, 1912.)
    E.&M.J., Vol. 93, 1912, p. 1238.
"Valuation of Mines"—T. A. Rickard.
    Min. & Sci. Press, Vol. 106, 1913, p. 766.
"Formulas for Mine Valuation"—D. B. Morkill.
    Min. & Sci. Press, Vol. 117, 1918, p. 276.
"Formulas for Mine Valuation"—H. D. Pallister.
    Min. & Sci. Press, Vol. 117, 1918, p. 682.
"Formulas for Mine Valuation"—W. W. Whitton.
    Min. & Sci. Press, Vol. 117, 1918, p. 179.
"Formulas for Valuation of Mines"—W. W. Whitton.
    Min. & Sci. Press, Vol. 116, 1918, p. 691.
"Formulas for Mine Valuation"—K. F. Hoffmann.
    Min. & Sci. Press, Vol. 116, 1918, p. 882.
"The Present Value of a Mine"—F. S. Schmidt.
    Min. & Sci. Press, Vol. 112, 1916, p. 207.
"Estimating and Valuing the Future of Mines"—M. Webber.
    Min. & Sci. Press, Vol. 103, 1911, p. 353.
"Vendors Valuation of Mining Property"—W. F. Disbrow.
    Min. & Sci. Press, Vol. 106, p. 954.

"Mine Valuation"—J. Channing.
    E.&M.J., Vol. 76, 1903, p. 383.
"Valuation of Iron Mines"—R. B. Brinsmade.
    A.I.M.E. Trans., Vol. 45, 1913, p. 322.
"Valuation of Iron Mines"—E. E. White.
    A.I.M.E. Trans., Vol. 45, 1913, p. 322.
"Computation of Present Value of Developed and Undeveloped
    Mines"—W. H. Goodchild.
    Inst. Min. & Met. Trans., Vol. 18, 1908-09, p. 367.
"Notes on the Valuation of Ores and Minerals, and on Metallurgical
    Calculations"—G. T. Holloway.
    Inst. Min. & Met. Trans., Vol. 21, 1911-12, p. 567.
"Determination of the Present Value of a Mine on the Rand"—F.
    Hellman. Inst. Min. & Met. Trans., Vol. 6, 1897-98, p. 229.
"Valuation of a Prospect"—
    Mining Magazine. London, Vol. 43, 1930, p. 371.
"Valuation of Ore-Bodies"—L. V. Melvill.
    Trans. Geol. Soc. of South Africa, 1929.
"Valuation of Iron Mines"—J. R. Finlay.
    A.I.M.E. Trans., Vol. 45, 1913, p. 282.
"Valuation of Iron Mines"—J. R. Finlay.
    A.I.M.E. Trans., Vol. 50, 1914, p. 188.
"Calculation of Mine Values"—R. B. Brinsmade.
    A.I.M.E. Trans., Vol. 39, 1908, p. 243.
"A Method of Calculating Sinking-Funds."—J. Langton.
    A.I.M.E. Trans., Vol. 42, 1911, p. 908.
"A Method of Calculating Sinking-Funds"—J. B. Dilworth.
    A.I.M.E. Trans., Vol. 41, 1910, p. 533.
"Capitalization of Mine Development"—J. B. Dilworth.
    A.I.M.E. Trans., Vol. 66, 1921, p. 715.
"Valuation of Prospects"—Geo. R. Fausett.
    Univ. of Arizona, Bureau of Mines, 1918.
"Depth & Minimum Thickness as a Limiting Factor in Valuation"—
    C. A. Fisher. Gov't. Printing Office, Wash., 1910.
"The Depreciation of Factories, Mines, and Industrial Undertakings
    and Their Valuation"—Ewing Mathewson. (4th Ed.)
    London, E. & F. N. Spon, Ltd., 1893.
    N. Y., Spon & Chamberlain, 1910.
"Curves for Ore-Valuation"—K. K. Hood.
    Min. & Sci. Press, Vol. 121, 1920, p. 270.
"Mine Sampling & Valuation"—H. S. Munroe.
    Min. & Met. Soc. of Amer. Bull. 1912, V. 118.

"The Deep-Level Mines of the Rand"—G. A. Denny.
    Crosby Lockwood & Son, London, 1902, Chap. 10.
"Retrospective Appraisals—Their Use in Determining Invested Capital, Depreciation, and Depletion"—W. I. Kiroaldie.
    Proc. of Amer. Mining Congress, Vol. 26, 1923, p. 193.
"Profit in Mining Ventures"—W. Kurtz.
    Proc. of Amer. Mining Congress, Vol. 26, 1923, p. 247.
"Invested Capital of Mining Corporations"—G. E. Holmes.
    Proc. of Amer. Mining Congress, Vol. 26, 1922, p. 670.
"The Valuation of Mining Areas on the Rand"—W. F. Wilkinson.
    A.I.M.E. Trans., Vol. 18, 1908-09, p. 377.
"Ore Valuation of a Witwatersrand Mine"—E. J. Way.
    A.I.M.E. Trans., Vol. 15, 1905-06, p. 134.
"Valuation of Mines"—Editorial.
    Min. & Sci. Press, Vol. 111, 1915, p. 541.
"Valuation of Metal Mines"—T. A. Rickard.
    Min. & Sci. Press, Vol. 111, 1915, p. 548.
"Valuation of Metal Mines"—P. B. McDonald.
    Min. & Sci. Press, Vol. 111, 1915, p. 699.
"Valuation of Metal Mines"—F. H. Probert.
    Min. & Sci. Press, Vol. 111, 1915, p. 657.
"Notes on the Valuation of Ores, Concentrates, and Smelter Product"
—L. C. Stuckey. I.M.M. Trans., Vol. 31, 1921-22, p. 336.
"Mine Sampling and Valuation"—H. B. Munroe.
    E.&M.J., Vol. 93, 1912, p. 1276.
"The Ownership & Valuation of Mineral Property in the United Kingdom"—Sir R. A. S. Redmayne & Gilbert Stone.
    Longmanns, Green & Co., London, N.Y., 1920.
"Valuation of Coal Land"—H. M. Chance.
    A.I.M.E. Trans., Vol. 47, 1913, p. 111.
"Valuation of Anthracite Mines"—R. V. Norris.
    Proc. of International Eng. Congress, San Francisco, 1915.
"Valuations of Coal Property"—R. V. Norris.
    Coal Age, Vol. 3, 1913, pp. 267, 423.
"Appraisal of Coal-Property Values"—H. M. Chance.
    A.I.M.E. Trans., Vol. 74, 1926, p. 443.
"Valuation of Coal Properties"—J. B. Dilworth.
    A.I.M.E. Trans., Vol. 76, 1928, p. 215.
"Valuation of Coal Mining Properties in the U. S."—Engineers Advisory Valuation Committee Report,
    A.I.M.E. Trans., Vol. 70, 1924, p. 794.

"Valuation of Coal Properties"—J. B. Dilworth.
   A.I.M.E. Tech. Pub. No. 1, N. Y., 1927. Tables.
"Coal, its Composition, Analysis, Utilization and Valuation"—E. E.
   Somermeier. McGraw-Hill, N. Y., 1912.
"Valuation of Public Coal Lands"—W. L. Fisher.
   Min. & Sci. Press, Vol. 103, 1911, p. 443.
"Valuation of Oil Lands"—W. Fostner.
   Min. & Sci. Press, Vol. 103, 1911, p. 578.
"Valuation of Oil and Gas Lands"—Robert Wesley Brown.
   McGraw-Hill Book Co., New York, 1924.
"Time to Pay Out as a Basis for Valuation of Oil Properties"—
   W. I. Mayer. A.I.M.E. Trans., Vol. 68, 1923, p. 1121.
"Essential Factors in Valuation of Oil Properties"—C. H. Beal.
   A.I.M.E. Trans., Vol. 65, 1921, p. 344.
"Modified Oil-Well Depletion Curves"—A. Knapp.
   A.I.M.E. Trans., Vol. 65, 1921, p. 405.
"The Valuation of Alluvial Deposits"—W. R. Rumbold.
   A.I.M.E. Trans., Vol. 37, 1927-28, p. 437.
"Dredging and Valuing Dredging Ground in Oroville, California"—
   N. B. Knox. I.M.M. Trans., Vol. 12, 1902-03, p. 452.
"The Valuation of Gold Mines"—H. C. Hoover.
   E.&M.J., Vol. 77, 1904, p. 801.
"Theory of Investment Value"—J. B. Williams.
   Harvard Univ. Press, 1938.
"The Ebb and Flow of Investment Values"—Mead & Gradinsky.
   Appleton-Century, 1939.
"Principles of Investment"—G. H. Evans & G. E. Barnett.
   Houghton Mifflin, 1940.
"Bond Ratings as an Investment Guide"—G. Harold.
   Ronald Press, 1938.
"Investment Principles & Practices"—R. E. Badger & H. G. Guth-
   mann. Prentice-Hall, Inc., 1937.
"Investments & Investment Policy"—F. F. Burtchett.
   Longmans, Green & Co., New York, London, 1939.
"Security Analysis"—B. Graham & D. L. Dodd.
   McGraw-Hill Book Co., 1940.
"World Prices and the Building Industry"—G. F. Warren & F. A.
   Pearson. John Wiley & Sons, 1937.
"Depreciation Principles and Applications"—E. A. Saliers.
   Ronald Press Co., 3rd Ed., 1939.
"Federal Reserve Bulletin"—Federal Reserve Board, Wash., D. C.

VALUATION OF OIL PROPERTY.

"Petroleum Development and Technology"—Annual.
   Petroleum Div., A.I.M.E.

"Bulletin, American Assoc. of Petroleum Geologists"

"Notes on Valuation of Oil and Gas Properties"—
   Corpus Christi Geologists Study Group.
   Corpus Christi, Texas, 1940. (With bibliography.)

"Oil Property Valuation"—P. Paine.
   John Wiley & Sons, Inc., 1942.

"Economics of the Petroleum Industry"—J. E. Pogue.
   Chase National Bank, New York, 1939.

"Petroleum Production"—P. J. Jones.
   Vol. I, Mechanics; Vol. II, Optimum Rate; Vol. III, Production
   by Water, Reinhold Pub. Co., New York, 1946-47.

"Essentials for Oil Pools"—K. C. Heald.
   Chap. IV, Elements of the Petroleum Industry, E. DeGolyer,
   A.I.M.E., 1940.

"Exploration by Geophysical Methods"—J. C. Karcher.
   Chap. V, Elements of the Petroleum Industry, E. DeGolyer,
   A.I.M.E., 1940.

"Petroleum Reservoir Efficiency and Well Spacing"—Committee on
   Reservoir Development and Operation.
   Stand. Oil Co., N. J., Humble Oil & Ref. Co., 1943.

"Changing Concepts in the Petroleum Industry"—J. B. Umpleby.
   Petroleum Dev. & Tech., 1932, A.I.M.E., pp. 38-50.

"Propositions and Corollaries in Petroleum Production"—L. C.
   Snider. Petroleum Dev. & Tech., 1932, A.I.M.E., pp. 51-68.

"Petroleum Production Engineering"—L. C. Uren.
   McGraw-Hill Book Co., Inc., 3rd Ed., 1946. (With bibliographies
   by subjects.)

"A Design for More Effective Proration"—J. E. Pogue.
   A.I.M.E., 1939.

"Our Oil Resources"—Leonard M. Fanning.
   McGraw-Hill Book Co., Inc., 1945.

"Appraisal of Oil Properties"—T. A. Hall.
   Oil Weekly, Vol. 93, Mar. 20, 1939.

"Principles of Well Spacing"—
   M. Muskat. A.I.M.E. Pet. Tech., Aug., 1939 (T.P. 1086).

"Salt Water Disposal and Pressure Maintenance in the East Texas
   Oil Fields"—W. S. Morris. Min. & Met., Dec., 1944, pp. 584-6.

"Economics of Well Spacing"—H. Gardesen.
    Oil Weekly, Vol. 96, Feb. 5, 1940.
Review of "Cutter's Rule of Well Spacing"—
    U.S.B.M. R.I. 3479.
"Factors Affecting Estimation of Recoverable Oil Reserves in Sand
    Fields"—O. L. Brace. Bull. Amer. Soc. Pet. Geol., Vol. 18, Mar.,
    1934.
"Flow of Homogeneous Fluids thru Porous Media"—M. Muskat.
    McGraw-Hill Book Co., Inc., 1937.
"Behavior of Fluids in Oil Reservoirs"—
    Bull. Amer. Assoc. of Pet. Geol., Sept., 1938.
"Connate Water in Oil & Gas Sands"—R. J. Schilthius.
    A.I.M.E. Pet. Tech., Feb., 1938 (T.P. 869).
"Influence of Connate Water on Permeability of Sands to Oil"—
    E. N. Dunlap. A.I.M.E. Pet. Tech., Feb., 1938 (T.P. 874).
"F rect of Pressure Reduction on Core Saturation"—H. G. Botset &
    M. Muskat. A.I.M.E. Pet. Tech., Feb., 1939 (T.P. 1025).
"Core Analysis"—H. C. Pyle & J. E. Sherborne.
    A.I.M.E. Pet. Tech., Feb., 1939 (T.P. 1024).
"New Device for Determining Porosity by Gas Expansion Method"—
    A. B. Stevens. A.I.M.E. Pet. Tech., May, 1939.
"A.P.I. Pressure Core Barrel—Progress Report"—D. B. Taliaferro
    and R. E. Heithecker. U.S.B.M., R.I. 3481, Nov., 1939.
"A Study of Bottom Hole Samples of East Texas Crude Oil"—B. E.
    Lindsly. U.S.B.M., R.I. 3212, May, 1933.
"Estimation of Underground Reserves by Oil Well Production
    Curves"—W. C. Cutler. U.S.B.M. Bull. 228, 1924.
"Petroleum Facts and Figures"—
    Amer. Pet. Inst., New York, 7th Ed., 1941.
"World Oil Atlas"—Annual.
    The Oil Weekly, Houston, Texas.
"The Petroleum Data Book", H. J. Struth, editor. Petroleum Eng.
    Pub. Co., Dallas, 1947.

VALUATION AND TAXATION.

"State Taxation of Metallic Deposits"—Warren A. Roberts.
    Harvard University Press, 1944.
"Taxation in Minnesota"—R. G. Blakey.
    University of Minnesota Press, 1932.
"Mine Economics"—S. J. Truscott.
    Mining Publications, Ltd., London, 1947.

"Rand Mine Taxation"—
    Economist. Vol. 123, 1936, p. 19.
Biennial Reports of the Minnesota Tax Commission,
    St. Paul, Minn.
Mich. State Tax Commission Reports and
    Mineral Resource Publications, Lansing, Mich.
"Mine Taxation"—H. B. Fernald.
    Min. & Met., Vol. 18, 1937, p. 8.
"Mine Taxation"—W. M. Ferry.
    Min. Cong. Jour., Vol. 23, 1937, p. 12.
"Equitable Mine Taxation"—H. B. Fernald.
    Min. Cong. Jour., Vol. 20, 1934, p. 10.
"Mine Taxation and the Law of the Diminishing Return"—P. H. Hunt.
    Min. Cong. Jour., Vol. 20, 1934, p. 22.
"Mine Taxation"—G. C. Jones.
    S. Af. Min. & Eng. Jour., July 24, 1943, p. 453.
"Barnes Income Tax Handbook"—A. W. Osborne.
    Butterworth & Co., Ltd., Africa.
"Percentage of Depletion"—J. R. Finlay.
    E.&M.J., Vol. 131, 1931, pp. 180, 230, 569.
"Mine Valuation for Taxation Purposes"—P. J. Stack.
    E.&M.J., Vol. 131, 1931, p. 27
"Michigan Iron Ore Reserves; Methods of Appraisal for Taxation"—
    R. C. Allen.
    L.S.M.I. Proceedings, Vol. 19, 1914, p. 229.
    Min. & Eng. World., Vol. 41, 1914, p. 463.
"Observations on the Appraisal of the Iron Mines of Michigan"—
    C. H. Baxter.
    (Michigan College of Mines "Alumnus," July, 1941.)
    E.&M.J., Vol. 99, 1915, p. 439.
"Taxation of Iron Lands in Michigan"—P. B. McDonald.
    Min. & Sci. Press, Vol. 106, 1913, p. 697.
"Michigan Copper Production, Costs and General Facts Pertaining
    to the Copper Mining Industry for 1929"—Dept. of Conservation,
    Mich. Geol. Survey. L.S.M.I. Proceedings, Vol. 28, 1930, p. 238.
"Summary of Facts of Michigan Iron Ore Production, Costs, Valua-
    tions, and Reserves"—Dept. of Conservation, Michigan Geological
    Survey. L.S.M.I. Proceedings, Vol. 28, 1930, p. 231.
"Factors for Determining Copper Mine Values"—L. C. Graton.
    Copper Producers Tax Committee, 1926.
"Taxation of Mines by States"—W. R. Ingalls.
    Proc. of Amer. Min. Congress, Vol. 26, 1922, p. 557.

"Mine Accounting Methods in Relation to Federal Taxes"—T. O. McGrath. Proc. of Amer. Min. Congress, Vol. 26, 1922, p. 573.

"Accounting for Depletion and Dividends of Mining Companies"— H. B. Fernald. Proc. of Amer. Min. Congress, Vol. 26, 1922, p. 629.

"Distributions from the Depletion Reserve under the Federal Tax Law"—P. Armitage. Proc. of Amer. Min. Congress, Vol. 26, 1922, p. 589.

"Inventories as Related to Federal Taxation of Mining Companies"— H. B. Fernald. Proc. of Amer. Min. Congress, Vol. 26, 1923, p. 166.

"Valuation of Mining Properties for Purposes of Federal Taxation" —R. V. Norris.
Proc. of Amer. Min. Congress, Vol. 26, 1922, p. 686.

"Is a Uniform Rate Per Cent of Extraction a 'Reasonable Allowance for Depletion' under the Federal Income Tax Laws?"—P. Armitage. Proc. of Amer. Min. Congress, Vol. 26, 1923, p. 210.

"Discovery Value—Practical Application of Provisions to Taxation of Mining Ventures"—E. H. Goodnor.
Proc. of Amer. Min. Congress, Vol. 26, 1923, p. 231.

"National Mine Tax Conference Proceedings"—
Proc. of Amer. Min. Congress, Vol. 27, 1924, p. 145.

"Taxation of Mines in Various Countries"—D. Bowen.
Proc. Amer. Mining Congress, Vol. 44, p. 560.

"Federal Taxation of Mines"—L. C. Graton.
A.I.M.E. Trans., Vol. 69, 1923, p. 1185.

"Assessing & Taxing Coal in the Ground"—W. Griffith.
Colliery Engineer, Vol. 33, 1913, p. 669.

"Principles of Mine Taxation"—T. W. Gibson.
A.I.M.E. Trans., Vol. 61, 1919, p. 639.

"Principles of Mine Taxation"—R. C. Allen, R. Arnold.
A.I.M.E. Trans., Vol. 61, 1919, p. 649.

"Mine Taxation in the United States"—L. E. Young.
Univ. of Illinois Graduate School, Vol. 5, No. 4, Dec., 1916.

"The Incidence of Taxation upon Metalliferous Mining in the British Isles"—H. Louis. I.M.M. Trans., Vol. 27, 1917-18, p. 203.

"Valuation of Lake Copper Mines—Statistics"—
Min. & Sci. Press, Vol. 106, 1913, p. 946.

"Arizona Valuation of Mines"—C. M. Zander.
Min. & Sci. Press, Vol. 112, 1916, p. 141.

"Valuation of Iron Mines in New York and New Jersey"—J. C. Smock. A.I.M.E. Trans., Vol. 10, 1881-1882, p. 268.

"Report of Appraisal of Mining Properties of New Mexico"—J. R. Finlay. New Mexico State Tax Commission, 1921-22.

"Mine Taxation"—H. Steele.
    E.&M.J., Vol. 98, 1914, p. 381.
"Mine Taxation in Nevada"—Editorial.
    Min. & Eng. World, Vol. 39, 1913, p. 499.
"Mine Taxation in Montana"—Editorial.
    Min. & Eng. World, Vol. 39, 1913, p. 583.
"Valuation of Mines by the Public"—H. Steele.
    Min. & Sci. Press, Vol. 106, 1913, p. 379.
"Valuation of Oil Properties for Federal Taxation"—
    Min. & Sci. Press, Vol. 120, 1920, p. 307.

MINING METHODS AND COSTS.

"U. S. Bureau of Mines Reports and Information Circulars"—
    U. S. Bureau of Mines and Gov't. Printing Office, Wash., D. C.
"Mining Engineers' Handbook"—R. Peele, 1918, 1927.
    R. Peele and J. A. Church, 3rd Ed., 1941.
    John Wiley & Sons, Inc., 1918, 1927.
"Metal Mining Practice"—C. F. Jackson & J. H. Hedges.
    U.S.B.M. Bull. 419, 1939.
"Copper Mining in North America"—E. D. Gardner, C. H. Johnson,
    and B. S. Butler. U.S.B.M. Bull. 405, 1938.
"Coal Mining in Europe"—G. S. Rice & I. Hartmann.
    U.S.B.M. Bull. 414, 1939.
"Mining Methods and Costs at Metal Mines of U. S."—C. W. Wright.
    U.S.B.M., I.C. No. 6503.
"Lead and Zinc Mining and Milling in the United States; Current
    Practices and Costs"—C. F. Jackson, J. B. Knaebel, C. A. Wright.
    U.S.B.M. Bull. 381, 1935.
"Gold Mining and Milling in the United States and Canada; Current
    Practices and Costs"—C. F. Jackson & J. B. Knaebel.
    U.S.B.M. Bull. 363, 1932.
"Shaft Sinking Practices and Costs"—E. D. Gardner & J. F. Johnson.
    U.S.B.M. Bull. 357, 1932.
"Ore and Stone Mining"—C. LeNeve Foster.
    Charles Griffin & Co., Ltd., London, W.C. 2, 7th Ed., 1910.
"Mining Methods"—C. A. Mitke.
    McGraw-Hill Book Co., Inc., 1930.
"Stoping Methods and Costs"—C. F. Jackson & E. D. Gardner.
    U.S.B.M., Bulletin 390, 1936.
"The Working of Unstratified Mineral Deposits"—G. J. Young.
    McGraw-Hill Book Co., Inc., 1927.

"Elements of Mining"—R. S. Lewis.
   John Wiley & Sons, Inc., 1933, 1941.
"The Working of Coal and Other Stratified Minerals"—H. F. Bulman.
   John Wiley & Sons, Inc., 1927.
"Elements of Mining"—G. J. Young.
   McGraw-Hill Book Co., Inc., 1916, 1923, 1932, 1946.
"Operating the Small Mine"—C. F. Jackson.
   E.&M.J., Aug., 1940, pp. 42-6.
"Placer Mining for Gold in California"—
   Bull. 135, Div. of Mines, State of California, Dept. of Min. Resources. San Francisco, 1946.
"Examination, Boring & Valuation of Alluvial and Kindred Ore Deposits"—H. L. H. Harrison. Mining Pub., Ltd., London, 1946.
"A General Theory of Rock Bursts"— R. G. K. Morrison.
   E.&M.J., Dec., 1947, pp. 70-73. (Bibliography.)
"New Metal Mining Methods"—P. B. Bucky.
   Min. Cong. Jour., Vol. 32, April, 1946, pp. 62-4.
"Shrink Fill Method of Mining Ore"—P. B. Bucky.
   Expl. Engr., Vol. 24, Sept., 1946, pp. 141-8.
"Lowering Mining Costs with Block Caving"—P. B. Bucky.
   E.&M.J., Vol. 147, Apr., 1946, pp. 75-9.
"Attacking Problems of Structure and Ground Support"—P. B. Bucky. E.&M.J., July, 1940, pp. 40-3.
"Stress in Mine Workings"—P. B. Bucky.
   E.&M.J., Nov., 1940, pp. 33-6.
"Ore Mining Methods"—W. R. Crane.
   John Wiley & Sons, Inc., 1910, 1917.
"Witwatersrand Mining Practice"—G. A. Watermeyer & S. N. Hoffenberg. Transvaal Chamber of Mines, Gold Producers' Committee, Johannesburg, South Africa, 1931.
"Mining Methods and Practices in the Mich. Copper Mines"—W. R. Crane. U.S.B.M. Bull. No. 306, 1929.
"Subsidence and Ground Movement in Mines of Michigan"—W.R. Crane. U.S.B.M. Bull. No. 295, 1929.
"Mining Subsidence"—Henry Briggs.
   Edward Arnold & Co., London, 1929.
"How Canada Develops Newest Porphyry Copper"—R. H. Ramsay.
   E.&M.J., Dec., 1944, p. 74-87.
"Making Low-Grade Iron Ore Pay"—A. J. Wiseley.
   Min. Cong. Jour., Vol. 32, Aug., 1946, pp. 22-4.
"Tomorrow's Mining Methods"—M. A. Smith.
   E.&M.J., 1940, Apr. 3, pp. 48-9; Oct. 10, pp. 33-7.

"Advances in Scraper-Hoist Mining"—R. V. Pierce. Mining World, San Francisco, Nov., Dec., 1947, and Jan., 1948.

"Mucking-Machine Draw Points Aid Sublevel Stoping"—L. E. Snow. E.&M.J., Dec., 1947, pp. 58-62.

"Choice of Methods in Mining and Metallurgy"— A.I.M.E. Series.

"Methods, Costs, and Safety in Stripping and Mining Coal, Copper, and Iron Ore, Bauxite and Phosphate"—F. E. Cash & M. von Bernewitz. U.S.B.M. Bull. 298, 1929.

"Underground Practice in Mining"—Bernard Beringer. Mining Publications, Ltd., Salisbury House, London E. C. 2, 1928.

"The Timbering of Metalliferous Mines"—J. F. Downey. Charles Griffin & Co., Ltd., London, W. C. 2, 1928.

"Timbering & Mining"—W. H. Storms. McGraw-Hill Book Co., Inc., 1909.

"Mining Methods in Europe"—L. W. Mayer. McGraw-Hill Book Co., Inc., 1909.

"Mine Timbering"—W. E. Sanders, N. W. Pardee, B. McDonald. Hill Publishing Co., 1907.

"Mining Without Timber"—R. B. Brinsmade. McGraw-Hill Book Co., Inc., 1911.

"Mechanical Underground Loading in Metal Mines"—C. E. Van-Barneveld. Missouri School of Mines Bulletin, 1924.

"Scraper Mucking"— Sullivan Machinery Co., 1930.

"Goodman Mining Handbook"— Goodman Mfg. Co., 5th Ed., 1927.

"Witwatersrand Banket and Mining Practice"—S. J. Truscott. Macmillan & Co., Ltd., London, 1905, Chap. 15.

"Gold Mines of the Rand"—F. H. Hatch, & J. A. Chalmers. Macmillan & Co., London & N. Y., 1895, Chap. 6.

"Handbook of Mining Details"—E.&M.J. Staff. McGraw-Hill Book Co., Inc., 1912.

"Mining Costs of the World"—E. N. Skinner, & H. R. Plate. McGraw-Hill Book Co., Inc., 1915.

"Notes and Records of Mining Costs"—A. E. Pettit. A.I.M.E. Trans., Vol. 30, 1920—21, p. 326.

"Steam Shovel Mining"—R. Marsh. McGraw-Hill Book Co., Inc., 1920.

"Practical Machine Mining"—M. D. Williams. Oxford University Press, London, Humphrey Milford, 1928.

"Oil Well Drilling Methods"—Victor Ziebler.
      John Wiley & Sons, Inc., 1923.
"Oil Field Practice"—Dorsey Hager.
      McGraw-Hill Book Co., Inc., 1921.
"Hydraulic Mine Filling, its use in Penn. Anthracite Fields"—Charles
   Enzian.
         U.S.B.M., Gov't. Print. Off., Wash., 1913, Bulletin No. 60.
"Practical Treatise on Hydraulic Mining"—A. J. Bowie, Jr.
      D. Van Nostrand Co., New York, 10th Ed., 1905.
"Hydraulic and Placer Mining"—E. B. Wilson.
      John Wiley & Sons, Inc., 1898, 1907, 1918.
"Tin Mining"—Moor.
      Isaac Pitman & Sons, 2 W. 45th, New York, 1928.
"A Sketch of Malayan Mining"—J. B. Srivenor.
      Mining Publications, Ltd., Salisbury House, London, E. C. 2, 1928.
"Mining of Alluvial Deposits by Dredging & Hydraulicking"—W. E.
   Thorne, & A. W. Hooke. Mining Publications, Ltd., London, 1929.
"Practical Mining"—John G. Murphy.
      D. Van Nostrand, N. Y., 1890.
"Shaft Sinking in Difficult Cases"—J. Riems. Trans. by J. W. Braugh.
      London, Griffin, 1907. (Has bibliography.)
"Observations on Subsidence"—L. Lea.
      Colliery Guardian, Vol. 139, 1929, p. 467.
"Notes on Mining Subsidence Theories"—Geo. Knox.
      Colliery Guardian, Vol. 138, 1929, pp. 825, 933.
"Costs of Production, Proceeds and Profits of British Coal Mining
   Industry"—Colliery Guardian. Each quarter.
A.I.M.E.; Transactions and Mining Technology.
I.M.M. Transactions.
L.S.M.I. Proceedings.
E. & M. J.
Mining Magazine of London.
Mining Congress Journal.
Hercules Powder Co., "The Explosives Engineer."
Canadian Mining Journal.
Coal Age.

MINE DEVELOPMENT, PLANT AND EQUIPMENT.

"Mine Plant"—B. F. Tillson.
      A.I.M.E., 1935.
"Mine Plant Design"—W. W. Staley.
      McGraw-Hill Book Co., Inc., 1936.

"Practical Mine Development and Equipment"—L. Eaton.
McGraw-Hill Book Co., Inc., 1934.

"Mining Engineers' Handbook"—R. Peele, 1918, 1927. R. Peele & J. A. Church, 3rd Ed., 1941,
John Wiley & Sons, Inc.

"Mechanical Loading of Coal Underground"—I. A. Given.
McGraw-Hill Book Co., Inc., 1943.

"Mining Practice and Mine Transportation, Minnesota Iron Ranges"
—G. J. Holt, Min. & Met., Aug., 1941, pp. 400-4.

MINING LAW.

"Mining Engineers' Handbook"—R. Peele and J. A. Church.
John Wiley & Sons, 3rd Ed., 1941.

"American Mining Law"—A. H. Ricketts.
Division of Mines, State of California, Bulletin 123, 1934.

"Law of Oil and Gas Leases and Royalties"—S. H. Glassmire.
Thomas Law Book Co., St. Louis, 2nd Ed., 1938.

"Land Tenure and Leasing"—R. Greenslade.
Chap. VI, Elements of the Petroleum Industry,
E. DeGolyer, A.I.M.E., 1940.

"Manner of Locating and Holding Mineral Claims in California"—
A. H. Ricketts and C. A. Logan.
California Journal of Mines and Geology, V. 44, No. 1, Jan., 1948.

"International Mining Law"—Theo. F. Van Wagensen.
McGraw-Hill Book Co., 1918.

"Royalties"—A. Deusseu.
Chap. VIII, Elements of the Petroleum Industry,
E. DeGolyer, A.I.M.E., 1940.

"Mining, Mineral & Geological Law"—C. H. Shamel.
Hill Pub. Co., London, New York, 1907. (Has bibliography.)

"Practical and Legal Aspects of Mine Financing"—P. S. Mathews.
Min. & Met., Vol. 17, Apr., 1936.

REPORT WRITING.

"Writing the Technical Report"—J. R. Nelson.
McGraw-Hill Book Co., Inc., 2nd Ed., 1947.

"Technical Report Writing"—F. H. Rhodes.
McGraw-Hill Book Co., Inc., 1st Ed., 1941.

"Technical Writing"—T. A. Rickard.
McGraw-Hill Book Co., Inc., 3rd Ed., 1931.

GENERAL.

U.S.B.M., List of Publications with Index.
    Gov't. Printing Office, Wash., D.C., 1930, 1937, 1942, 1946.

U. S. Geological Survey, List of Publications.
    Gov't. Printing Office, Wash., D. C., 1947.

A.I.M.E.—A Catalog of Periodical Publications in the Library of the
    Institute, New York, 1904.

Great Brit. Patent Office Library.
    Subject List of Works on Mineral Industries & Allied Science in
    the library of the Patent Office. London. H.M., Stationery Office,
        Carling & Son (printers), 1903, 1912.

Canada—Dept. of Mines—Mines Branch.
    Catalog of Mines Branch Publications with alphabetical guide.
    Ottawa, 1927, 14th Ed. rev.

Index Catalog of Books & Papers relating to Mining, Metallurgy &
    Manufactures—H. T. Folkard, librarian. Southport, Johnson, 1910.
    Wigan, Eng. Free Public Library, Reference Department.

The Mining World Index of Current Literature Vols. 1-10, 1912-16,
    Chicago, Mining World Company 1912-16.

"Index to Mining Engineering Literature"—W. R. Crane.
    John Wiley & Sons, Inc., 1909, 1912.

Indices to Names of Authors and Subjects of papers presented to
    Canadian Mining Institute, the Federated Canadian Min. Inst. &
    the antecedent provincial mining societies—B. T. A. Bell. 1891 to
    1903, Ottawa, 1904.

Location of Mineral Fields; Modern Procedure in the Investigation of
    Mineral Areas and Subsequent Verification of their Extent—M. H.
    Haddock, Lockwood, London, 1926. (Bibliography each chapter.)

Annotated & Classified Catalogue of Ancient & Modern Books on
    Exact and Applied Sciences, London, 1927, Sotheran, Henry & Co.

Annotated Bibliography of Economic Geol., Semiannually 1928 to
    date.
    Econ. Geol. Pub. Co., Wash., D. C. (Has section on geophysical
    prospecting.)

Bibliography and Index of Geology, Annual,
    Geological Society of America, New York.

A selected list of books and references on Geophysical Prospecting—
    C. A. Heiland & D. Wautlund.
    Colo. Sch. Mines Quarterly, Vol. 26, No. 3, Golden, 1931.

Applied Geophysics in the Search for Minerals—A. S. Eve & D. A.
Keys. Cambridge, Univ. Press, 1929. (Has bibliography.)

Handy Lists of Technical Literature 1889-93—H. E. Haperkorn.
Library of Congress.

Bibliography on Mines and Mining in the Philippines—Perez and
Estrella-Villanueva.
Scientific Library, Bureau of Science, Manila, P. I., 1937.

"Bibliography of Diamond Drilling"—E. J. Longyear Co.
Minneapolis, 1947. (Indexed by subjects.)

INDEX

NOTE: *Index is not inclusive of footnotes and bibliography.* (*Numbers refer to pages.*)